Longman

Listening
mentor joy

5
LEVEL

PEARSON

Longman
Listening Mentor Joy 5

지은이 교재개발연구소
편집 및 기획 English Nine
발행처 Pearson Education South Asia Pte Ltd.
판매처 inkedu(inkbooks)
전화 02-455-9620(주문 및 고객지원)
팩스 02-455-9619
등록 제13-579호

ISBN 979-11-88228-62-1
잘못된 책은 구입처에서 바꿔 드립니다.

INTRODUCTION

Listening Mentor Joy 시리즈는 총 5권 5레벨로 구성되어 있으며,
각 권마다 15회의 모의고사가 수록되어 있습니다.

단계	대상	활용 방안
	초등 3학년	● 정확한 알파벳 소리를 익힌다. ● 영어 단어의 정확한 발음과 의미를 익힌다. ● 한 문장으로 된 간단한 지시, 명령을 이해한다. ● 간단한 대화의 내용을 이해한다. ● 간단한 질문을 이해하고 대답할 수 있는 능력을 키운다.
	초등 3-4학년	● 영어 단어의 정확한 발음과 의미를 익힌다. ● 한 문장으로 된 간단한 지시, 명령을 이해한다. ● 일상생활에 관련된 쉽고 간단한 대화를 듣고 이해한다. ● 수와 시각에 관한 간단한 대화를 듣고 이해한다. ● 간단한 대화를 듣고, 대화가 일어난 장소와 시간 등을 안다.
	초등 4-5학년	● 한두 문장으로 된 명령이나 지시를 듣고 이해한다. ● 간단한 대화를 듣고, 대화가 일어난 장소와 시간 등을 안다. ● 일상생활과 관련된 쉽고 간단한 말을 듣고, 중심 낱말을 찾는다. ● 시간과 수량에 관한 대화를 이해하고 대답할 수 있다. ● 두 사람 간의 대화를 통해 내용을 이해할 수 있다. ● 의문사를 이용한 질문을 이해하고 대답할 수 있다.
	초등 5-6학년	● 일상생활에 관한 쉽고 간단한 내용을 듣고, 의도나 목적을 이해한다. ● 간단한 대화를 듣고 주제를 이해한다. ● 간단한 말을 듣고 세부 사항을 이해한다. ● 앞으로 일어날 일에 관한 간단한 말을 듣고 이해한다. ● 의문사를 이용한 질문을 이해하고 답할 수 있다. ● 대상을 비교하는 쉬운 말을 듣고 이해한다. ● 간단한 전화 대화를 이해한다.
	예비중학생	● 자기소개를 하거나 위치를 묻고 말하는 내용을 이해한다. ● 과거시제를 이용한 대화를 이해한다. ● 대화를 듣고 세부 정보를 파악하거나 화자 간 관계를 추론할 수 있다. ● 대화를 통해 화자의 의도나 목적을 추론할 수 있다. ● 대화를 듣고 화자의 심정이나 태도 추론이 가능하고 관용적인 표현을 이해한다. ● 간단한 전화 대화를 이해할 수 있으며, 좀 더 복잡한 시간과 수를 영어로 이해한다.

CONSTRUCTION

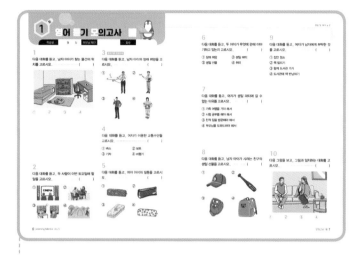

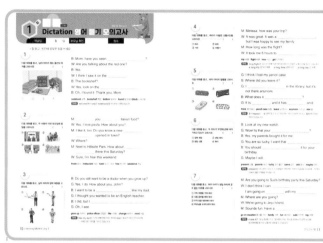

영어 듣기 모의고사

실제 모의고사에 나오는 다양한 문제들을 풀면서
영어 듣기 평가 시험에 대비합니다.

Dictation 영어 듣기 모의고사

모의고사에 나오는 단어와 문장, 표현들을 Dictation을
통해서 확인하고, 듣기 집중력과 청취력을 향상시킵니다.

Word Check

모의고사에 등장하는
핵심 단어들을 듣고
확인합니다.

Sentence Check

모의고사에 등장하는
핵심 문장을 듣고
확인합니다.

Vocabulary

모의고사 15회에
등장하는 모든 단어들을
회별로 다시 한 번 더
확인합니다.

정답 및 해석

모의고사와 Dictation의
답을 확인할 수 있으며,
모의고사에 등장하는
단어와 문장, 대화의
해석을 확인합니다.

CONTENTS

1

다음 대화를 듣고, 남자 아이가 찾는 물건의 위치를 고르시오. ···················· (   )

①   ②   ③   ④

2

다음 대화를 듣고, 두 사람이 이번 토요일에 할 일을 고르시오. ···················· (   )

①
②
③
④

3 중학기출 변형문제

다음 대화를 듣고, 남자 아이의 장래 희망을 고르시오. ···················· (   )

①
②
③
④

4

다음 대화를 듣고, 여자가 이용한 교통수단을 고르시오. ···················· (   )

① 버스   ② 보트
③ 기차   ④ 비행기

5

다음 대화를 듣고, 여자 아이의 필통을 고르시오. ···················· (   )

①
②
③
④

6

다음 대화를 듣고, 두 아이가 무엇에 관해 이야기하고 있는지 고르시오. ········· (　　　)

① 장래 희망　　　② 생일 파티
③ 생일 선물　　　④ 취미

7

다음 대화를 듣고, 여자가 생일 파티에 갈 수 <u>없는</u> 이유를 고르시오. ·········· (　　　)

① 가족 여행을 가야 해서
② 시험 공부를 해야 해서
③ 친척 집을 방문해야 해서
④ 부모님을 도와드려야 해서

8

다음 대화를 듣고, 남자 아이가 사려는 친구의 생일 선물을 고르시오. ·········· (　　　)

① 　　②

③ 　　④

9

다음 대화를 듣고, 여자가 남자에게 부탁한 것을 고르시오. ····················· (　　　)

① 집안 청소
② 책 빌리기
③ 함께 도서관 가기
④ 도서관에 책 반납하기

10

다음 그림을 보고, 그림과 일치하는 대화를 고르시오. ····················· (　　　)

① 　　② 　　③ 　　④

11

다음 대화를 듣고, 남자 아이가 대화 후 할 일을 고르시오. ·····················( )

① 청소　　　② 피아노 연습
③ 컴퓨터 게임　　　④ 숙제

12

다음 대화를 듣고, 여자가 지불할 금액을 고르시오. ·····················( )

① $2　　　② $3
③ $4　　　④ $5

13

다음 대화를 듣고, 대화가 자연스럽지 않은 것을 고르시오. ·····················( )

①　　　②　　　③　　　④

14

다음을 듣고, 내용과 일치하지 않는 것을 고르시오. ·····················( )

① 캐시는 옆집에 산다.
② 나는 방과 후 캐시와 자주 논다.
③ 캐시는 춤추는 것을 좋아한다.
④ 캐시는 K-pop을 자주 듣는다.

15 중학기출 변형문제

다음 대화를 듣고, 두 사람이 만날 시각과 장소를 고르시오. ·····················( )

① 11시 – 버스 정류장
② 11시 30분 – 버스 정류장
③ 11시 – 지하철역
④ 11시 30분 – 지하철역

16

다음 대화를 듣고, 여자가 하는 운동을 고르시오. ·····················( )

17

다음 대화를 듣고, 이어질 말로 알맞은 것을 고르시오. ···························· (　　　)

B _____

① No, it's not my toy.

② How much is it?

③ No, he doesn't have a toy.

④ Yes, I hope he likes it.

19

다음 대화를 듣고, 이어질 말로 알맞은 것을 고르시오. ···························· (　　　)

B _____

① Yes, I like him.

② He's a taxi driver.

③ He lives in Seoul.

④ He's from Italy.

18

다음 대화를 듣고, 이어질 말로 알맞은 것을 고르시오. ···························· (　　　)

G _____

① Yes, I like spicy food.

② I don't like ice skating.

③ Yes, it's in front of the gym.

④ Great. See you on Sunday.

20

다음 대화를 듣고, 이어질 말로 알맞은 것을 고르시오. ···························· (　　　)

M _____

① It's my pleasure.

② Oh, that's too bad.

③ You're welcome.

④ Long time no see.

1회 Dictation 영어 듣기 모의고사

학습일 | 월 | 일 | 부모님 확인 | 점수

● 잘 듣고, 빈칸에 알맞은 말을 쓰세요.

1

다음 대화를 듣고, 남자 아이가 찾는 물건의 위치를 고르시오. ·················· ( )

① ② ③ ④

B: Mom, have you seen _____ _____?

W: Are you talking about the red one?

B: Yes.

W: I think I saw it on the _____.

B: The bookshelf?

W: Yes, look on the _____ _____.

B: Oh, I found it. Thank you, Mom.

notebook 공책 | **bookshelf** 책장 | **bottom** 밑바닥 | **found** 발견하다(find)의 과거형

TIPS red one에서 one은 notebook을 대신하는 대명사입니다.

2

다음 대화를 듣고, 두 사람이 이번 토요일에 할 일을 고르시오. ·················· ( )

① CINEMA ②
③ ④

M: _____ you _____ Italian food?

W: Yes, I love pasta. How about you?

M: I like it, too. Do you know a new _____ _____ opened in town?

W: Where?

M: Next to Hillside Park. How about _____ _____ there this Saturday?

W: Sure, I'm free this weekend.

know 알다 | **restaurant** 식당 | **town** 도시, 시내 | **free** 한가한 | **weekend** 주말

3

다음 대화를 듣고, 남자 아이의 장래 희망을 고르시오. ·················· ( )

① ② ③ ④

B: Do you still want to be a doctor when you grow up?

G: Yes, I do. How about you, John?

B: I want to be a _____ _____ like my dad.

G: I thought you wanted to be an English teacher.

B: I did, but I _____ _____ _____.

G: Oh, I see.

grow up 자라다 | **police officer** 경찰관 | **like** ~처럼 | **change** 바꾸다 | **mind** 마음

TIPS like my dad는 '나의 아빠처럼'이란 의미로 like는 동사가 아닌 전치사이며, '~처럼'이란 의미를 가지고 있습니다.

4

다음 대화를 듣고, 여자가 이용한 교통수단을
고르시오. ·························· (   )

① 버스　　　　② 보트
③ 기차　　　　④ 비행기

M: Melissa, how was your trip?

W: It was great. It was a _____ _____,
　 but I was happy to see my family.

M: How long was the flight?

W: It took me 6 hours to _____ _____.

trip 여행 | **flight** 비행 | **hour** 시간 | **get** 도착하다

TIPS long flight은 '장시간 비행'이란 의미로 여자가 이용한 교통수단을 알 수 있습니다.
　　　 a long trip 장거리 여행　　a long time 오랜 시간　　a long day 긴 하루

5

다음 대화를 듣고, 여자 아이의 필통을 고르시
오. ···························· (   )

① ② ③ ④

G: I think I lost my pencil case.

B: Where did you leave it?

G: I _____ _____ in the library, but it's
　 not there anymore.

B: What does it _____ _____?

G: It is _____, and it has _____ on it.

think 생각하다 | **pencil case** 필통 | **leave** 남겨두다 | **anymore** 더 이상 | **star** 별

TIPS 동사 leave는 '~을 깜박 잊고 두고 가다'라는 의미 이외에 '떠나다, 출발하다'라는
　　　 의미가 있습니다.

6

다음 대화를 듣고, 두 아이가 무엇에 관해 이야
기하고 있는지 고르시오. ········· (   )

① 장래 희망　　　② 생일 파티
③ 생일 선물　　　④ 취미

B: Look at my new watch.

G: Wow! Is that your _____ _____?

B: Yes, my parents bought it for me.

G: You are so lucky. I want that _____ _____.

B: You should _____ _____ it for your
　 birthday.

G: Maybe I will.

present 선물 | **parents** 부모 | **lucky** 운이 좋은 | **same** 같은 | **ask** 묻다 | **maybe** 아마

TIPS present는 주고받는 사이가 스스럼없는 개인적인 친분이 있음을 시사하며, 가격이
　　　 비싸지 않은 선물을 의미합니다.

7

다음 대화를 듣고, 여자가 생일 파티에 갈 수
없는 이유를 고르시오. ··········· (   )

① 가족 여행을 가야 해서
② 시험 공부를 해야 해서
③ 친척 집을 방문해야 해서
④ 부모님을 도와드려야 해서

M: Are you going to Sue's birthday party this Saturday?

W: I don't think I can _____ _____.
　 I am going on _____ with my _____.

M: Where are you going?

W: We're going to Jeju Island.

M: Sounds fun. Have a _____ _____.

go on vacation 휴가를 가다 | **family** 가족 | **fun** 재미있는 | **safe** 안전한 | **trip** 여행

TIPS make it은 '(모임 등에) 가다, 참석하다'라는 의미로 앞에서 언급한 모임에
　　　 참가여부를 묻거나 답할 때 사용할 수 있습니다.

8

다음 대화를 듣고, 남자 아이가 사려는 친구의 생일 선물을 고르시오. ········· (   )

① ② ③ ④

B: Alice, did you buy a birthday present for Smith?

G: Yes, I bought a baseball cap. How about you?

B: I'm going to buy a backpack. What do you think?

G: He _____ has two backpacks.

B: Then, how about a _____ _____?

G: That's a _____ _____.

present 선물 | backpack 배낭 | think 생각하다 | already 이미, 벌써 |
baseball glove 야구 글러브 | idea 생각

TIPS [How/What about + 명사/동명사?]는 '~은 어때요?'라는 의미로 상대방에게
제의를 할 때 사용합니다.

9

다음 대화를 듣고, 여자가 남자에게 부탁한 것을 고르시오. ················· (   )

① 집안 청소
② 책 빌리기
③ 함께 도서관 가기
④ 도서관에 책 반납하기

W: Mike, what are you going to do today?

M: I'm going to the _____.

W: Can you do me a _____?

M: What is it?

W: Do you mind _____ _____ _____
   to the library?

M: No, that won't be a problem. I can do that.

library 도서관 | favor 부탁 | mind ~을 꺼리다 | return 반납하다 | problem 문제

TIPS [Do you mind + 동명사?]는 '~하여 주지 않으시겠습니까?'라는 의미입니다.
   A: Do[Would] you mind turning on the light?
      미안하지만 전등을 좀 켜 주시겠어요?
   B: No, not at all. 그렇게 하지요.

10

다음 그림을 보고, 그림과 일치하는 대화를 고르시오. ················· (   )

① ② ③ ④

❶ M: Do you enjoy watching baseball games?
   W: Yes, why?
❷ M: What happened to your arm?
   W: I fell from a tree.
❸ M: What's wrong? You _____ _____.
   W: I have _____ _____.
❹ M: Where are you going?
   W: I'm going to the _____.

enjoy 즐기다 | happen 일어나다 | arm 팔 | fall 넘어지다 | sick 아픈 | flu 독감

TIPS '병에 걸리다'라고 할 때 동사 have를 이용합니다.
   have a headache 머리가 아프다   have a toothache 이가 아프다

11

다음 대화를 듣고, 남자 아이가 대화 후 할 일을 고르시오. ·····················( )

① 청소 　　　　　② 피아노 연습
③ 컴퓨터 게임 　　④ 숙제

W: Jack, your piano teacher is _____ _____. Clean up your room.

B: I've already cleaned it.

W: Okay, _____ _____ until your teacher gets here.

B: Alright, Mom.

soon 곧 | **clean up** 청소하다 | **practice** 연습하다 | **get** 도착하다

TIPS go practice는 go and practice를 줄여서 사용한 표현입니다.

12

다음 대화를 듣고, 여자가 지불할 금액을 고르시오. ·····················( )

① $2 　　　　　② $3
③ $4 　　　　　④ $5

M: May I help you?

W: Yes, I'm _____ _____ mangos.

M: They're here.

W: _____ _____ are these mangos?

M: It's _____ _____ each.

W: Okay. I'll _____ _____.

look for ~을 찾다 | **mango** 망고 | **here** 여기에

TIPS these 다음에 명사가 올 경우에는 반드시 복수형으로 써야 합니다.
these pencils 이 연필들　　these books 이 책들

13

다음 대화를 듣고, 대화가 자연스럽지 않은 것을 고르시오. ·····················( )

①　　②　　③　　④

❶ M: Would you like anything to drink?

　W: Yes, I'd like some orange juice.

❷ M: Thank you for helping me.

　W: It was _____ _____!

❸ M: What are you doing now?

　W: I'm watching TV.

❹ M: What's your _____ _____?

　W: I like _____ books.

anything 무언가 | **pleasure** 즐거움 | **favorite** 좋아하는

14

다음을 듣고, 내용과 일치하지 않는 것을 고르시오. ·····················( )

① 캐시는 옆집에 산다.
② 나는 방과 후 캐시와 자주 논다.
③ 캐시는 춤추는 것을 좋아한다.
④ 캐시는 K-pop을 자주 듣는다.

G: I'd like to introduce my friend Cathy to you. She is from Canada, and she lives _____ _____. We often play together after school. She likes dancing. She _____ _____ to K-pop.

introduce 소개하다 | **next door** 옆집 | **often** 종종 | **sometimes** 때때로

15

다음 대화를 듣고, 두 사람이 만날 시각과 장소를 고르시오. ························· (　　)

① 11시 – 버스 정류장
② 11시 30분 – 버스 정류장
③ 11시 – 지하철역
④ 11시 30분 – 지하철역

[Cellphone rings.]

W: Hello.

M: Hello, Julia. What's up?

W: Ted and I are going to the aquarium tomorrow. Do you want to come with us?

M: Sure, _____ _____ shall we meet?

W: How about 11 o'clock?

M: That's _____ _____. Let's meet _____ _____ at the subway station.

W: Okay.

aquarium 아쿠아리움, 수족관 | tomorrow 내일 | meet 만나다 | too early 너무 이른 | subway station 지하철 역

TIPS 시각이나 비교적 좁은 장소 앞에는 전치사 at을 사용합니다.

16

다음 대화를 듣고, 여자가 하는 운동을 고르시오. ························· (　　)

① ② ③ ④

M: Michelle, you _____ _____ these days.

W: Really? I _____ every day.

M: Do you go jogging every day?

W: No, I _____ _____ every day.

M: Jump rope?

W: Yes, jumping rope is good for health.

healthy 건강한 | these days 요즘 | exercise 운동하다 | jump rope 줄넘기하다

TIPS exercise는 동사(운동하다)와 명사(운동)로 둘 다 이용하여 사용할 수 있습니다. work out도 '운동하다'라는 의미이나, 주로 체육관에서 근육 운동을 할 때 사용하는 표현입니다

17

다음 대화를 듣고, 이어질 말로 알맞은 것을 고르시오. ························· (　　)

B _____

① No, it's not my toy.
② How much is it?
③ No, he doesn't have a toy.
④ Yes, I hope he likes it.

G: Jim! Where are you going?

B: I'm going to the mall.

G: Why are you going to the mall?

B: It's my brother's birthday tomorrow, so I am getting his _____ _____.

G: Your brother will be _____ _____.

B: _____

mall 쇼핑몰 | toy 장난감 | hope 바라다

TIPS Yes, I hope he likes it. 은 '그가 그것을 좋아하면 좋겠어.'라는 의미로 it은 toy를 의미합니다.

18

다음 대화를 듣고, 이어질 말로 알맞은 것을 고르시오. ····················· (   )

G _____

① Yes, I like spicy food.
② I don't like ice skating.
③ Yes, it's in front of the gym.
④ Great. See you on Sunday.

[Cellphone rings.]

G: Hello.

B: Hi. Jessica! It's Nick.

G: Oh, hi, Nick.

B: If you are free this Sunday, do you want to
_____ _____ _____?

G: Sure, that sounds fun! What time shall we meet?

B: _____ _____ 2 o'clock in front of the gym?

G: _____

cellphone 휴대폰 | go ice skating 스케이팅 타다 | in front of ~ 앞에 | gym 체육관

19

다음 대화를 듣고, 이어질 말로 알맞은 것을 고르시오. ····················· (   )

B _____

① Yes, I like him.
② He's a taxi driver.
③ He lives in Seoul.
④ He's from Italy.

G: Is this a picture of your family?

B: Yes, it is.

G: Is this your dad?

B: No, he's _____ _____, Brian.

G: Your uncle is very tall. _____ _____ he do?

B: _____

picture 사진 | uncle 삼촌 | taxi driver 택시 운전사

20

다음 대화를 듣고, 이어질 말로 알맞은 것을 고르시오. ····················· (   )

M _____

① It's my pleasure.
② Oh, that's too bad.
③ You're welcome.
④ Long time no see.

W: Hi, Ted. Did you hear about Tony? He's in the hospital now.

M: _____ _____ to him?

W: He fell off his bike and _____ his _____.

M: _____

hear 듣다 | hospital 병원 | fall off ~에서 떨어지다 | leg 다리

TIPS It's my pleasure. '별말씀을, 천만에요'이란 의미로 상대방이 감사의 표현을 할 때 사용합니다.
A: Thank you for your support. 도와주셔서 감사합니다.
B: It's my pleasure. 천만에요.

● 다음 들려주는 단어와 그 의미를 쓰세요.

단어	의미
01 bookshelf	책장
02	
03	
04	
05	
06	
07	
08	
09	
10	
11	
12	
13	
14	
15	

앞에 모의고사에 나오는 문장들을 잘 듣고, 빈칸을 완성하세요.

01 I think I saw it ___on___ ___the___ ___bookshelf___.

02 Do you know a new Italian restaurant opened _____ _____?

03 I want to be a police officer _____ _____ _____.

04 It took me 6 hours to _____ _____.

05 You should _____ _____ it for your birthday.

06 Have a _____ _____.

07 I _____ _____ a tree.

08 Go practice _____ your teacher gets _____.

09 Thank you for _____ _____.

10 I'd like to _____ my friend Cathy _____ you.

11 Let's meet at 11:30 at the _____ _____.

12 You _____ _____ these days.

13 Your brother will be _____ _____.

14 _____ _____ shall we meet?

15 He fell off his bike and _____ _____ _____.

2^회 영어 듣기 모의고사

보통 속도 빠른 속도

학습일   월   일   부모님 확인   점수

1

다음 대화를 듣고, 대화가 일어나는 장소를 고르시오. ·························· (   )

① 집   ② 옷 가게
③ 교실   ④ 서점

2

다음 그림을 보고, 그림과 일치하는 대화를 고르시오. ···························· (   )

①   ②   ③   ④

3

다음을 듣고, 무엇에 대해 설명하고 있는지 고르시오. ······························ (   )

①    ②

③    ④

4

다음 대화를 듣고, 두 사람이 만날 장소와 시각을 고르시오. ························ (   )

① 버스 정류장 – 10시
② 쇼핑센터 앞 – 10시 30분
③ 버스 정류장 – 12시 30분
④ 쇼핑센터 앞 – 12시 30분

5

다음 대화를 듣고, 대화가 끝난 후 남자 아이가 할 일을 고르시오. ················ (   )

① 청소하기   ② 설거지하기
③ 요리하기   ④ 시장에 가기

6

다음 대화를 듣고, 무엇에 관해 이야기하고 있는지 고르시오. ····················· (   )

① 시험 성적   ② 장래 희망
③ 좋아하는 음식   ④ 좋아하는 과목

7

다음 대화를 듣고, 남자 아이의 여동생을 고르시오. ································· (   )

①   ②

③   ④

8

다음 대화를 듣고, 남자 아이가 이번 주 토요일에 할 일을 고르시오. ·············· (   )

①   ②

③   ④

9

다음 대화를 듣고, 여자 아이가 말한 내용과 일치하지 <u>않는</u> 것을 고르시오. ······ (   )

① 학교에 걸어간다.
② 집 근처에 학교가 있다.
③ 일주일에 세 번 개를 산책시킨다.
④ 독서 모임에 가입했다.

10 　중학기출 변형문제

다음 대화를 듣고, 남자 아이가 전화를 건 목적을 고르시오. ····················· (   )

① 안부를 물으려고
② 약속을 취소하려고
③ 파티에 초대하려고
④ 도움을 요청하려고

11

다음 대화를 듣고, 대화가 자연스럽지 <u>않은</u> 것을 고르시오. ···················· (   )

①   ②   ③   ④

12

다음 그림을 보고, 그림과 일치하는 대화를 고르시오. ·················· (   )

① ② ③ ④

13

다음 대화를 듣고, 남자가 찾고 있는 장소를 고르시오. ····························· (   )

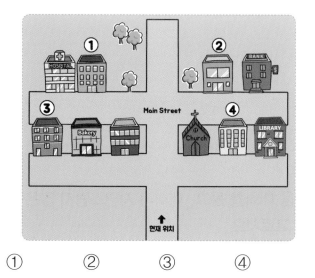

① ② ③ ④

14

다음 대화를 듣고, 여자가 찾고 있는 것이 어디에 있는지 고르시오. ················· (   )

① ② ③ ④

15

다음 대화를 듣고, 여자 아이가 살 케이크의 종류와 금액을 고르시오. ·············· (   )

① 치즈케이크 – 20달러

② 치즈케이크 – 25달러

③ 딸기 케이크 – 25달러

④ 초콜릿 케이크 – 20달러

16 중학기출 변형문제

다음 대화를 듣고, 남자 아이가 부탁한 일을 고르시오. ································· (   )

① 숙제 함께하기 ② 책 빌리기
③ 동생 돌보기 ④ 돈 빌리기

17 중학기출 변형문제

다음 대화를 듣고, 이어질 말로 알맞은 것을 고르시오. ································· (   )

B _____

① I'm not good at basketball.
② I play basketball in the gym.
③ I play with my friends.
④ I play basketball once a week.

18

다음 대화를 듣고, 이어질 말로 알맞은 것을 고르시오. ································· (   )

G _____

① This Friday.
② It's on the desk.
③ I was busy yesterday.
④ History is my favorite subject.

19

다음 대화를 듣고, 이어질 말로 알맞은 것을 고르시오. ································· (   )

W _____

① I think you will like her.
② I'm sure she will be a great artist.
③ Yes, I like drawing flowers.
④ I have art classes on Monday.

20

다음 대화를 듣고, 이어질 말로 알맞지 않은 것을 고르시오. ································· (   )

W _____

① Yes, I'd love to. Thank you,
② Yes, I like watching baseball on TV.
③ I'd like to, but I have another plan.
④ Sure. What time shall we meet?

| 학습일 | 월 일 | 부모님 확인 | | 점수 |

● 잘 듣고, 빈칸에 알맞은 말을 쓰세요.

1

다음 대화를 듣고, 대화가 일어나는 장소를 고르시오. ·········· ( )

① 집　　　　② 옷 가게
③ 교실　　　④ 서점

M: I'm looking for _____ _____ for my son.

W: How about _____ _____?
This just came in.

M: How much is it?

W: It's 50 dollars.

M: Okay. I'll _____ _____.

clothes 옷 | **son** 아들 | **just** 방금

TIPS look for new clothes, coat 등의 표현으로 대화가 일어나는 장소를 알 수 있습니다.

2

다음 그림을 보고, 그림과 일치하는 대화를 고르시오. ·········· ( )

① ② ③ ④

❶ B: It smells so good in here. What are you doing?
G: I'm making some cookies for you.

❷ B: What a _____ _____!
It looks so nice on you.
G: Thank you, Kevin.

❸ B: Can you _____ _____, please?
G: Okay. I'm sorry.

❹ B: Jane, what are you looking for?
G: I'm _____ _____ my scarf.

smell 냄새가 나다 | **pretty** 예쁜 | **scarf** 스카프 | **quiet** 조용한

TIPS 감탄문은 [What + [a/an]+ 형용사 + 명사!]의 어순으로 만듭니다.
What a wonderful world! 매우 아름다운 세상이구나!

3

다음을 듣고, 무엇에 대해 설명하고 있는지 고르시오. ·········· ( )

W: They are long and _____ _____.
They are made of wood, bamboo, or metal.
We use these to _____ _____ or eat food. These are used especially by Asians.

stick 막대기 | **bamboo** 대나무 | **metal** 금속 | **pick up** ~을 들다 | **especially** 특별히 | **Asian** 아시아인

4

다음 대화를 듣고, 두 사람이 만날 장소와 시각을 고르시오. …………… (   )

① 버스 정류장 – 10시
② 쇼핑센터 앞 – 10시 30분
③ 버스 정류장 – 12시 30분
④ 쇼핑센터 앞 – 12시 30분

M: Are we still going to the shopping mall tomorrow?

W: Of course. Where and when should we meet?

M: The shopping mall opens at 10 a.m. Let's meet _____ _____ _____ the mall at 10:30.

W: That's too early. How about _____? Let's have pizza for lunch _____ _____.

M: Great. See you then.

still 여전히 | **shopping mall** 쇼핑몰 | **of course** 물론 | **in front of** ~ 앞에

TIPS [let's + 동사원형]은 '~하자'라는 의미로 제안을 할 때 사용합니다.

5

다음 대화를 듣고, 대화가 끝난 후 남자 아이가 할 일을 고르시오. …………… (   )

① 청소하기   ② 설거지하기
③ 요리하기   ④ 시장에 가기

W: Chris! I'm thinking about cooking bulgogi tonight.

B: That sounds so delicious.

W: Can you do me _____ _____?

B: What is it?

W: Can you _____ _____ _____ _____ and get some onions?

B: Sure.

think about ~에 대해 생각하다, 고려 중이다 | **cook** 요리하다 | **tonight** 오늘 저녁에 | **delicious** 맛있는 | **favor** 부탁 | **market** 시장 | **onion** 양파

TIPS 동사 get은 '~을 사다(buy)'라는 의미가 있습니다.

6

다음 대화를 듣고, 무엇에 관해 이야기하고 있는지 고르시오. …………… (   )

① 시험 성적   ② 장래 희망
③ 좋아하는 음식   ④ 좋아하는 과목

B: Amy, do you like _____?

G: No, I don't. It's too hard.

B: What is your _____ _____?

G: I enjoy learning _____. How about you?

B: I like _____. I want to become an English teacher when I grow up.

science 과학 | **hard** 어려운 | **subject** 과목 | **learn** 배우다 | **become** 되다

TIPS 학교 과목: history 역사, music 음악, P.E. 체육, arts 미술, geography 지리

7

다음 대화를 듣고, 남자 아이의 여동생을 고르시오. …………… (   )

①   ②   ③   ④

B: I lost my sister. Can you help me find her?

W: What does she look like?

B: She has long brown hair and she's _____ _____.

W: Is she wearing a dress?

B: Yes, she's wearing a _____ _____.

lost 잃어버리다(lose)의 과거형 | **wear** 입다 | **hair** 머리 | **glasses** 안경

8

다음 대화를 듣고, 남자 아이가 이번 주 토요일에 할 일을 고르시오. ·············· (　　)

①
②
③
④

G: Jim, do you want to go to the _____ _____ with me this Saturday?

B: I'm sorry, but I can't.

G: Do you have _____ _____?

B: Yes, I have an _____ with the _____ this Saturday.

art museum 미술관 | Saturday 토요일 | plan 계획 | appointment 약속 | dentist 치과의사

TIPS appointment는 '(시간) 예약'으로 쓰입니다. 주로 일과 관련된 시간 약속을 나타내고, promise는 '특정한 행동을 하겠다는 약속'입니다.
She kept her promise to visit them.
그녀는 그들을 방문하겠다는 약속을 지켰다.

9

다음 대화를 듣고, 여자 아이가 말한 내용과 일치하지 <u>않는</u> 것을 고르시오. ······ (　　)

① 학교에 걸어간다.
② 집 근처에 학교가 있다.
③ 일주일에 세 번 개를 산책시킨다.
④ 독서 모임에 가입했다.

B: Cindy, how do you go to school?

G: My school is near my house, so I _____ _____ _____ every day.

B: What do you do after school?

G: I walk _____ _____ on Monday and Thursday.

B: What after-school activities do you do?

G: I joined a _____ _____.

walk 걷다, 산책시키다 | every day 매일 | after-school activity 방과 후 활동

TIPS 여자 아이는 일주일에 두 번 개를 산책시킵니다.

10

다음 대화를 듣고, 남자 아이가 전화를 건 목적을 고르시오. ·················· (　　)

① 안부를 물으려고
② 약속을 취소하려고
③ 파티에 초대하려고
④ 도움을 요청하려고

[Cellphone rings.]

G: Hello.

B: Hi, Susan. It's David.

G: Oh, hi, David. What's up?

B: I'm calling to ask you _____ _____.

G: What is it?

B: I have a _____ _____ tomorrow, but these math problems are _____ _____ for me. Can you help me?

G: Sure. Let's meet at the library.

call 전화하다 | favor 부탁 | problem 문제 | difficult 어려운 | library 도서관

TIPS very와 too는 '매우', '너무'라는 의미의 부사로 형용사를 수식하지만 very가 긍정적이지도 부정적이지도 않은 '중립적(neutral)'인 의미를 가지는데 반해 too는 '부정적'인 의미를 가집니다.

11

다음 대화를 듣고, 대화가 자연스럽지 않은 것을 고르시오. ·················· (   )

①   ②   ③   ④

① W: Can I talk to you for a minute?

   M: Sorry, I'm busy _____ _____.

② W: Would you like something to drink?

   M: No, thank you.

③ W: Can I use your computer for a minute?

   M: Sure. Go ahead.

④ W: _____ _____ you come home?

   M: Yes, I came back _____ _____.

for a minute 잠시 동안 | right now 지금 당장 | something 무언가 | go ahead 계속하다

TIPS · 의문사(why, when, where, what, how 등)로 묻는 질문에는 yes나 no를 이용해서 대답할 수 없습니다.
· will은 미래를 의미하므로 대답도 미래를 나타내어 답해야 합니다.

12

다음 그림을 보고, 그림과 일치하는 대화를 고르시오. ·················· (   )

①   ②   ③   ④

① M: Can I take your order?

   W: Sure. I'd like the chicken curry, please.

② M: Excuse me. You _____ _____ here.

   W: Sorry, I didn't know that.

③ M: Where are you going?

   W: I'm going to the bus stop.

④ M: How was your vacation?

   W: It was _____ _____ _____ fun.

order 주문 | curry 카레 | park 주차하다 | bus stop 버스 정류장 | vacation 휴가 | fun 재미

13

다음 대화를 듣고, 남자가 찾고 있는 장소를 고르시오. ·················· (   )

①   ②   ③   ④

M: Excuse me, can I ask you something?

W: Sure. What is it?

M: Where is the bookstore?

W: Just _____ _____ ahead for two blocks and _____ _____.

M: Go straight ahead for _____ _____ and turn left, and then?

W: It's on your _____. It is next to the hospital.

bookstore 서점 | straight 곧장 | ahead 앞으로 | turn left 왼쪽으로 돌다 | next to ~ 옆에

14

다음 대화를 듣고, 여자가 찾고 있는 것이 어디에 있는지 고르시오. ·············· (   )

①   ②   ③   ④

W: Mike, did you see _____ _____?

B: No, Mom. Where did you leave them?

W: I don't know, but maybe I put them on the sofa.

B: Nothing's there, Mom. Did you check the bookshelf?

W: Yes, I did.

B: Mom, I found your sunglasses.
They are _____ the _____.

sunglasses 선글라스 | leave 두다, 남기다 | maybe 아마도 | put on ~에 놓다 | check 확인하다 | found 찾다(find)의 과거형

TIPS   sunglasses는 복수형으로 써야 하며, 대명사로 쓸 때에도 it이 아닌 they나 them을 사용해야 합니다.

15

다음 대화를 듣고, 여자 아이가 살 케이크의 종류와 금액을 고르시오. ·············· (   )

① 치즈케이크 – 20달러
② 치즈케이크 – 25달러
③ 딸기 케이크 – 25달러
④ 초콜릿 케이크 – 20달러

M: Good morning, may I help you?

G: Yes, I want to buy a chocolate cake.

M: Sorry, we _____ _____ any chocolate cake now. How about a cheesecake or a strawberry cake?

G: I'll take the _____. How much is it?

M: The large one is 25 dollars, and the small one is 20 dollars.

G: I would like the _____ _____, please.

chocolate 초콜릿 | cheese 치즈 | strawberry 딸기

16

다음 대화를 듣고, 남자 아이가 부탁한 일을 고르시오. ·············· (   )

① 숙제 함께하기   ② 책 빌리기
③ 동생 돌보기   ④ 돈 빌리기

G: John, how was Christmas?

B: It was great. My parents gave me a baseball bat. What presents did you get?

G: I got _____ _____ about American history.

B: Really? I'm very interested in history.
Can you _____ _____ to me?

G: Sure.

Christmas 크리스마스 | history 역사 | be interested in ~에 관심 있다 | lend 빌려주다

17

다음 대화를 듣고, 이어질 말로 알맞은 것을 고르시오. ·························· (   )

B _____

① I'm not good at basketball.
② I play basketball in the gym.
③ I play with my friends.
④ I play basketball once a week.

G: Hi, Minsu. What are you going to do after school?

B: I will _____ _____ with my friends.

G: Do you play any _____ _____?

B: I also play basketball.

G: _____ _____ do you play basketball?

B: _____

play tennis 테니스를 치다 | too 역시 | sport 운동 | often 자주

18

다음 대화를 듣고, 이어질 말로 알맞은 것을 고르시오. ·························· (   )

G _____

① This Friday.
② It's on the desk.
③ I was busy yesterday.
④ History is my favorite subject.

G: Kevin, did you do the history homework?

B: Not yet. _____ is the deadline?

G: _____

history 역사 | homework 숙제 | yet 아직 | deadline 마감일

TIPS 의문사 When을 이용해 물으면 구체적인 날짜나 시각 등으로 답해야 합니다.
　　A: When did you see him? 그를 언제 봤어?
　　B: I saw him yesterday. 어제 봤어.

19

다음 대화를 듣고, 이어질 말로 알맞은 것을 고르시오. ·························· (   )

W _____

① I think you will like her.
② I'm sure she will be a great artist.
③ Yes, I like drawing flowers.
④ I have art classes on Monday.

M: Kelly, look at this beautiful painting!

W: Wow, it is very beautiful. Who drew it?

M: My _____ _____. She wants to become _____ _____.

W: _____

beautiful 아름다운 | painting 그림 | drew 그리다(draw)의 과거형 | cousin 사촌

20

다음 대화를 듣고, 이어질 말로 알맞지 <u>않은</u> 것을 고르시오. ·························· (   )

W _____

① Yes, I'd love to. Thank you,
② Yes, I like watching baseball on TV.
③ I'd like to, but I have another plan.
④ Sure. What time shall we meet?

M: Amy, do you like watching _____ _____?

W: Yes, why?

M: I have two tickets to tomorrow's game. _____ _____ _____ to come with me?

W: _____

baseball game 야구 경기 | ticket 표

TIPS [Would you like to + 동사원형?]은 상대방에게 제의하거나 초대할 때 사용하는 표현으로 Okay. / Sure, / Yes, sounds good. / Yes, I'd love to. Thank you. / Sorry, I can't. 등으로 대답할 수 있습니다.

Word Check

● 다음 들려주는 단어와 그 의미를 쓰세요.

	단어	의미
01	stick	막대기
02		
03		
04		
05		
06		
07		
08		
09		
10		
11		
12		
13		
14		
15		

● 앞에 모의고사에 나오는 문장들을 잘 듣고, 빈칸을 완성하세요.

01 This just ___came___ ___in___.

02 It _____ so _____ on you.

03 They _____ _____ _____ wood, bamboo, or metal.

04 _____ and _____ should we meet?

05 That sounds _____ _____.

06 I _____ _____ math.

07 I have an _____ with the _____.

08 I walk to school _____ _____.

09 I'm calling to _____ you a _____.

10 Would you like _____ _____ _____?

11 I _____ _____ last week.

12 Just go _____ _____ for two blocks and turn left.

13 I _____ _____ the large one, please.

14 I'm very _____ _____ history.

15 She wants to become _____ _____.

보통 속도   빠른 속도

| 학습일 | 월 일 | 부모님 확인 | | 점수 |

1

다음 대화를 듣고, 남자가 선택한 물건을 고르시오. ································ (   )

①  ②

③  ④

2

다음 대화를 듣고, 남자 아이가 내일 할 일을 고르시오. ····························· (   )

① 숙제   ② 청소
③ 축구   ④ 요리

3

다음 대화를 듣고, 대화가 일어나는 장소를 고르시오. ····························· (   )

① 도서관   ② 놀이공원
③ 동물원   ④ 식당

4

다음 대화를 듣고, 두 사람이 할 일을 고르시오. ····························· (   )

①   ②

③  ④

5

다음 대화를 듣고, 여자 아이 부모의 직업이 바르게 짝지어진 것을 고르시오. ··· (   )

① 어머니 아버지   ② 어머니 아버지

③ 어머니 아버지   ④ 어머니 아버지

정답 및 해석 p. 10

6

다음 대화를 듣고, 무엇에 관해 이야기하고 있는지 고르시오. ················ (   )

① 방과 후 활동   ② 장래 희망
③ 주말 계획   ④ 휴가 계획

7

다음 그림을 보고, 그림과 일치하는 대화를 고르시오. ····················· (   )

①   ②   ③   ④

8 중학기출 변형문제

다음 대화를 듣고, 여자 아이의 장래 희망을 고르시오. ····················· (   )

① 의사   ② 피아니스트
③ 요리사   ④ 선생님

9

다음 대화를 듣고, 남자가 지불해야 할 금액을 고르시오. ····················· (   )

① 2달러   ② 4달러
③ 6달러   ④ 8달러

10

다음 대화를 듣고, 현재의 날씨를 고르시오.
······························· (   )

①

②

③

④

11

다음을 듣고, 여자 아이가 말한 내용과 <u>다른</u> 것을 고르시오. ··························· (　　　)

① 12살이다.
② 인천에 살고 있다.
③ 음악 듣는 것을 좋아한다.
④ 기타를 잘 친다.

14

다음 대화를 듣고, 남자가 사려는 과일과 지불할 가격이 바르게 짝지어진 것을 고르시오.
··························· (　　　)

① 배 − 2달러　　　　포도 − 5달러
② 배 − 2달러　　　　포도 − 10달러
③ 사과 − 2달러　　　배 − 10달러
④ 배 − 10달러　　　포도 − 2달러

12

다음 대화를 듣고, 대화가 자연스럽지 <u>않은</u> 것을 고르시오. ··························· (　　　)

①　　　　②　　　　③　　　　④

15

다음 대화를 듣고, 남자 아이가 내일 소풍에 가져올 물건을 고르시오. ··············· (　　　)

① 　　②

③ 　　④

13

다음 그림을 보고, 그림과 일치하는 대화를 고르시오. ··························· (　　　)

① 　　② 　　③　　④

16 중학기출 변형문제

다음 대화를 듣고, 여자 아이 엄마의 직업으로 알맞은 것을 고르시오. ············ (   )

① 패션모델
② 가방 제작자
③ 자동차 디자이너
④ 의류회사 디자이너

17

다음 대화를 듣고, 이어질 말로 알맞은 것을 고르시오. ···························· (   )

G _____

① How about meeting at 7 o'clock?
② Oh, that's too bad. I hope she will feel better soon.
③ I want to play with your sister.
④ I don't have any plans tonight.

18

다음 대화를 듣고, 이어질 말로 알맞은 것을 고르시오. ···························· (   )

B _____

① I like all kinds of gimbap.
② I'm eating gimbap now.
③ Gimbap is my favorite food.
④ I have gimbap once a week.

19

다음 대화를 듣고, 이어질 말로 알맞은 것을 고르시오. ···························· (   )

M _____

① I'd like to, but I have to watch TV.
② Yes, I like watching TV.
③ Sure. What time shall we meet?
④ Of course. It's very interesting. You will like it.

20

다음 대화를 듣고, 이어질 말로 알맞지 <u>않은</u> 것을 고르시오. ···························· (   )

W _____

① Sure, what's your dog's name?
② Everything will be okay.
③ Sorry, I'm allergic to dogs.
④ No problem.

학습일   월   일   부모님 확인   점수

● 잘 듣고, 빈칸에 알맞은 말을 쓰세요.

1

다음 대화를 듣고, 남자가 선택한 물건을 고르시오. ························· (   )

① ② ③ ④

W: Hello. Can I help you?

M: Yes, I want a backpack for my daughter.

W: Okay. What about this one with the star on it?

M: It looks good, but it's not her favorite color.
  I want that _____ one with the _____ on it. She likes flowers.

W: _____ _____. Many girls like that backpack.

backpack 배낭 | **daughter** 딸 | **favorite** 좋아하는 | **choice** 선택

TIPS yellow one은 yellow backpack을 의미합니다.

2

다음 대화를 듣고, 남자 아이가 내일 할 일을 고르시오. ························· (   )

① 숙제   ② 청소
③ 축구   ④ 요리

W: Damon, did you finish your homework?

B: Yes, I finished it last night.

W: When are you going to _____ your room?

B: I'll do it _____. I can't do it now.

W: Why?

B: I'm _____ _____ to play soccer now.

finish 끝내다 | **homework** 숙제 | **last night** 어젯밤에 | **clean** 청소하다 | **go out** 나가다

3

다음 대화를 듣고, 대화가 일어나는 장소를 고르시오. ························· (   )

① 도서관   ② 놀이공원
③ 동물원   ④ 식당

B: Am I _____ _____ to ride the roller coaster?

W: Let me check. Yes, you are!

B: Great!

W: But for _____ _____, you need an adult to ride with you.

B: Okay, my dad will ride the roller coaster with me.

enough 충분한 | **roller coaster** 롤러코스터 | **check** 확인하다 | **ride** 탈것 | **adult** 어른

TIPS [enough to + 동사원형]은 '~하기에 충분할 만큼'이란 의미로 enough가 부사로 쓰일 경우 형용사 뒤에서 수식합니다.
He is old enough to drive. 그는 자동차를 운전할 수 있는 나이가 되었다.

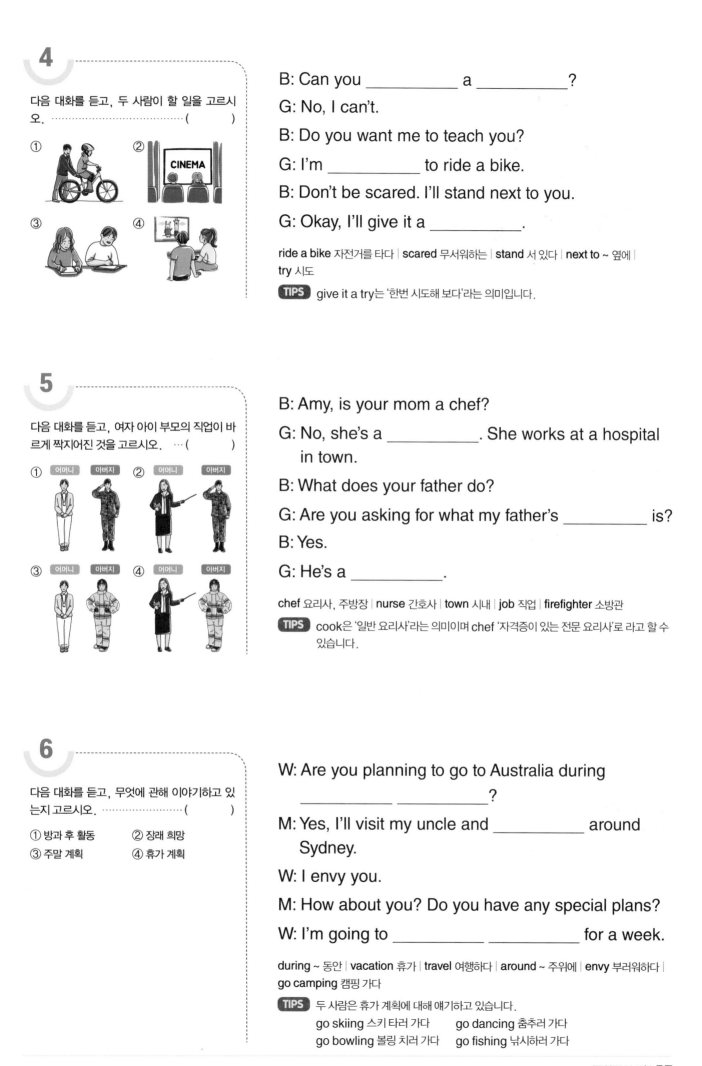

4

다음 대화를 듣고, 두 사람이 할 일을 고르시오. ·········· (　　)

① ② CINEMA
③ ④

B: Can you _____ a _____?
G: No, I can't.
B: Do you want me to teach you?
G: I'm _____ to ride a bike.
B: Don't be scared. I'll stand next to you.
G: Okay, I'll give it a _____.

ride a bike 자전거를 타다 | **scared** 무서워하는 | **stand** 서 있다 | **next to ~** 옆에 | **try** 시도

TIPS give it a try는 '한번 시도해 보다'라는 의미입니다.

5

다음 대화를 듣고, 여자 아이 부모의 직업이 바르게 짝지어진 것을 고르시오. ··· (　　)

① 어머니 아버지 ② 어머니 아버지
③ 어머니 아버지 ④ 어머니 아버지

B: Amy, is your mom a chef?
G: No, she's a _____. She works at a hospital in town.
B: What does your father do?
G: Are you asking for what my father's _____ is?
B: Yes.
G: He's a _____.

chef 요리사, 주방장 | **nurse** 간호사 | **town** 시내 | **job** 직업 | **firefighter** 소방관

TIPS cook은 '일반 요리사'라는 의미이며 chef '자격증이 있는 전문 요리사'로 라고 할 수 있습니다.

6

다음 대화를 듣고, 무엇에 관해 이야기하고 있는지 고르시오. ·················· (　　)

① 방과 후 활동　　② 장래 희망
③ 주말 계획　　　④ 휴가 계획

W: Are you planning to go to Australia during _____ _____?
M: Yes, I'll visit my uncle and _____ around Sydney.
W: I envy you.
M: How about you? Do you have any special plans?
W: I'm going to _____ _____ for a week.

during ~ 동안 | **vacation** 휴가 | **travel** 여행하다 | **around ~** 주위에 | **envy** 부러워하다 | **go camping** 캠핑 가다

TIPS 두 사람은 휴가 계획에 대해 얘기하고 있습니다.
go skiing 스키 타러 가다　　　go dancing 춤추러 가다
go bowling 볼링 치러 가다　　go fishing 낚시하러 가다

7

다음 그림을 보고, 그림과 일치하는 대화를 고르시오. ······( )

① ② ③ ④

❶ M: May I help you?

W: Yes, I'd like to _____ this _____ to London.

❷ M: What would you like to have?

W: I'd like two donuts and an iced tea.

❸ M: Could you please help me _____ this _____?

W: Sure.

❹ M: Good afternoon. How may I help you?

W: I need two tickets to Busan, please.

send 보내다 | package 소포 | move 옮기다 | afternoon 오후 | ticket 표

TIPS 우체국에서 한 여자가 소포를 붙이려하는 그림이므로 ①번이 그림의 상황과 어울립니다.

8

다음 대화를 듣고, 여자 아이의 장래 희망을 고르시오. ······( )

① 의사　　　　② 피아니스트
③ 요리사　　　④ 선생님

G: What do you want to be _____ _____ _____?

B: I want to be a doctor. What about you?

G: When I was young, I wanted to be a pianist.

But now, I really want to _____ _____ _____ like my dad.

B: Your dad's food is really good.

G: Thanks.

in the future 장래에 | young 어린 | pianist 피아니스트 | really 정말 |
chef 요리사, 주방장

TIPS like my dad는 '나의 아버지처럼'이란 의미로 여기서 like는 '~처럼'이란 의미의 전치사입니다.

9

다음 대화를 듣고, 남자가 지불해야 할 금액을 고르시오. ······( )

① 2달러　　　　② 4달러
③ 6달러　　　　④ 8달러

W: May I help you?

M: Yes, I'd like to order a tuna sandwich and a soda. How much is it?

W: The tuna sandwich is _____ dollars, and the soda is _____ dollars.

M: Here's _____ dollars.

W: Here's your _____.

order 주문하다 | tuna 참치 | change 잔돈

TIPS Here's ten dollars.에서 주어는 ten dollars이고 here는 '여기에'라는 부사로 문장의 순서가 도치되어 있습니다. 회화체에서는 복수명사가 뒤에 오더라도 Here are 대신 Here's로 사용할 수 있습니다.

10

다음 대화를 듣고, 현재의 날씨를 고르시오.
.... (   )

① ② ③ ④

G: Mom, can I go to Jessica's house?

W: Sure, but what time would you be back?

G: I will be home for dinner.

W: Okay, do you want me to _____ you _____?

G: No, it's a _____ weather to _____.

W: Okay, give me a call when you get there.

house 집 | be back 돌아오다 | drive 운전하다 | perfect 완벽한 | give a call 전화하다

TIPS a perfect weather to walk는 '걷기에 좋은 날씨'라는 의미로 오늘의 날씨를 유추할 수 있습니다.

11

다음을 듣고, 여자 아이가 말한 내용과 다른 것을 고르시오. .... (   )

① 12살이다.
② 인천에 살고 있다.
③ 음악 듣는 것을 좋아한다.
④ 기타를 잘 친다.

G: Hello, everyone. My name is Jessica Brown.
   I'm 12 years old. I'm from Germany.
   I live in Incheon. My favorite food is fried chicken.
   I like _____ to music.
   I'm good at _____ _____ _____.

Germany 독일 | favorite 좋아하는 | listen to music 음악을 듣다 |
play the violin 바이올린을 연주하다

TIPS 기타를 잘 친다는 내용은 없습니다. 내가 무엇을 잘한다고 말할 때는 [I am good at + 명사/ 동명사]를 이용합니다.

12

다음 대화를 듣고, 대화가 자연스럽지 않은 것을 고르시오. .... (   )

① ② ③ ④

❶ W: What is your favorite _____?
   M: I like _____.
❷ W: Is there a bank near here?
   M: Yes, there is one at the corner.
❸ W: How are you doing?
   M: _____ _____.
❹ W: Dinner is ready. Wash your hands first.
   M: All right.

subject 과목 | baseball 야구 | near 가까운 | corner 모퉁이 | pretty 꽤 | ready 준비된

TIPS I like baseball.이 올바른 대답이 되기 위해서는 What is your favorite subject? 대신 What is your favorite sport?라고 물어야 합니다.

13

다음 그림을 보고, 그림과 일치하는 대화를 고르시오. ·················· (　)

① ② ③ ④

❶ W: How much is it?

　M: It's 10 dollars.

❷ W: Can I help you?

　M: Oh, yes. I'm _____ _____ a wallet.

❸ W: How much money do you have?

　M: I have 20 dollars.

❹ W: Excuse me. Is _____ your _____?

　M: Oh, yes. Thank you.

wallet (남성용)지갑 | money 돈

TIPS 여자가 남자가 떨어뜨린 지갑을 찾아주는 그림이므로 ④번의 대화가 그림과 가장 어울립니다. wallet은 남성용 지갑, purse는 여성용 지갑을 의미합니다.

14

다음 대화를 듣고, 남자가 사려는 과일과 지불할 가격이 바르게 짝지어진 것을 고르시오. ·················· (　)

① 배 – 2달러　　　　포도 – 5달러
② 배 – 2달러　　　　포도 – 10달러
③ 사과 – 2달러　　　배 – 10달러
④ 배 – 10달러　　　포도 – 2달러

M: How much are these pears?

W: _____ dollars each.

M: Okay, I'll just _____ _____.

W: Do you need anything else?

M: Can I get a box of grapes?

W: Sure, it's _____ dollars.

pear 배 | take 사다 | need 필요하다 | grapes 포도

15

다음 대화를 듣고, 남자 아이가 내일 소풍에 가져올 물건을 고르시오. ············· (　)

①　　　　　　　②

③　　　　　　　④

G: Eric, what are you going to do tomorrow?

B: I don't have any _____ _____.

G: How about going on a picnic with me?

B: I would _____ _____.

G: Could you bring a picnic _____ and a _____?

B: Okay!

tomorrow 내일 | special 특별한 | picnic 소풍 | blanket 담요 | basket 바구니

16

다음 대화를 듣고, 여자 아이 엄마의 직업으로 알맞은 것을 고르시오. ············· (　)

① 패션모델　　　　② 가방 제작자
③ 자동차 디자이너　④ 의류회사 디자이너

B: Wow, Susan. What a _____ _____!

G: Thanks, my mom made it for me.

B: Really? I like that style. What does your mother do?

G: She works at a _____ company as a _____.

B: That sounds great!

nice 멋진 | style 스타일 | clothing company 의류 회사 | designer 디자이너

TIPS as a designer에서 as는 전치사로 '~으로서(의)'의 의미를 가지고 있습니다.
　　　　He works as a taxi driver at night. 그 사람은 밤에 택시기사로 일한다.

17

다음 대화를 듣고, 이어질 말로 알맞은 것을 고르시오. ············· ( )

G _____

① How about meeting at 7 o'clock?
② Oh, that's too bad. I hope she will feel better soon.
③ I want to play with your sister.
④ I don't have any plans tonight.

18

다음 대화를 듣고, 이어질 말로 알맞은 것을 고르시오. ············· ( )

B _____

① I like all kinds of gimbap.
② I'm eating gimbap now.
③ Gimbap is my favorite food.
④ I have gimbap once a week.

19

다음 대화를 듣고, 이어질 말로 알맞은 것을 고르시오. ············· ( )

M _____

① I'd like to, but I have to watch TV.
② Yes, I like watching TV.
③ Sure. What time shall we meet?
④ Of course. It's very interesting.

20

다음 대화를 듣고, 이어질 말로 알맞지 <u>않은</u> 것을 고르시오. ············· ( )

W _____

① Sure, what's your dog's name?
② Everything will be okay.
③ Sorry, I'm allergic to dogs.
④ No problem.

[Cellphone rings.]

G: Hello?

B: Hi, Sara. This is Mike.

G: What's up, Mike?

B: I'm afraid I _____ _____ you tonight.

G: What's wrong?

B: My sister _____ _____ . So I have to take care of her.

G: _____

afraid 유감인 | tonight 오늘 저녁 | wrong 잘못된 | sick 아픈 | take care of ~을 돌보다

B: Mom, what are we having for lunch?

W: I'm _____ _____ making gimbap.

B: I love gimbap.

W: _____ _____ of gimbap do you want?

B: _____

think 생각하다 | kind 종류

TIPS I have gimbap once a week.이 정답이 되려면 How often do you have gimbap?으로 질문해야 합니다.

W: What are you doing?

M: I'm _____ _____ .

W: What program are you watching?

M: It's a documentary about sharks.

W: Wow, awesome. _____ _____ watch it with you?

M: _____

program 프로그램 | documentary 다큐멘터리 | awesome 멋진

TIPS Of course.는 상대방의 질문에 대한 강한 긍정의 대답입니다.

M: What are you going to do after school?

W: _____ special. Why?

M: _____ _____ take care of my dog?

W: _____

after school 방과 후에 | special 특별한 | take care of ~을 돌보다

TIPS Everything will be okay.는 '모두 잘 될 거야.'라는 의미입니다.

● 다음 들려주는 단어와 그 의미를 쓰세요.

	단어	의미
01	daughter	딸
02		
03		
04		
05		
06		
07		
08		
09		
10		
11		
12		
13		
14		
15		

● 앞에 모의고사에 나오는 문장들을 잘 듣고, 빈칸을 완성하세요.

01 I'm ___going___ ___out___ to play soccer now.

02 You need an _____ _____ ride with you.

03 _____ _____ to ride a bike.

04 I'll _____ _____ _____ _____.

05 She _____ _____ a hospital in town.

06 Do you have any _____ _____?

07 I'd like to _____ _____ _____ to London.

08 I really _____ _____ _____ a chef like my dad.

09 Here's _____ _____.

10 It's _____ _____ to walk.

11 I'm good at _____ _____ _____.

12 There is one _____ _____ _____.

13 _____ _____ going on a picnic with me?

14 She works at a _____ _____ as a designer.

15 _____ _____ I can't meet you tonight.

영어 듣기 모의고사

 보통 속도 빠른 속도

| 학습일 | 월 일 | 부모님 확인 | 점수 |

1

다음 대화를 듣고, 남자가 사려는 스웨터를 고르시오. ················· (   )

①  ②

③  ④

2

다음 대화를 듣고, 음악 축제가 열리는 날짜를 고르시오. ················· (   )

October

Sun	Mon	Tue	Wed	Thu	Fri	Sat
1	2	① 3	4	5	② 6	7
8	9	③ 10	11	④ 12	13	14

① ② ③ ④

3

다음 대화를 듣고, 대화가 끝난 후 남자 아이가 할 일을 고르시오. ··············· (   )

① 심부름 ② 숙제
③ 농구   ④ 방 청소

4

다음 대화를 듣고, 여자 아이가 어제 한 일을 고르시오. ··············· (   )

①  ②

③  ④

5

다음 대화를 듣고, 대화가 일어나는 장소를 고르시오. ··············· (   )

① 기차역   ② 버스 정류장
③ 미술관   ④ 극장

6

다음 대화를 듣고, 무엇에 관해 이야기하고 있는지 고르시오. ·························· (　　　)

① 영어 수업　　　　② 좋아하는 과목
③ 한국어 수업　　　④ 영어선생님

7

다음 그림을 보고, 그림과 일치하는 대화를 고르시오. ·························· (　　　)

①　　　　②　　　　③　　　　④

8

다음 대화를 듣고, 두 사람이 점심으로 먹을 음식을 고르시오. ·················· (　　　)

①　　　　　　　　②

③　　　　　　　　④

9

다음 대화를 듣고, 여자가 지불할 금액을 고르시오. ·························· (　　　)

① 15달러　　　　② 20달러
③ 25달러　　　　④ 30달러

10

다음 대화를 듣고, 대화가 자연스럽지 <u>않은</u> 것을 고르시오. ·················· (　　　)

①　　　　②　　　　③　　　　④

11

다음 대화를 듣고, 두 사람이 이용할 교통수단을 고르시오. ·················· (   )

①

②

③

④

12

다음 대화를 듣고, 대화의 내용으로 알 수 <u>없는</u> 것을 고르시오. ·················· (   )

① Mike의 취미
② Mike가 좋아하는 음악
③ Mike가 음악을 듣는 횟수
④ Mike가 좋아하는 가수

13

다음 대화를 듣고, 남자 아이가 전화한 이유를 고르시오. ·················· (   )

① 숙제를 함께 하려고
② 두고 온 물건을 찾으려고
③ 학교에 함께 가기 위해
④ 공책을 빌리려고

14

다음 대화를 듣고, 두 사람이 내일 만날 시각과 장소를 고르시오. ·················· (   )

① 10시 – 버스 정류장
② 11시 – 지하철역
③ 10시 – 지하철역
④ 11시 – 도서관 앞

15

다음 대화를 듣고, 남자 아이가 찾는 물건의 위치를 고르시오. ·················· (   )

①   ②   ③   ④

16

다음 대화를 듣고, 여자 아이의 취미로 알맞은 것을 고르시오. ·················· (   )

① 낚시   ② 그림 그리기
③ 노래 부르기   ④ 사진 찍기

17

다음 대화를 듣고, 이어질 말로 알맞은 것을 고르시오. ·························· (   )

B _____

① Good luck. I'm sure you will do fine.
② Wow, it's wonderful.
③ Really? That sounds interesting.
④ Thank you very much.

18 중학기출 변형문제

다음 대화를 듣고, 이어질 말로 알맞은 것을 고르시오. ·························· (   )

W _____

① Here you are.
② I'm sorry, but I can't.
③ I'm sorry to hear that.
④ Where is his house?

19

다음 대화를 듣고, 이어질 말로 알맞은 것을 고르시오. ·························· (   )

B _____

① I don't like ice skating.
② I was in the hospital.
③ So, I stayed in bed.
④ I hope you get better soon.

20

다음 대화를 듣고, 이어질 말로 적절하지 않은 것을 고르시오. ·················· (   )

M _____

① Okay. I'll take it.
② It's not my bag.
③ How much is it?
④ It's not my style. Do you have another one?

4 회 Dictation 영어 듣기 모의고사

| 학습일 · | 월 일 | 부모님 확인 | 점수 |

● 잘 듣고, 빈칸에 알맞은 말을 쓰세요.

1

다음 대화를 듣고, 남자가 사려는 스웨터를 고르시오. ·················· (   )

W: Can I help you?

M: Yes, I'm looking for a _____.

W: How about this red one?

M: I don't like its color. Can you show me the _____ sweater?

W: Do you mean the one with the _____ on it?

M: Yes, I'll take that. How much is it?

sweater 스웨터 | show 보여주다 | mean 의미하다 | deer 사슴

TIPS the one with the deer는 the sweater with the deer란 의미입니다.

2

다음 대화를 듣고, 음악 축제가 열리는 날짜를 고르시오. ·················· (   )

October

Sun	Mon	Tue	Wed	Thu	Fri	Sat
1	2	① 3	4	5	② 6	7
8	9	③ 10	11	④ 12	13	14

①   ②   ③   ④

G: Hi, Jack. Can you come to the music festival?

B: When is the festival?

G: It's _____ _____.

B: Next Tuesday? Do you mean _____ _____?

G: Yes, it is.

B: I'm not sure. I have a swimming lesson on that day.

festival 축제 | Tuesday 화요일 | sure 확실한 | lesson 수업

TIPS 날짜를 표시할 때 기수를 사용해서 쓸 수 있지만, 읽을 때나 말할 때에는 서수로 말해야 합니다.

3

다음 대화를 듣고, 대화가 끝난 후 남자 아이가 할 일을 고르시오. ·················· (   )

① 심부름   ② 숙제
③ 농구   ④ 방 청소

B: Mom, can I go out and play basketball with Steve?

W: Yes, but did you _____ your _____?

B: Yes, I did.

W: What about cleaning your room?

B: Oh, I forgot. Can I do it when I come back?

W: No, _____ your _____, and then you can go out.

B: Okay.

go out 외출하다 | basketball 농구 | finish 끝나다 | clean 청소하다 |
forgot 잊다(forget)의 과거형

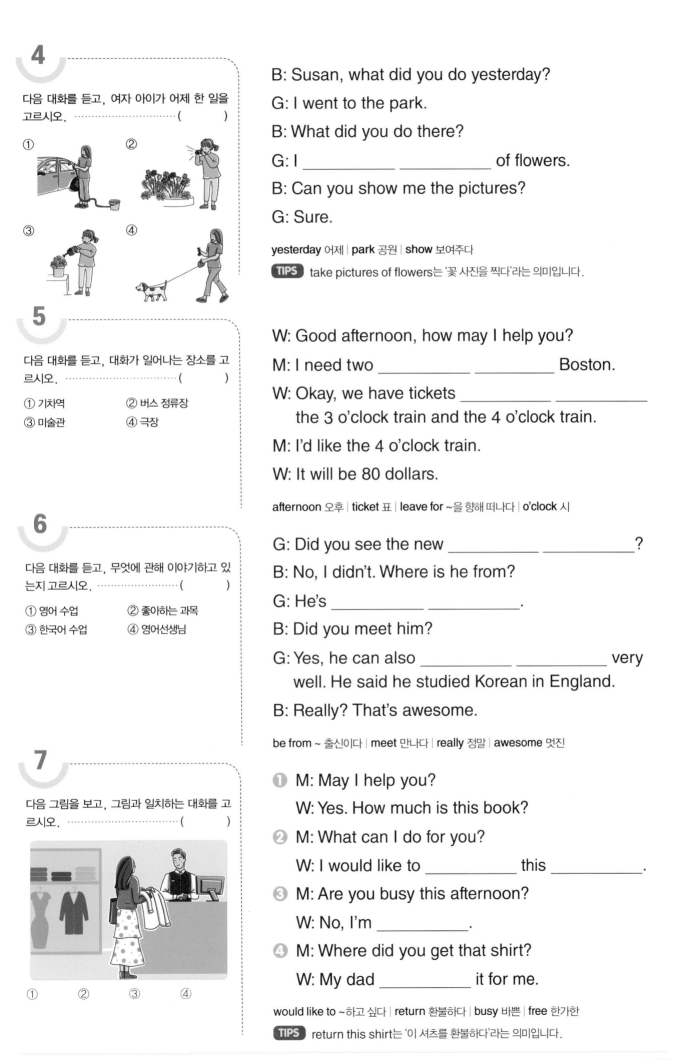

4

다음 대화를 듣고, 여자 아이가 어제 한 일을 고르시오. ………………… ( )

① ② ③ ④

B: Susan, what did you do yesterday?

G: I went to the park.

B: What did you do there?

G: I _____ _____ of flowers.

B: Can you show me the pictures?

G: Sure.

yesterday 어제 | **park** 공원 | **show** 보여주다

TIPS take pictures of flowers는 '꽃 사진을 찍다'라는 의미입니다.

5

다음 대화를 듣고, 대화가 일어나는 장소를 고르시오. ………………… ( )

① 기차역　　　② 버스 정류장
③ 미술관　　　④ 극장

W: Good afternoon, how may I help you?

M: I need two _____ _____ Boston.

W: Okay, we have tickets _____ _____ the 3 o'clock train and the 4 o'clock train.

M: I'd like the 4 o'clock train.

W: It will be 80 dollars.

afternoon 오후 | **ticket** 표 | **leave for** ~을 향해 떠나다 | **o'clock** 시

6

다음 대화를 듣고, 무엇에 관해 이야기하고 있는지 고르시오. ………………… ( )

① 영어 수업　　　② 좋아하는 과목
③ 한국어 수업　　　④ 영어선생님

G: Did you see the new _____ _____?

B: No, I didn't. Where is he from?

G: He's _____ _____.

B: Did you meet him?

G: Yes, he can also _____ _____ very well. He said he studied Korean in England.

B: Really? That's awesome.

be from ~ 출신이다 | **meet** 만나다 | **really** 정말 | **awesome** 멋진

7

다음 그림을 보고, 그림과 일치하는 대화를 고르시오. ………………… ( )

① ② ③ ④

❶ M: May I help you?
　 W: Yes. How much is this book?

❷ M: What can I do for you?
　 W: I would like to _____ this _____.

❸ M: Are you busy this afternoon?
　 W: No, I'm _____.

❹ M: Where did you get that shirt?
　 W: My dad _____ it for me.

would like to ~하고 싶다 | **return** 환불하다 | **busy** 바쁜 | **free** 한가한

TIPS return this shirt는 '이 셔츠를 환불하다'라는 의미입니다.

8

다음 대화를 듣고, 두 사람이 점심으로 먹을 음식을 고르시오. ································· (   )

① ② ③ ④

W: What do you want for _____?

M: I want a cheese sandwich.

W: We don't have any cheese now.

M: Then, how about we eat creamy _____ _____?

W: Sounds good. We should _____ _____, too.

M: Great. I will help you cook.

cheese sandwich 치즈 샌드위치 | **creamy shrimp pasta** 새우 크림 파스타 | **add** 첨가하다 | **bacon** 베이컨

TIPS [how about + we + 동사]는 '우리 ~하는 게 어떨까?'라는 의미입니다.
How about we go out for Korean food tonight?
오늘 저녁에 한국 요리 먹으러 가는 게 어때?

9

다음 대화를 듣고, 여자가 지불할 금액을 고르시오. ································· (   )

① 15달러   ② 20달러
③ 25달러   ④ 30달러

M: Can I help you?

W: Yes, I'm looking for a cake.

M: We have two kinds: cheesecake and chocolate cake.

W: They look delicious. _____ _____ are they?

M: The cheesecake is _____ dollars, and the chocolate cake is _____ dollars.

W: Okay. I'll _____ the _____.

look for ~을 찾다 | **chocolate** 초콜릿 | **delicious** 맛있는 | **take** 사다

10

다음 대화를 듣고, 대화가 자연스럽지 <u>않은</u> 것을 고르시오. ································· (   )

①   ②   ③   ④

❶ W: What kind of movie do you like?
   M: I like action movies.

❷ W: _____ _____ I get to the bookstore?
   M: It _____ 30 minutes.

❸ W: What do you have for breakfast?
   M: I have some bread and milk.

❹ W: How was your weekend, Tom?
   M: It was _____ _____.

action movie 액션영화 | **bookstore** 서점 | **weekend** 주말 | **pretty** 꽤

TIPS It takes 30 minutes.(30분 걸려요.)가 올바른 대답이 되려면 How long does it take from here to the bookstore?(여기서 서점까지 (시간이) 얼마쯤 걸립니까?)로 질문해야 합니다.

11

다음 대화를 듣고, 두 사람이 이용할 교통수단을 고르시오. .... (   )

① (image of train)
② (image of ship)
③ (image of airplane)
④ (image of car)

M: What time is it now?

W: It's _____ 1:30.

M: We _____ _____. Let's take the subway.

W: The subway station is far from here.
   Let's _____ _____ _____.

M: Sounds great.

now 지금 | already 이미 | be late 늦다 | subway 지하철 | taxi 택시

TIPS take the bus 버스를 타다   take the plane 비행기를 타다

12

다음 대화를 듣고, 대화의 내용으로 알 수 없는 것을 고르시오. .... (   )

① Mike의 취미
② Mike가 좋아하는 음악
③ Mike가 음악을 듣는 횟수
④ Mike가 좋아하는 가수

G: Do you have _____ _____, Mike?

B: Yes, I love listening to _____ _____.

G: How often do you listen to classical music?

B: I listen to it _____ _____.

G: Wow, you really like listening to music.

hobby 취미 | listen to music 음악을 듣다 | classical music 고전음악 | every day 매일

TIPS Mike는 고전음악을 좋아하고 매일 고전음악을 듣지만, 좋아하는 가수에 대한 언급은 없습니다.

13

다음 대화를 듣고, 남자 아이가 전화한 이유를 고르시오. .... (   )

① 숙제를 함께 하려고
② 두고 온 물건을 찾으려고
③ 학교에 함께 가기 위해
④ 공책을 빌리려고

[Cellphone rings.]

G: Hello?

B: Hi, Cathy! This is Tony.
   I think I _____ my _____ at your house.

G: Your notebook?

B: Yes, can you check the table by the bookshelf?

G: Is it the one with a cartoon character on it?

B: Yes, that's the one! Can you _____ it _____ school tomorrow?

cellphone 휴대폰 | notebook 공책 | check 확인하다 | bookshelf 책장 | cartoon 만화 | character 캐릭터

14

다음 대화를 듣고, 두 사람이 내일 만날 시각과 장소를 고르시오. ·················· (　　)

① 10시 – 버스 정류장
② 11시 – 지하철역
③ 10시 – 지하철역
④ 11시 – 도서관 앞

G: Jack, how about going to the zoo tomorrow?

B: Sounds good. Let's go there by bike.

G: I don't have a bike. Let's _____ the _____.

B: Okay. _____ and _____ shall we meet tomorrow?

G: Let's meet at _____ at the subway station.

B: Okay. See you tomorrow.

zoo 동물원 | by bike 자전거로 | subway 지하철 | station 역

15

다음 대화를 듣고, 남자 아이가 찾는 물건의 위치를 고르시오. ·················· (　　)

① ② ③ ④

W: Jim, make sure you wear warm clothes today. It's going to snow all day today.

B: Did you see _____ _____?

W: I saw them _____ your desk.

B: They're not there.

W: Then, why don't you look _____ the _____.

B: Here they are. Thank you, Mom.

make sure 반드시 ～하다 | warm 따뜻한 | all day 하루 종일 | gloves 장갑 | under ~ 아래에

16

다음 대화를 듣고, 여자 아이의 취미로 알맞은 것을 고르시오. ·················· (　　)

① 낚시
② 그림 그리기
③ 노래 부르기
④ 사진 찍기

G: What do you do when you are free?

B: I _____ _____ once a month.

G: Sounds interesting!

B: Do you have any hobbies?

G: I _____ _____. I want to be an artist when I grow up.

free 한가한 | go fishing 낚시하다 | once 한 번 | interesting 재미있는 | hobby 취미 | artist 화가 | grow up 자라다

17

다음 대화를 듣고, 이어질 말로 알맞은 것을 고르시오. ·················· (　　)

B _____

① Good luck. I'm sure you will do fine.
② Wow, it's wonderful.
③ Really? That sounds interesting.
④ Thank you very much.

B: What are you doing?

G: I am practicing for the _____ _____.

B: When is the contest?

G: It's _____ _____.

B: _____

practice 연습하다 | speech contest 말하기 대회 | sure 확실한 | wonderful 멋진

TIPS　I'll keep my fingers crossed.(행운을 빌게.) 등의 상대방을 격려하는 표현이 와야 자연스럽습니다.

18

다음 대화를 듣고, 이어질 말로 알맞은 것을 고르시오. ·············· ( )

W _____

① Here you are.
② I'm sorry, but I can't.
③ I'm sorry to hear that.
④ Where is his house?

M: Happy birthday, Susie.

W: Thank you for coming, Jack. _____ _____ _____, have you seen Tom today? I called him, but he didn't answer his phone.

M: No. I think he is in the _____. Yesterday, he had a _____ _____.

W: _____

by the way 그런데 | **call** 전화하다 | **be in (the) hospital** 입원해 있다 | **car accident** 자동차 사고

19

다음 대화를 듣고, 이어질 말로 알맞은 것을 고르시오. ·············· ( )

B _____

① I don't like ice skating.
② I was in the hospital.
③ So, I stayed in bed.
④ I hope you get better soon.

B: What _____ to your foot?

G: I went ice skating with my family, and I _____.

B: Oh no, did you _____ it?

G: Unfortunately, _____.

B: _____

happen 일어나다 | **foot** 발 | **fell** 넘어지다(fall)의 과거형 | **break** 부러지다 | **unfortunately** 불행하게도

TIPS 다리가 부러진 상대방에게 위로하는 표현이 와야 합니다.

20

다음 대화를 듣고, 이어질 말로 적절하지 않은 것을 고르시오. ·············· ( )

M _____

① Okay. I'll take it.
② It's not my bag.
③ How much is it?
④ It's not my style. Do you have another one?

W: Hi, how can I help you?

M: I am looking for a bag.

W: _____ _____ this blue one? It's _____ _____.

M: _____

look for ~을 찾다 | **on sale** 세일 중

TIPS another는 '또 다른'이란 의미이며, [an + other]로 볼 수 있습니다. 하나를 나타내는 an이 붙어 있기 때문에 another 다음에는 셀 수 있는 단수명사만 오게 됩니다.
Can I ask you another question? 또 다른 질문을 해도 될까요?

● 다음 들려주는 단어와 그 의미를 쓰세요.

	단어	의미
01	sweater	스웨터
02		
03		
04		
05		
06		
07		
08		
09		
10		
11		
12		
13		
14		
15		

Sentence Check

● 앞에 모의고사에 나오는 문장들을 잘 듣고, 빈칸을 완성하세요.

01 Can you _____ show _____ me _____ the blue sweater?

02 I have a _____ _____ on that day.

03 Clean your room, and then _____ _____ _____ out.

04 I _____ _____ of flowers.

05 He can also _____ _____ very well.

06 I would like to _____ _____ _____.

07 How can I _____ _____ the bookstore?

08 The subway station is _____ _____ here.

09 Do you have _____ _____?

10 _____ _____ I left my notebook at your house.

11 Let's _____ _____ _____.

12 It's going to snow _____ _____ today.

13 I want to be an artist when I _____ _____.

14 I am practicing for the _____ _____.

15 Yesterday, he had a _____ _____.

보통 속도

빠른 속도

학습일   월   일   부모님 확인   점수

1

다음 대화를 듣고, 남자 아이가 대화가 끝난 후 할 일을 고르시오. ················ (   )

① 피자 만들기   ② 피자 주문하기
③ 시장에 가기   ④ 비빔밥 만들기

2

다음 대화를 듣고, 여자가 가려는 장소를 고르시오. ··························· (   )

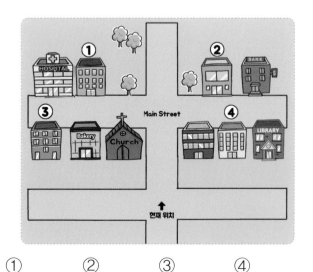

①   ②   ③   ④

3

다음 대화를 듣고, 여자 아이 언니의 장래 희망을 고르시오. ····················· (   )

① 작가   ② 선생님
③ 의사   ④ 요리사

4

다음 대화를 듣고, 남자 아이가 먹을 간식을 고르시오. ···························· (   )

①   ②
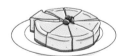

③   ④

5

다음 대화를 듣고, 여자 아이의 생일을 고르시오. ···························· (   )

① 8월 10일   ② 9월 10일
③ 9월 11일   ④ 10월 10일

6

다음 그림을 보고, 그림과 일치하는 대화를 고르시오. ···························· (   )

①   ②   ③   ④

7

다음 대화를 듣고, 여자가 찾는 물건이 있는 곳을 고르시오. ···················· (   )

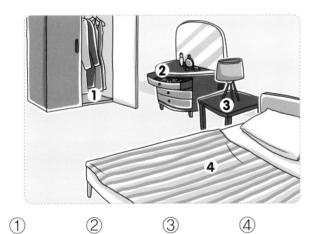

①   ②   ③   ④

8

다음 대화를 듣고, 여자 아이가 4월을 좋아하는 이유를 고르시오. ················ (   )

① 친구들을 만날 수 있어서
② 생일이 4월에 있어서
③ 꽃을 볼 수 있어서
④ 새 학기가 시작되어서

9

다음 대화를 듣고, 남자 아이 친구의 모습을 고르시오. ······················ (   )

①    ②

③    ④

10

다음 대화를 듣고, 남자 아이가 동생의 선물로 사려는 것을 고르시오. ············· (   )

①    ②

③   ④

11

다음 대화를 듣고, 여자 아이가 주말에 한 일을 고르시오. ···················· (   )

① 영화 감상　　　② 공연 관람
③ 독서　　　　　④ 낚시

12

다음 대화를 듣고, 대화가 자연스럽지 않은 것을 고르시오. ····················· (   )

①　　　　②　　　　③　　　　④

13

다음 그림을 보고, 그림과 일치하는 대화를 고르시오. ···························· (   )

①　　　　②　　　　③　　　　④

14

다음 대화를 듣고, 남자 아이가 산 도넛의 개수와 지불한 금액을 고르시오. ········ (   )

①
3개 – 5달러

②
4개 – 5달러

③
3개 – 6달러

④
4개 – 6달러

15

다음 대화를 듣고, 남자가 전화한 이유를 고르시오. ···························· (   )

① 약속을 취소하려고
② 물건을 빌리려고
③ 파티 장소를 알아보려고
④ 파티에 늦을 거라고 알리려고

16

다음을 듣고, 내용과 일치하지 <u>않는</u> 것을 고르시오. ·························· (   )

① 누나의 이름은 Nancy다.
② 누나는 나보다 4살 많다.
③ 누나는 키가 크다.
④ 누나의 장래 희망은 선생님이 되는 것이다.

17

다음 대화를 듣고, 이어질 말로 알맞은 것을 고르시오. ·························· (   )

B _____

① No, that's all. Thank you.
② No, I like tulips.
③ How many roses do you want?
④ Sorry, we don't have tulips.

18 중학기출 변형문제

다음 대화를 듣고, 이어질 말로 알맞은 것을 고르시오. ·························· (   )

B _____

① Here you are.
② I'm free today.
③ Sure. What is it?
④ It's my pleasure.

19

다음 대화를 듣고, 이어질 말로 알맞은 것을 고르시오. ·························· (   )

M _____

① I think it will be lots of fun.
② Where is the store?
③ What kind of chocolate do you like?
④ No, thank you. I'm on a diet.

20

다음 대화를 듣고, 이어질 말로 알맞은 것을 고르시오. ·························· (   )

M _____

① How much is it?
② I think it's expensive.
③ Let's find it together.
④ I think your computer has a virus.

학습일   월   일   부모님 확인   점수

● 잘 듣고, 빈칸에 알맞은 말을 쓰세요.

1

다음 대화를 듣고, 남자 아이가 대화가 끝난 후 할 일을 고르시오. ·············· (   )

① 피자 만들기   ② 피자 주문하기
③ 시장에 가기   ④ 비빔밥 만들기

B: Mom, what are we having _____ _____?
W: How about bibimbap?
B: We had bibimbap yesterday.
W: Then, how about we _____ _____?
B: Sounds great, Mom! Let me order pizza _____.

yesterday 어제 | order 주문하다 | online 온라인으로

TIPS [Let me + 동사원형]은 '제가 ~하게 해 주세요, 제가 ~할게요.'라는 의미입니다.
Let me do it. 제가 할게요.

2

다음 대화를 듣고, 여자가 가려는 장소를 고르시오. ·············· (   )

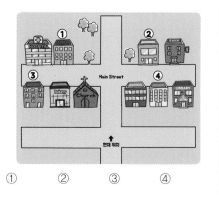

① ② ③ ④

W: Can you tell me how I can get to the post office?
M: You have to go straight and _____ _____ when you see the church.
   It's _____ from the hospital.
W: Is it far from here?
M: It will _____ _____ ten minutes.
W: Okay, thank you.

get to ~에 도착하다 | post office 우체국 | church 교회 | across 맞은편에 |
hospital 병원 | take 걸리다

TIPS 동사 take는 '시간이 걸리다'라는 의미입니다.

3

다음 대화를 듣고, 여자 아이 언니의 장래 희망을 고르시오. ·············· (   )

① 작가   ② 선생님
③ 의사   ④ 요리사

G: My sister wrote this poem.
B: Wow. She _____ _____ very well.
G: Yes. She loves writing. When she is free, she _____ writes poems.
B: I think she will become a great writer.
G: It is her dream to _____ _____ _____.

poem 시 | write 쓰다 | think 생각하다 | become 되다 | writer 작가 | dream 꿈

TIPS It is her dream to become a writer.에서 It은 가주어 to become은 진주어입니다.

4

다음 대화를 듣고, 남자 아이가 먹을 간식을 고르시오. ·················· ( )

① ② ③ ④

B: Mom, I am hungry. Can I have _____ _____ _____?

W: Sure, I baked some cookies. Do you want some?

B: No, I want chocolate cake.

W: You ate that last night. How about some _____ _____?

B: Okay, Mom. I will _____ _____.

hungry 배고픈 | something 무언가 | bake 굽다 | sweet potato 고구마

TIPS something을 수식하는 형용사 또는 to부정사는 something 뒤에 위치합니다.
something new 무언가 새로운 것[일]   something to drink (무언가) 마실 것

5

다음 대화를 듣고, 여자 아이의 생일을 고르시오. ·················· ( )

① 8월 10일   ② 9월 10일
③ 9월 11일   ④ 10월 10일

G: Paul, do you know that my birthday is _____ _____ _____?

B: When is it?

G: It's _____ _____.

B: _____ 10?

G: Yes, my birthday is September 10.
   Can you come to my birthday party?

B: Of course.

know 알다 | come up soon 곧 다가오다 | of course 물론

TIPS 날짜를 표시할 때 기수를 사용해서 쓸 수 있지만, 읽을 때나 말할 때에는 서수로 말해야 합니다.

6

다음 그림을 보고, 그림과 일치하는 대화를 고르시오. ·················· ( )

① ② ③ ④

❶ W: How often do you take a shower?
   M: I take a shower _____ _____.

❷ W: What do you want for dinner?
   M: What about noodles?

❸ W: How are you doing today?
   M: Not bad.

❹ W: Can you help me _____ _____ _____?
   M: Sure. _____ _____.

take a shower 샤워하다 | every day 매일 | noodles 국수 |
wash the dishes 설거지하다

7

다음 대화를 듣고, 여자가 찾는 물건이 있는 곳을 고르시오. ·························· (   )

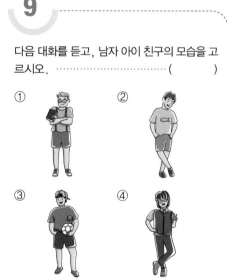

①   ②   ③   ④

W: Sam, did you see my swimming _____?

B: No, Mom. Where did you leave them?

W: I thought I put them in the _____.

B: Nothing's there, Mom. Did you check the table?

W: Yes, I did.

B: Oh, I found them, Mom. They are _____ _____ _____.

swimming goggles 물안경 | leave 놓다 | thought 생각하다(think)의 과거형 | drawer 서랍 | check 확인하다

TIPS goggles를 대명사로 쓸 경우에는 it이 아닌 them으로 써야 합니다.

8

다음 대화를 듣고, 여자 아이가 4월을 좋아하는 이유를 고르시오. ·············· (   )

① 친구들을 만날 수 있어서
② 생일이 4월에 있어서
③ 꽃을 볼 수 있어서
④ 새 학기가 시작되어서

B: Can you believe today is the last day of March?

G: Time goes by fast, doesn't it? But I like the _____ _____ _____.

B: Why?

G: _____ _____ is in April.

B: Oh, that's why you like April.

G: Yes, I will have a birthday party. Can you come?

B: _____.

believe 믿다 | time goes by fast 시간이 빠르다 | month 달

TIPS 달, 계절, 연도 앞에는 전치사 in을 씁니다.
I was born in 2002. 나는 2002년에 태어났다.
It's very cold in winter. 겨울에는 날씨가 매우 춥다.

9

다음 대화를 듣고, 남자 아이 친구의 모습을 고르시오. ·························· (   )

①   ②
③   ④

G: Tim, is your friend Mike in _____ _____?

B: Yes, he is in the picture.

G: Is he wearing blue jeans?

B: No, he's _____ _____.

G: Is he reading a book?

B: No, he's _____ _____ _____ in his hand.

picture 사진 | blue jeans 청바지 | shorts 반바지 | hold 들다, 잡다 | ball 공

TIPS 반바지를 입고 공을 손에 들고 있는 소년이 Mike입니다.
반바지(shorts)는 반드시 복수형으로 써야 합니다.

10

다음 대화를 듣고, 남자 아이가 동생의 선물로 사려는 것을 고르시오. ·········· (   )

① ② ③ ④

B: Did you buy a Christmas _____ for your younger sister?

G: No, not yet, but I will buy a backpack for her.

B: That's good. I don't know what to get for my brother.

G: How about a _____ _____?

B: He has many toy robots.

G: Then, how about a toy train?

B: That's a _____ _____.
He doesn't have a _____ _____.

present 선물 | younger sister 여동생 | backpack 배낭 | toy robot 장난감 로봇 | idea 생각

11

다음 대화를 듣고, 여자 아이가 주말에 한 일을 고르시오. ···························· (   )

① 영화 감상   ② 공연 관람
③ 독서   ④ 낚시

B: How was your weekend?

G: It was great.

B: Did you _____ to the _____?

G: No, I didn't.

B: What did you do?

G: I _____ to a K-pop _____ with my cousins.

B: Really? Sounds interesting.

G: Yeah, the concert was _____.

weekend 주말 | movie 영화 | concert 콘서트 | cousin 사촌 | interesting 재미있는

TIPS go to the movies는 '영화를 보러 가다'라는 의미로 go to a movie로 바꿔 쓸 수 있습니다.

12

다음 대화를 듣고, 대화가 자연스럽지 않은 것을 고르시오. ···························· (   )

① ② ③ ④

❶ W: Hi, John. How's it going?
M: Pretty good.

❷ W: _____ _____ does your school begin?
M: It's _____ _____ the hospital.

❸ M: Hi. My name is Scott Brown.
W: I'm Jane Smith. Nice to _____ _____.

❹ W: What would you like to have?
M: I'll _____ French fries and a Coke.

begin 시작하다 | next to ~ 옆에 | meet 만나다 | French fries 감자튀김

TIPS It's next to the hospital.의 대답에 어울리는 질문은 Where is ~?입니다.

13

다음 그림을 보고, 그림과 일치하는 대화를 고르시오. ·························· (   )

① ② ③ ④

M: ❶ The woman is _____ in the kitchen.
　 ❷ The woman is _____ _____ at a restaurant.
　 ❸ The woman is _____ food at a restaurant.
　 ❹ The woman is wearing a baseball cap.

cook 요리하다 | order 주문하다 | restaurant 식당 | baseball cap 야구모자

14

다음 대화를 듣고, 남자 아이가 산 도넛의 개수와 지불한 금액을 고르시오. ········· (   )

① 3개 – 5달러　② 4개 – 5달러
③ 3개 – 6달러　④ 4개 – 6달러

W: How may I help you?
B: I want to buy these _____.
W: _____ _____ donuts do you want?
B: _____ please.
W: Okay, that will be _____ dollars.
B: Here you are.

donut 도넛 | here you are 여기 있다

15

다음 대화를 듣고, 남자가 전화한 이유를 고르시오. ·························· (   )

① 약속을 취소하려고
② 물건을 빌리려고
③ 파티 장소를 알아보려고
④ 파티에 늦을 거라고 알리려고

[Cellphone rings.]
W: Hello.
M: Hello, Alice. Where are you?
W: I'm _____ _____. I'm making a cake for the party.
M: Alice, I will _____ _____ for the party.
W: Why?
M: It's raining, and the _____ is very _____.
W: Oh, I see.

party 파티 | be late 늦다 | rain 비가 오다 | traffic 교통 | heavy 많은, 심한
TIPS be late for는 '~에 늦다, 지각하다'라는 의미입니다.

16

다음을 듣고, 내용과 일치하지 않는 것을 고르시오. ·························· (   )

① 누나의 이름은 Nancy다.
② 누나는 나보다 4살 많다.
③ 누나는 키가 크다.
④ 누나의 장래 희망은 선생님이 되는 것이다.

B: I have an older sister. Her name is Nancy.
　 She is _____ _____ older than me.
　 She is _____ _____ and has short curly hair. She loves to play the violin. When she grows up, she wants to _____ _____ _____.

older sister 누나 | curly hair 곱슬머리 | violin 바이올린 | grow up 자라다
TIPS old의 비교급은 older, 최상급은 oldest입니다.

17

다음 대화를 듣고, 이어질 말로 알맞은 것을 고르시오. ································( )

B _____

① No, that's all. Thank you.
② No, I like tulips.
③ How many roses do you want?
④ Sorry, we don't have tulips.

W: How may I help you?
B: I want to buy _____ _____ for my mom's birthday.
W: Okay, which ones would you like?
B: Can I get these roses and tulips?
W: Sure. _____ _____?
B: _____

flower 꽃 | which one 어느 것 | rose 장미 | tulip 튤립 | anything else 그밖에 다른 것

TIPS Anything else?는 Would you like anything else?의 줄임말입니다.

18

다음 대화를 듣고, 이어질 말로 알맞은 것을 고르시오. ································( )

B _____

① Here you are.
② I'm free today.
③ Sure. What is it?
④ It's my pleasure.

W: Charlie, did you _____ your _____?
B: Yes, I did.
W: Then, can you _____ me a _____?
B: _____

finish 끝내다 | homework 숙제 | favor 부탁, 요청

19

다음 대화를 듣고, 이어질 말로 알맞은 것을 고르시오. ································( )

M _____

① I think it will be lots of fun.
② Where is the store?
③ What kind of chocolate do you like?
④ No, thank you. I'm on a diet.

M: Where are you going, Julie?
W: I'm going to the _____ _____.
M: Why are you going there?
W: I will buy some water and ice cream. _____ _____ want me to _____ you some chocolate?
M: _____

convenience store 편의점 | water 물 | ice cream 아이스크림

TIPS '초콜릿을 사다주겠다'는 말에 올바른 대답은 ④ No, thank you. I'm on a diet. 가 가장 어울립니다.

20

다음 대화를 듣고, 이어질 말로 알맞은 것을 고르시오. ································( )

M _____

① How much is it?
② I think it's expensive.
③ Let's find it together.
④ I think your computer has a virus.

M: May I help you?
G: There is _____ _____ with my computer.
M: Okay. Let me take a look at it.
G: _____ you _____ any problems?
M: _____

wrong 잘못된 | take a look 보다, 확인하다 | problem 문제

TIPS 의문문·부정문·조건문에서 any를, 긍정문에서는 some을 사용합니다.
Do you have any questions? 무슨 질문이 있습니까?

● 다음 들려주는 단어와 그 의미를 쓰세요.

단어	의미
01 online	온라인으로
02	
03	
04	
05	
06	
07	
08	
09	
10	
11	
12	
13	
14	
15	

● 앞에 모의고사에 나오는 문장들을 잘 듣고, 빈칸을 완성하세요.

01 ___Sounds___ ___great___ .

02 _____ _____ _____ about ten minutes.

03 It is her dream _____ _____ a writer.

04 Can I have _____ _____?

05 My birthday is _____ _____ soon.

06 I _____ _____ _____ every day.

07 I thought I put them _____ _____.

08 _____ _____ _____ fast, doesn't it?

09 He is _____ _____ _____ in his hand.

10 The woman is _____ _____ at a restaurant.

11 It's raining, and the _____ is very _____.

12 She is very tall and has short _____ _____.

13 Can you do me _____ _____?

14 I'm going to the _____ _____.

15 There is _____ _____ with my computer.

| 학습일 | 월　일 | 부모님 확인 | 점수 |

1
중학기출 변형문제

다음 대화를 듣고, 여자의 여동생을 고르시오.
.... (　　　)

① 　②

③ 　④

2

다음 대화를 듣고, 남자가 전화를 건 목적을 고르시오. .... (　　　)

① 책을 빌리려고
② 생일 선물을 함께 사려고
③ 생일 파티에 함께 가려고
④ 생일 파티 장소를 물어보려고

3

다음 대화를 듣고, 여자 아이가 생일선물로 받은 것을 고르시오. .... (　　　)

① 　②

③ 　④

4
중학기출 변형문제

다음 대화를 듣고, 여자의 전화번호를 고르시오. .... (　　　)

① 012-733-3528
② 012-733-4528
③ 012-733-4535
④ 012-733-4538

5

다음 대화를 듣고, 남자 아이가 어제 한 일을
고르시오. ································· (   )

①    ②

③    ④

7

다음을 듣고, 여자 아이가 말한 내용과 일치하
지 <u>않는</u> 것을 고르시오. ··········· (   )

① 캐나다에서 왔다.

② 현재 서울에 살고 있다.

③ 4년 전에 서울로 이사 왔다.

④ 장래 희망은 가수가 되는 것이다.

8

다음 대화를 듣고, 여자 아이가 좋아하는 꽃과
이유를 고르시오. ·················· (   )

① 튤립 – 색이 예쁘다

② 튤립 – 냄새가 좋다

③ 장미 – 냄새가 좋다

④ 장미 – 색이 예쁘다

6

다음 그림을 보고, 그림과 일치하는 대화를 고
르시오. ···························· (   )

①   ②   ③   ④

9

다음을 듣고, 인천의 오늘 날씨를 고르시오.
··································· (   )

①    ②

③    ④

10

다음 그림을 보고, 질문에 알맞은 대답을 고르시오. ·························· (   )

①   ②   ③   ④

11

다음 대화를 듣고, 대화 직후 두 사람이 할 일을 고르시오. ·························· (   )

① 공원에 간다.   ② 수영장에 간다.
③ 도서관에 간다.   ④ 서점에 간다.

12

다음 대화를 듣고, 대화가 자연스럽지 <u>않은</u> 것을 고르시오. ·························· (   )

①   ②   ③   ④

13

다음 대화를 듣고, 남자 아이가 오늘 해야 할 일을 고르시오. ·························· (   )

① 시험 공부   ② 숙제
③ 컴퓨터 게임   ④ 심부름

14

다음 대화를 듣고, 여자가 산 채소와 지불한 금액을 고르시오. ·························· (   )

①  – 5달러   ② – 5달러

③  – 15달러   ④ – 15달러

15 중학기출 변형문제

다음 대화를 듣고, 여자 아이의 장래 희망을 고르시오. ·························· (   )

① 의사   ② 선생님
③ 화가   ④ 작가

16

다음 대화를 듣고, 두 사람이 만나기로 한 장소와 시각을 고르시오. ……………… (   )

① 지하철역 – 2시 30분
② 버스 정류장 – 2시 30분
③ 지하철역 – 3시 30분
④ 버스 정류장 – 3시 30분

17

다음 대화를 듣고, 이어질 말로 알맞은 것을 고르시오. ……………………………… (   )

G _____

① I like Italian food.
② I don't like pasta.
③ I like potato pizza.
④ We had tomato shrimp pasta.

18

다음 대화를 듣고, 이어질 말로 알맞은 것을 고르시오. ……………………………… (   )

M _____

① I want a large size.
② No thanks. I'm full.
③ I want a blue one.
④ It's 20 dollars.

19 중학기출 변형문제

다음 대화를 듣고, 이어질 말로 알맞은 것을 고르시오. ……………………………… (   )

W _____

① Size six.
② Good. May I try it on?
③ Yes, that's all.
④ How was it?

20

다음 대화를 듣고, 이어질 말로 적절하지 <u>않은</u> 것을 고르시오. ……………… (   )

W _____

① It's not mine.
② No problem. You should be careful.
③ You're welcome.
④ It's my pleasure.

6회 Dictation 영어 듣기 모의고사

| 학습일 | 월 일 | 부모님 확인 | 점수 |

● 잘 듣고, 빈칸에 알맞은 말을 쓰세요.

1

다음 대화를 듣고, 여자의 여동생을 고르시오. .... ( )

① ② ③ ④

M: Lisa, which one is your sister?

W: There she is. She's wearing a _____ and _____.

M: Does she have long hair?

W: Yes, she has _____ _____ hair.

dress 원피스 | **glasses** 안경 | **long hair** 긴 머리 | **curly hair** 곱슬머리

TIPS 의문사 which는 '어떤 ~, 어느 ~' 등의 의미를 가지고 있으며, 어떤 선택된 사항 중에서 고를 때 사용합니다.
Which is better exercise, swimming or tennis?
수영이나 테니스 중에서 어느 게 더 좋은 운동이니?

2

다음 대화를 듣고, 남자가 전화를 건 목적을 고르시오. .... ( )

① 책을 빌리려고
② 생일 선물을 함께 사려고
③ 생일 파티에 함께 가려고
④ 생일 파티 장소를 물어보려고

[Cellphone rings.]

W: Hello?

M: Jane, it's me Kevin.

W: Oh, Hi Kevin! _____ _____?

M: It's Mike's birthday tomorrow. Can you _____ to his birthday party _____ _____?

W: Sure. Where is the party?

M: He's going to have a party at his home at 1 o'clock.

W: Okay, let's meet at the bus stop _____ _____.

birthday 생일 | **tomorrow** 내일 | **meet** 만나다 | **bus stop** 버스 정류장 | **noon** 정오

3

다음 대화를 듣고, 여자 아이가 생일선물로 받은 것을 고르시오. .... ( )

① ② ③ ④

G: Check this out.

B: Awesome! Did you get a _____ _____?

G: Yes, it was a birthday _____ from my aunt.

B: I love the color.

G: Me too. Let's _____ _____ a ride.

B: Okay, let's go!

check this out 이것 봐 | **awesome** 멋진 | **present** 선물 | **aunt** 고모, 이모

TIPS bike는 bicycle의 줄임말입니다.
[go for + 명사/동명사]는 '~하러 가다'라는 의미입니다.
go for a walk 산책하러 가다   go for a jog 조깅하러 가다

4

다음 대화를 듣고, 여자의 전화번호를 고르시오. ·········· (　　)

① 012-733-3528
② 012-733-4528
③ 012-733-4535
④ 012-733-4538

W: Hello. Can I speak to Mr. Wilson, please?

M: Sorry. He's not in. Can I take a _____?

W: Yes, my name is Cindy. Please _____ him to _____ me.

M: Okay. What's your phone number?

W: It's 012-_____-4528.

M: Excuse me? Can you repeat that, please?

W: 012-733-_____.

speak 말하다 | **message** 메시지 | **call** 전화하다 | **phone number** 전화번호 | **repeat** 반복하다

TIPS 영어로 전화번호를 말할 때에는 숫자 하나하나를 읽어주면 됩니다. 0는 zero라고 할 수도 있지만 oh라고 주로 말합니다. What's your phone number? 대신 May I have your phone number?라고 할 수도 있습니다.

5

다음 대화를 듣고, 남자 아이가 어제 한 일을 고르시오. ·········· (　　)

① ② ③ ④

G: Jack, what did you do yesterday?

B: I went to the _____ with my friends.

G: Oh, did you? What did you do there?

B: I _____ in the sea.

G: It must have been _____. Can I join you next time?

B: Sure. I will call you later.

beach 해변 | **swam** 수영하다(swim)의 과거형 | **fun** 재미있는 | **join** 함께하다 | **next time** 다음 번에 | **later** 나중에

6

다음 그림을 보고, 그림과 일치하는 대화를 고르시오. ·········· (　　)

① ② ③ ④

❶ W: What are you doing?
   M: I'm _____ on the _____.
❷ W: Do you have a cellphone?
   M: No, I don't.
❸ W: What do you want for your birthday?
   M: I want a cellphone.
❹ W: What's wrong with your cellphone?
   M: I _____ it, and the screen _____.

phone 전화기 | **cellphone** 휴대폰 | **wrong** 잘못된 | **drop** 떨어뜨리다 | **screen** 화면 | **crack** 금이 가다

TIPS talk on the phone은 '통화하다'라는 의미입니다. 바닥에 떨어진 휴대폰이 있으므로 ④번의 대화가 그림과 가장 어울립니다.

7

다음을 듣고, 여자 아이가 말한 내용과 일치하지 **않**는 것을 고르시오. ·········· (　　)

① 캐나다에서 왔다.
② 현재 서울에 살고 있다.
③ 4년 전에 서울로 이사 왔다.
④ 장래 희망은 가수가 되는 것이다.

G: Hello, everyone. I'll introduce myself to you.
My name is Cindy. I'm from Canada.
I _____ _____ Seoul.
We moved to Seoul _____ years ago.
I like to listen to K-pop and watch K-dramas.
I want to be a _____ when I grow. I hope my dream will come true.

introduce 소개하다 | myself 나 자신 | move 이사하다 | ago 전에 | grow 자라다 | dream 꿈 | come true 실현되다

TIPS 여자 아이는 3년 전에 서울로 이사를 왔습니다.

8

다음 대화를 듣고, 여자 아이가 좋아하는 꽃과 이유를 고르시오. ·········· (　　)

① 튤립 – 색이 예쁘다
② 튤립 – 냄새가 좋다
③ 장미 – 냄새가 좋다
④ 장미 – 색이 예쁘다

B: Amy, look at those flowers! They are so beautiful.
G: Do you like flowers?
B: Yes, I do. I like _____ _____.
How about you?
G: The _____ is my favorite flower.
B: Why do you like it?
G: I love its _____ _____.

those 저 | beautiful 아름다운 | tulip 튤립 | most 가장 | rose 장미

TIPS 여자 아이는 장미의 빨간색을 좋아한다고 했습니다.
lily 백합, violet 제비꽃, cherry blossom 벚꽃, sunflower 해바라기

9

다음을 듣고, 인천의 오늘 날씨를 고르시오.
·········· (　　)

① ② ③ ④

W: Good morning, Here's the weather for today.
It will be _____ in Seoul and Suwon.
In Incheon, it will _____ _____, but it will be _____ in Busan.

weather 날씨 | cloudy 흐린 | rainy 비오는 | sunny 맑은

10

다음 그림을 보고, 질문에 알맞은 대답을 고르시오. ·········· (　　)

① ② ③ ④

M: Can I _____ a _____ here?
W: ❶ Sure, no problem.
❷ Sorry, you can't.
❸ No, you _____ _____ here.
❹ Of course, you can.

campfire 캠프파이어, 모닥불 | here 여기에 | problem 문제 | smoke 담배 피우다 | of course 물론

11

다음 대화를 듣고, 대화 직후 두 사람이 할 일을 고르시오. ·················· (   )

① 공원에 간다.　　② 수영장에 간다.
③ 도서관에 간다.　④ 서점에 간다.

B: Hi, Susan, where are you going?

G: I'm going to the park. Will you come with me?

B: Sure. But can we go to the _____ _____?
   I have to _____ these books.

G: Okay. _____ _____ there first.

park 공원 | **library** 도서관 | **first** 먼저 | **return** 반납하다

TIPS return books는 '책을 반납하다'라는 의미입니다.
Let's go there first.에서 there는 도서관을 의미합니다.

12

다음 대화를 듣고, 대화가 자연스럽지 <u>않은</u> 것을 고르시오. ·················· (   )

①　　②　　③　　④

❶ B: How was the musical?

G: It was great.

❷ B: Can I borrow a pencil?

G: I'm sorry. I don't have an extra pencil.

❸ B: What are you _____ _____
   _____ today?

G: I'm eating dinner _____.

❹ B: What's your favorite _____?

G: I like history.

musical 뮤지컬 | **borrow** 빌리다 | **extra** 여분의 | **subject** 과목

TIPS I'm eating dinner now.에 대한 알맞은 질문은 What are you doing? 입니다.

13

다음 대화를 듣고, 남자 아이가 오늘 해야 할 일을 고르시오. ·················· (   )

① 시험 공부　　② 숙제
③ 컴퓨터 게임　④ 심부름

G: Do you want to come to my house and play computer games?

B: Today?

G: Yes.

B: I'd like to, but I can't today.

G: _____ _____?

B: I have an English _____ _____, and I have to _____ for it.
   How about tomorrow after school?

G: Okay, tomorrow is _____ _____ me.

house 집 | **test** 시험 | **tomorrow** 내일

TIPS That's fine with me.는 상대방의 제안에 동의할 때 사용합니다.
Anytime is fine with me. 전 아무 때나 괜찮아요.

14

다음 대화를 듣고, 여자가 산 채소와 지불한 금액을 고르시오. ·················· (   )

① 🥒 – 5달러   ② 🥕 – 5달러

③ 🥒 – 15달러   ④ 🥕 – 15달러

W: Excuse me. How much are these carrots?

M: It's _____ dollars for a bag.

W: Can I get _____ _____ of carrots?

M: Okay. That will be _____ dollars.
Do you need anything else?

W: No, it's okay. I came to the market just for carrots.

carrot 당근 | bag 봉지 | anything else 그밖에 다른 것 | market 시장

TIPS 당근 1봉지에 5달러이고, 여자는 3봉지를 샀습니다.

15

다음 대화를 듣고, 여자 아이의 장래 희망을 고르시오. ·················· (   )

① 의사   ② 선생님
③ 화가   ④ 작가

B: Wow, great! Where did you draw these pictures?

G: I drew them at the park last week.

B: I think you're really _____ _____ drawing.

G: Thank you.

B: Do you want to become _____ _____?

G: Yes, I do.

B: I think you will be a _____ _____.

draw 그리다 | really 정말 | be good at ~을 잘하다 | become 되다 | artist 예술가, 화가

16

다음 대화를 듣고, 두 사람이 만나기로 한 장소와 시각을 고르시오. ·················· (   )

① 지하철역 – 2시 30분
② 버스 정류장 – 2시 30분
③ 지하철역 – 3시 30분
④ 버스 정류장 – 3시 30분

M: Cathy, how about going to the museum tomorrow?

W: Great! _____ _____ shall we meet?

M: Let's meet at _____.
Do you want to meet me at the bus stop?

W: Sure. Let's meet at the _____ _____ at 2:30.

M: Okay. See you tomorrow.

museum 박물관 | meet 만나다 | bus stop 버스 정류장

TIPS 영어로 시각 말하기
1시 10분: It's one ten. / It's ten past one.
1시 50분: It's one fifty. / It's ten to two.
*to나 past를 이용할 때에는 분을 먼저 말해야 합니다.

17

다음 대화를 듣고, 이어질 말로 알맞은 것을 고르시오. ············· ( )

G _____

① I like Italian food.
② I don't like pasta.
③ I like potato pizza.
④ We had tomato shrimp pasta.

G: Jim, what did you eat for lunch today?

B: I had a slice of pizza.

G: That's it?

B: Yes. I wasn't that hungry. What did you eat, Kelly?

G: I _____ _____ with my mom.

B: Sounds yummy. _____ _____ of pasta did you have?

G: _____

slice 조각 | hungry 배고픈 | yummy 맛있는 | kind 종류

TIPS What kind of는 '무슨 종류의'란 의미로 ④번의 We had tomato shrimp pasta.가 가장 어울리는 대답입니다.

18

다음 대화를 듣고, 이어질 말로 알맞은 것을 고르시오. ············· ( )

M _____

① I want a large size.
② No thanks. I'm full.
③ I want a blue one.
④ It's 20 dollars.

W: May I help you?

M: Yes, I'm _____ _____ a T-shirt.

W: _____ _____ would you like?

M: _____

look for ~을 찾다 | what color 무슨 색

19

다음 대화를 듣고, 이어질 말로 알맞은 것을 고르시오. ············· ( )

W _____

① Size six.
② Good. May I try it on?
③ Yes, that's all.
④ How was it?

M: May I help you?

W: Yes, please. I'm _____ _____ a skirt.

M: _____ _____ do you want?

W: I want a red one.

M: How about this one?

W: _____

skirt 치마 | what color 무슨 색 | red 빨간

TIPS try on 은 '~을 (시험 삼아) 해보다, 입어보다'라는 의미입니다.

20

다음 대화를 듣고, 이어질 말로 적절하지 <u>않은</u> 것을 고르시오. ············· ( )

W _____

① It's not mine.
② No problem. You should be careful.
③ You're welcome.
④ It's my pleasure.

W: Excuse me.

M: Yes? How may I help you?

W: You _____ your wallet.

M: Oh, _____ _____ very much.

W: _____

drop 떨어뜨리다 | wallet 지갑 | so much 무척

TIPS Thank You.에 대답하는 방법으로는 You are welcome. / No problem. / My pleasure. / Don't mention it 등이 있습니다.

● 다음 들려주는 단어와 그 의미를 쓰세요.

	단어	의미
01	noon	정오
02		
03		
04		
05		
06		
07		
08		
09		
10		
11		
12		
13		
14		
15		

Sentence Check

● 앞에 모의고사에 나오는 문장들을 잘 듣고, 빈칸을 완성하세요.

01 ___Which___ ___one___ is your sister?

02 Let's meet at the bus stop _____ _____.

03 Let's _____ _____ _____ _____.

04 Please _____ _____ _____ call me.

05 Can I _____ _____ _____?

06 I _____ _____, and the screen cracked.

07 I'll _____ _____ to you.

08 Here's the weather _____ _____.

09 I have to _____ _____ _____.

10 _____ _____ _____, but I can't today.

11 Tomorrow is _____ _____ _____.

12 I came _____ _____ just for carrots.

13 I think you will be a _____ _____.

14 _____ _____ _____ pasta did you have?

15 You dropped _____ _____.

영어 듣기 모의고사

보통 속도

빠른 속도

학습일   월   일   부모님 확인   점수

1

다음을 듣고, 그림과 일치하는 설명을 고르시오. ······················· (   )

①   ②   ③   ④

3

다음 대화를 듣고, 남자 아이의 자전거를 고르시오. ····························· (   )

①    ②

③   ④

4   중학기출 변형문제

다음 대화를 듣고, 남자 아이가 기분이 좋은 이유를 고르시오. ························ (   )

① 축구시합에 이겨서
② 선생님에게 칭찬을 받아서
③ 용돈을 받아서
④ 시험을 잘 봐서

2   중학기출 변형문제

다음 대화를 듣고, 대화가 일어나는 장소를 고르시오. ····························· (   )

① 은행   ② 학교
③ 서점   ④ 병원

5

다음 대화를 듣고, 여자 아이가 이번 주 토요일에 할 일을 고르시오. ·············· (   )

① 병문안   ② 피아노 공연
③ 캠핑   ④ 할머니댁 방문

6

다음 그림을 보고, 그림과 일치하는 대화를 고르시오. ·················· (   )

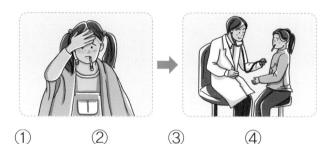

①   ②   ③   ④

7

다음 대화를 듣고, 남자 아이가 대화가 끝난 후 할 일을 고르시오. ·············· (   )

① 게임 하기   ② 숙제하기
③ 청소하기   ④ 설거지하기

8

다음 대화를 듣고, 여자 아이가 찾는 물건의 위치를 고르시오. ·············· (   )

①   ②   ③   ④

9

다음 대화를 듣고, 남자 아이의 생일 날짜와 원하는 생일 선물을 고르시오. ······ (   )

① 9월 11일 – 자전거
② 9월 11일 – 컴퓨터
③ 11월 11일 – 자전거
④ 11월 11일 – 컴퓨터

10

다음을 듣고, 남자 아이가 말한 내용과 일치하지 않는 것을 고르시오. ··········· (   )

① Kevin은 가장 친한 친구이다.
② Kevin과 나는 같은 학교에 다닌다.
③ Kevin은 형들이 있다.
④ Kevin은 나보다 키가 작다.

11

다음 대화를 듣고, 상황에 알맞은 그림을 고르시오. ·················· ( )

①

②

③

④

12

다음 대화를 듣고, 남자 아이가 백화점에 가야 하는 이유를 고르시오. ············· ( )

① 아버지를 만나려고
② 피자 사려고
③ 생일 케이크를 사려고
④ 생일 선물을 사려고

13

다음 대화를 듣고, 대화가 자연스럽지 <u>않은</u> 것을 고르시오. ··················· ( )

① 　　 ② 　　 ③ 　　 ④

14

다음 대화를 듣고, 두 사람이 보고 있는 사진을 고르시오. ··················· ( )

①

②

③

④

15 　중학기출 변형문제

다음을 듣고, 오늘 오후 날씨로 알맞은 것을 고르시오. ··················· ( )

①

②

③

④

16

다음 대화를 듣고, 남자가 지불해야 할 금액을 고르시오. ·························· (   )

① 2달러   ② 4달러
③ 6달러   ④ 8달러

17

다음 대화를 듣고, 이어질 말로 알맞은 것을 고르시오. ·························· (   )

M _____

① Milk is good for your health.
② I like Korean food.
③ No, thanks. I'm full.
④ We have soda and orange juice.

18

다음 대화를 듣고, 이어질 말로 알맞은 것을 고르시오. ·························· (   )

B _____

① I want to visit Korea.
② Yes, I went to Busan with my family.
③ I stayed at the hotel.
④ I lived in Seoul.

19 중학기출 변형문제

다음 대화를 듣고, 이어질 말로 알맞은 것을 고르시오. ·························· (   )

M _____

① I watched a movie until midnight.
② I was very tired.
③ I will do my homework.
④ I was very hungry last night.

20

다음 대화를 듣고, 이어질 말로 알맞은 것을 고르시오. ·························· (   )

G _____

① We have lunch at noon.
② Yes, I like pizza very much.
③ Okay. See you tomorrow.
④ I don't drink coffee.

학습일   월   일   부모님 확인   점수

● 잘 듣고, 빈칸에 알맞은 말을 쓰세요.

1

다음을 듣고, 그림과 일치하는 설명을 고르시오. ·························· (   )

W: ❶ A man is taking a shower.

　❷ A man is using a computer.

　❸ A man is _____ on the _____.

　❹ A man is _____ a _____ with his cellphone.

take a shower 샤워하다 | use 사용하다 | talk on the phone 전화통화하다 | take a picture 사진 찍다

TIPS 한 남자가 전화를 하고 있는 그림이므로 talk on the phone(전화통화하다)의 표현이 들어간 ③이 그림과 가장 어울립니다.

① ② ③ ④

2

다음 대화를 듣고, 대화가 일어나는 장소를 고르시오. ·························· (   )

① 은행　　　 ② 학교
③ 서점　　　 ④ 병원

W: Jim! You're _____ _____.
Why don't you get up early?

B: I'm really sorry. I'll try.

W: Good! You have to be _____ _____ by 8:30. Don't be late tomorrow.

always 언제나 | try 노력하다 | get up 일어나다 | early 일찍 | class 수업, 교실

TIPS by는 종료 시점에 초점이 맞춰져 있고, until은 종료 시점까지의 과정에 초점이 맞춰져 있습니다.
I have to go to school by 8:20. 나는 8시 20분까지 학교에 가야 한다.
I have to study until 6:00. 나는 6시까지 공부를 해야 한다.
(6시까지 계속해서 공부를 해야 한다는 과정이 중요하기 때문에 until을 사용합니다.)

3

다음 대화를 듣고, 남자 아이의 자전거를 고르시오. ·························· (   )

① ②
③ ④

G: Jack, _____ _____ is your bicycle?

B: Do you see the bicycle over there?

G: Oh, the green one?

B: No, the _____ _____.

G: There are two blue bicycles.

B: My bicycle has a _____ in the _____.

bicycle 자전거 | over there 저쪽에 | basket 바구니 | front 앞

4

다음 대화를 듣고, 남자 아이가 기분이 좋은 이유를 고르시오. ·························· (   )

① 축구시합에 이겨서
② 선생님에게 칭찬을 받아서
③ 용돈을 받아서
④ 시험을 잘 봐서

B: Mom, I'm home.

W: David, you look happy. Did you _____ _____ at school?

B: I had a _____ _____.

W: So how did it go?

B: I got _____ percent.

W: Good for you.

happy 행복한 | fun 재미 | test 시험 | percent 퍼센트

TIPS have fun은 '즐거운 시간을 보내다'라는 의미입니다. fun 대신 funny를 사용하지 않도록 합니다. fun은 '재미, 즐거움'이란 의미의 명사이고, funny는 '우스운, 웃기는'이란 의미의 형용사입니다.

5

다음 대화를 듣고, 여자 아이가 이번 주 토요일에 할 일을 고르시오. ·············· (   )

① 병문안   ② 피아노 공연
③ 캠핑   ④ 할머니댁 방문

G: Jack, where are you going?

B: I'm going to my piano lesson.
   I have a _____ _____ this Saturday.

G: Oh, I see. Are you nervous?

B: Yes, I am. Can you come to the competition?

G: Sorry, I can't. I have to _____ my grandmother.
   She's in _____ _____ now.

lesson 수업 | competition 대회 | nervous 긴장한 | visit 방문하다 |
be in (the) hospital 입원하다

6

다음 그림을 보고, 그림과 일치하는 대화를 고르시오. ·············· (   )

①   ②   ③   ④

❶ G: What time do you get up?
   B: I get up at 7.

❷ G: Where are you going?
   B: I'm going to the dentist.

❸ G: I _____ _____ _____.
   B: That's too bad. Go and _____ _____
   _____.

❹ G: I'm hungry.
   B: Dinner will _____ _____ soon.

get up 일어나다 | dentist 치과의사 | have a cold 감기 걸리다 |
see a doctor 병원에 가다 | ready 준비된 | soon 곧

TIPS have a cold는 '감기에 걸리다'라는 의미입니다. 우리가 아프면 병원에 간다고 말을 하는데 이때 우리는 '병원'(hospital)이라고 하지만 hospital은 '종합병원'으로 큰 병이 있을 때 가는 병원입니다. 따라서 비교적 가벼운 병인 '감기에 걸려 병원에 갈 거야.'라고 할 경우에는 I'm going to the doctor.라고 해야 합니다.

7

다음 대화를 듣고, 남자 아이가 대화가 끝난 후 할 일을 고르시오. ·············· (　　)

① 게임 하기　　② 숙제하기
③ 청소하기　　④ 설거지하기

W: Tony, can you come here?

B: Mom, I'm playing a computer game.

W: Come here _____ _____ .

B: What's wrong?

W: I told you to _____ _____ _____ , and you still didn't.

B: I'm sorry. Can I do it after the game?

W: No. _____ _____ right now.

right now 지금 당장 | wash the dishes 설거지하다 | still 여전히

8

다음 대화를 듣고, 여자 아이가 찾는 물건의 위치를 고르시오. ·············· (　　)

① ② ③ ④

G: Dad, _____ you _____ my watch?

M: It's on your desk.

G: My desk? It isn't there. I have already checked.

M: Did you _____ in the _____ ?

G: Oh, _____ it is. Thank you, Dad.

watch 손목시계 | check 확인하다 | already 이미 | drawer 서랍

TIPS [have + 과거분사]는 현재완료라고 하며, 과거에 시작된 일이 현재에 완료, 경험, 계속, 결과로 나타나는 시제를 현재완료시제라고 합니다.

9

다음 대화를 듣고, 남자 아이의 생일 날짜와 원하는 생일 선물을 고르시오. ····· (　　)

① 9월 11일 – 자전거
② 9월 11일 – 컴퓨터
③ 11월 11일 – 자전거
④ 11월 11일 – 컴퓨터

B: My birthday is coming soon.

G: When is it?

B: It's _____ 11.

G: What do you want for your birthday?

B: Well. I'd like to have a _____ _____ .

G: Did you tell your parents _____ you want?

B: Yes, I did.

come 오다 | soon 곧 | November 11월 | parents 부모

TIPS 날짜를 표시할 때 기수를 사용해서 쓰지만 읽을 때나 말할 때에는 서수로 말해야 합니다.

10

다음을 듣고, 남자 아이가 말한 내용과 일치하지 않는 것을 고르시오. ·············· (　　)

① Kevin은 가장 친한 친구이다.
② Kevin과 나는 같은 학교에 다닌다.
③ Kevin은 형들이 있다.
④ Kevin은 나보다 키가 작다.

B: Today, I played with my best friend Kevin. Kevin and I go to the _____ _____ . He is _____ _____ me, and he has two _____ brothers. We like to play baseball and computer games.

best friend 가장 친한 친구 | same school 같은 학교 | older brother 형 | baseball 야구

TIPS tall의 비교급은 taller이고, short의 비교급 shorter입니다.
I am shorter than him. 나는 그보다 키가 더 작다.

11

다음 대화를 듣고, 상황에 알맞은 그림을 고르시오. ·············· (   )

① ② ③ ④

W: Thomas, can I _____ you a _____?

M: Sure. What is it?

W: Could you _____ the music _____ a little?

M: Sorry. I didn't know it was _____ _____. I'll turn it down now.

W: Thanks.

ask 요청하다 | **favor** 부탁 | **turn down** (소리 등) 줄이다 | **a little** 조금 | **loud** 시끄러운

TIPS turn the music down은 '음악소리를 줄이다'라는 표현입니다.
turn the music down = turn down the music

12

다음 대화를 듣고, 남자 아이가 백화점에 가야 하는 이유를 고르시오. ·············· (   )

① 아버지를 만나려고
② 피자 사려고
③ 생일 케이크를 사려고
④ 생일 선물을 사려고

G: Are you hungry?

B: Yeah, I'm hungry.

G: Do you want to _____ _____ some pizza?

B: I would love to, but I _____ _____ go to the department store before it closes.

G: Why?

B: It's my dad's _____ tomorrow, and I didn't buy a _____ for him yet.

hungry 배고픈 | **department store** 백화점 | **close** 닫다 | **yet** 아직

TIPS go get은 go and get에서 and를 생략한 형태입니다.
go get을 이용해서 다음과 같이 표현할 수 있습니다.
I'll go get the coffee. 내가 커피 사 올게.
Let's go get a drink during recess. 휴식 시간에 음료수를 마시러 가자.

13

다음 대화를 듣고, 대화가 자연스럽지 <u>않은</u> 것을 고르시오. ·············· (   )

① ② ③ ④

❶ G: Eric, what are you going to do tomorrow?

B: I don't have any plans. Why?

❷ G: What do you do in your _____ _____?

B: I play with my pet.

❸ G: How about playing tennis after school?

B: Sounds great!

❹ G: Hi, Tom. _____ _____ you doing?

B: I'm doing my _____.

plan 계획 | **free time** 여가시간 | **pet** 반려동물 | **play tennis** 테니스를 치다

TIPS How are you doing?에 대한 질문에 Not bad. / Very well, thanks. / Pretty good. 등으로 대답할 수 있습니다.

14

다음 대화를 듣고, 두 사람이 보고 있는 사진을 고르시오. ·············· (   )

① ② ③ ④

G: Sam, is this you in this picture?

B: Yes, my family went to the _____ last summer.

G: Who is the girl?

B: She's my _____ sister, Jessie.

G: You were making a sandcastle.

B: Yes, Jessie and I like _____ _____ at the beach.

beach 해변 | younger sister 여동생 | sandcastle 모래성

15

다음을 듣고, 오늘 오후 날씨로 알맞은 것을 고르시오. ·············· (   )

① ② ③ ④

W: Good morning! It's Monday! This is Susan with the _____ _____. It is cloudy at the moment, but this _____, it's going to _____. If you're going out in the afternoon, don't _____ your umbrella.

weather report 일기예보 | cloudy 흐린 | at the moment 지금 | go out 외출하다 | forget 잊다

TIPS 부정명령문은 [Don't + 동사원형.] 의 형태를 취합니다.
Don't open the window. 창문 열지 마.

16

다음 대화를 듣고, 남자가 지불해야 할 금액을 고르시오. ·············· (   )

① 2달러　　　　② 4달러
③ 6달러　　　　④ 8달러

W: May I help you?

M: Yes, I'm looking for _____ _____. Where can I find them?

W: They're over there.

M: How much is this red pencil?

W: It's _____ dollars.

M: Okay. I'll _____ _____.

help 돕다 | over there 저쪽에 | take 사다

TIPS 연필이 한 개에 2달러이며, 남자는 세 개를 구입한다고 했습니다.

17

다음 대화를 듣고, 이어질 말로 알맞은 것을 고르시오. ·············· (   )

M _____

① Milk is good for your health.
② I like Korean food.
③ No, thanks. I'm full.
④ We have soda and orange juice.

W: Mike, your party is great! I'm having a lot of fun.

M: Thank you, Helen. I'm really happy you are here. Do you want _____ to _____?

W: Sure. _____ _____ of drink do you have?

M: _____

really 정말 | something 무언가 | kind 종류

18

다음 대화를 듣고, 이어질 말로 알맞은 것을 고르시오. ·············· (   )

B _____

① I want to visit Korea.
② Yes, I went to Busan with my family.
③ I stayed at the hotel.
④ I lived in Seoul.

G: Hi, Robin! How was your vacation?

B: Hello, Lisa. My vacation was great.
   I had a lot of fun.

G: _____ you go _____?

B: _____

vacation 방학, 휴가 | fun 재미 | somewhere 어딘가

TIPS Did you go somewhere?는 '어디에 갔다 왔니?'라는 의미이므로 Yes, I went to Busan with my family.이 가장 어울리는 대답입니다. I stayed at the hotel.의 대답에 알맞은 질문은 Where did you stay?입니다.

19

다음 대화를 듣고, 이어질 말로 알맞은 것을 고르시오. ·············· (   )

M _____

① I watched a movie until midnight.
② I was very tired.
③ I will do my homework.
④ I was very hungry last night.

W: You _____ _____ today.

M: Yes, I am. I'm very sleepy right now.

W: Did you play computer games late last night?

M: No, I didn't.

W: Then, _____ _____ you do?

M: _____

tired 피곤한 | sleepy 졸린 | right now 지금 당장 | last night 지난밤에

TIPS What did you do?로 묻고 있으므로, 과거의 한 행위나, 동작을 구체적으로 대답해야 합니다. 따라서 I watched a movie.가 대답으로 가장 어울립니다.

20

다음 대화를 듣고, 이어질 말로 알맞은 것을 고르시오. ·············· (   )

G _____

① We have lunch at noon.
② Yes, I like pizza very much.
③ Okay. See you tomorrow.
④ I don't drink coffee.

G: Ted, I'm going to the concert tomorrow.
   Can you come with me?

B: Sure. _____ _____ shall we meet?

G: Let's meet at 3 o'clock.

B: Well, how about 1 o'clock at the bus stop?
   Let's _____ _____ before the concert.

G: _____

concert 콘서트 | tomorrow 내일 | what time 몇 시 | before ~ 전에

TIPS What time shall we meet?은 '몇 시에 만나고 싶니?'라는 의미로 What time would you like to meet?으로 바꿔 표현할 수 있습니다.

Word Check

● 다음 들려주는 단어와 그 의미를 쓰세요.

	단어	의미
01	always	언제나
02		
03		
04		
05		
06		
07		
08		
09		
10		
11		
12		
13		
14		
15		

● 앞에 모의고사에 나오는 문장들을 잘 듣고, 빈칸을 완성하세요.

01 A man ___is___ ___talking___ on the phone.

02 You have to _____ _____ _____ by 8:30.

03 My bicycle has a basket _____ _____ _____.

04 I had a _____ _____.

05 I have a _____ _____ this Saturday.

06 Dinner will _____ _____ _____.

07 _____ _____ _____ in the drawer?

08 Kevin and I go to the _____ _____.

09 Could you _____ the music _____ a little?

10 Jessie and I like _____ _____ at the beach.

11 This is Susan with the _____ _____.

12 I'm _____ _____ you are here.

13 _____ _____ your vacation?

14 I'm _____ _____ right now.

15 Let's have lunch _____ _____ _____.

영어 듣기 모의고사

보통 속도　빠른 속도

학습일　월　일　부모님 확인　점수

1

다음 대화를 듣고, 남자 아이가 오늘 이용할 교통수단을 고르시오. ················· (　　　)

①

②

③

④

3

다음 대화를 듣고, 두 사람이 주말에 할 일을 고르시오. ····························· (　　　)

①

②

③

④

2

다음을 듣고, 그림과 일치하는 설명을 고르시오. ······························· (　　　)

①　　②　　③　　④

4

다음 그림을 보고, 그림과 일치하는 대화를 고르시오. ······························· (　　　)

①　　②　　③　　④

5

다음 대화를 듣고, 여자가 사려는 신발과 신발 사이즈를 고르시오. ·············· (   )

①
size 9

②
size 10

③
size 9

④
size 10

6 중학기출 변형문제

다음 대화를 듣고, 여자가 전화를 건 목적을 고르시오. ························· (   )

① 음식을 주문하기 위해
② 식당을 예약을 하기 위해
③ 놓고 온 지갑을 찾기 위해
④ 식당 위치를 알아보기 위해

7

다음 대화를 듣고, 여자 아이가 대화 후 할 일을 고르시오. ·················· (   )

① 청소하기   ② 숙제하기
③ 컴퓨터게임하기   ④ 설거지하기

8

다음 대화를 듣고, 남자 아이가 일주일에 테니스를 하는 횟수를 고르시오. ······ (   )

① 2번   ② 3번
③ 4번   ④ 5번

9

다음을 듣고, 남자 아이가 말한 내용과 일치하지 않는 것을 고르시오. ··········· (   )

① 형은 나보다 3살 많다.
② 형은 키가 크다.
③ 형은 야구하는 것을 좋아한다.
④ 형은 내가 숙제하는 것을 도와준다.

10

다음 대화를 듣고, 두 사람이 공원에 가기로 한 날짜를 고르시오. ·················· (   )

① 4월 3일   ② 4월 6일
③ 5월 6일   ④ 6월 6일

11

다음 대화를 듣고, 남자 아이가 좋아하는 운동과 그 이유를 고르시오. ·········· (   )

① 축구 – 활동적이고 재미있다.
② 탁구 – 누구나 할 수 있다.
③ 야구 – 활동적이고 흥미롭다.
④ 테니스 – 흥미롭다.

12

다음 대화를 듣고, 두 사람이 있는 장소를 고르시오. ······························· (   )

① 식당   ② 옷 가게
③ 호텔   ④ 가구점

13

다음 대화를 듣고, 대화가 자연스럽지 않은 것을 고르시오. ···················· (   )

①   ②   ③   ④

14

다음 대화를 듣고, 두 사람이 방과 후 할 일을 고르시오. ······························ (   )

15 중학기출 변형문제

다음 대화를 듣고, 두 사람이 어머니를 위해 할 일을 고르시오. ····················· (   )

① 청소하기   ② 쓰레기 버리기
③ 심부름하기   ④ 저녁식사 만들기

16

다음을 듣고, 여자의 직업을 고르시오.
································· (   )

①

②

③

④

17

다음 대화를 듣고, 두 아이가 만나서 할 일과 만나기로 한 시각을 고르시오. ······ (   )

① 청소하기 – 2시   ② 숙제하기 – 3시
③ 선물 사기 – 3시   ④ 생일파티 가기 – 3시

18

다음 대화를 듣고, 이어질 말로 알맞은 것을 고르시오. ······························· (   )

G _____

① I like all kinds of books.
② I like action movies.
③ I want to be a writer.
④ I read books every day.

19 중학기출 변형문제

다음 대화를 듣고, 이어질 말로 알맞은 것을 고르시오. ····························· (   )

G _____

① Yes, I want to go home.
② No, I don't like sports.
③ Thanks, but I'm full.
④ I'd love to, but I have to go home for dinner.

20 중학기출 변형문제

다음 대화를 듣고, 이어질 말로 알맞은 것을 고르시오. ····························· (   )

G _____

① I'm okay. Thank you.
② Oh, I'm sorry to hear that.
③ Don't worry. He will be all right.
④ When did you find it?

Dictation 영어 듣기 모의고사

학습일　월　일　부모님 확인　점수

● 잘 듣고, 빈칸에 알맞은 말을 쓰세요.

1

다음 대화를 듣고, 남자 아이가 오늘 이용할 교통수단을 고르시오. ·············· ( )

① 　②

③ 　④

B: Mom, can you _____ me _____ _____ to school today? It's raining.

W: Sure. What time do we need to _____ the house?

B: We need to leave in about 20 minutes. Can we also _____ _____ James?

W: Not a problem.

give me a ride 나를 태워주다 | leave 출발하다 | pick up 태워주다 | about 대략

TIPS [give A a ride]는 'A(사람)를 차에 태워주다'라는 의미입니다.
Can you give me a ride home? 집까지 태워줄 수 있니?

2

다음을 듣고, 그림과 일치하는 설명을 고르시오. ·············· ( )

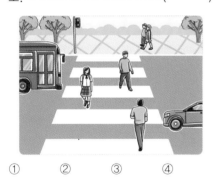

① ② ③ ④

W: ❶ People are waiting for the traffic light to change.

❷ People are _____ the _____.

❸ There is a blue bus on the road.

❹ Some children are running _____ the _____.

people 사람들 | wait for ~을 기다리다 | traffic light 교통신호 | change 바뀌다 | cross 건너다 | street 길 | road 도로 | children 아이들

TIPS 사람들이 길을 건너고 있으므로 People are crossing the street.이 그림과 가장 일치합니다.

3

다음 대화를 듣고, 두 사람이 주말에 할 일을 고르시오. ·············· ( )

① 　②

③ 　④

G: James, what are you going to do _____ _____?

B: I don't have any special plans. What about you?

G: I will _____ _____ with my cousins.

B: Wow. That sounds very exciting!

G: Would you like to _____ _____?

B: Sure, I'd love to.

weekend 주말 | special 특별한 | cousin 사촌 | exciting 재미있는 | join 함께하다

TIPS Would you like to join us? 대신 Do you want to come with us?(우리와 함께 갈래?)라고 표현할 수 있습니다.

4

다음 그림을 보고, 그림과 일치하는 대화를 고르시오. ·························· (   )

① ② ③ ④

① G: Jack, I got a new cellphone.

B: What a _____ _____!
Where did you _____ it?

② G: Can I use your cellphone?

B: Sorry, it's not my cellphone.

③ G: Jack, what are you doing?

B: I'm _____ _____ _____ on
my phone.

④ G: What do you want for your birthday?

B: I want a new bicycle.

cellphone 휴대전화 | use 사용하다 | birthday 생일

TIPS 여자 아이가 친구에게 휴대전화기를 보여 주고 있으므로 ①번의 대화가 가장
어울립니다.

5

다음 대화를 듣고, 여자가 사려는 신발과 신발
사이즈를 고르시오. ·············· (   )

① ②

size 9   size 10

③ ④

size 9   size 10

M: May I help you?

W: Yes, I'm looking for _____ _____ for
my husband.

M: What size do you want?

W: _____ _____, please.

M: How about these _____ _____?
They just came in.

W: Oh, I like them. How much are they?

running shoes 운동화 | husband 남편

6

다음 대화를 듣고, 여자가 전화를 건 목적을 고르시오. ·························· (   )

① 음식을 주문하기 위해
② 식당을 예약을 하기 위해
③ 놓고 온 지갑을 찾기 위해
④ 식당 위치를 알아보기 위해

[Telephone rings.]

M: Rainbow Restaurant. How may I help you?

W: I _____ my _____ at your restaurant
yesterday.

M: What does it _____ _____?

W: It's small and red. It has a star on it.

M: Yes, we have it _____.

W: Oh, thank you. I'll pick it up this afternoon.

rainbow 무지개 | purse 지갑 | small 작은 | star 별 | pick up 가지러 가다

TIPS 여성이 두고 온 지갑은 빨간색이고 지갑에 별모양이 있다.
purse는 여성용 지갑이고, wallet은 남성용 지갑입니다.

7

다음 대화를 듣고, 여자 아이가 대화 후 할 일을 고르시오. ·········· (   )

① 청소하기　　② 숙제하기
③ 컴퓨터게임하기　　④ 설거지하기

G: Mom, can I play computer games?

W: Sure. Did you clean your room?

G: Yes, I cleaned up my room and vacuumed the living room.

W: Did you _____ your _____?

G: No, I didn't.

W: You know the rules. You have to finish your homework _____ you play computer games.

G: Okay, Mom. I'll _____ _____ right now.

clean 청소하다 | **vacuum** 진공청소하다 | **finish** 끝내다 | **know** 알다 | **rule** 규칙

TIPS I'll do it right now.에서 it은 to do homework을 의미합니다.
[have to + 동사원형]은 '~해야 한다'라는 의미입니다.

8

다음 대화를 듣고, 남자 아이가 일주일에 테니스를 하는 횟수를 고르시오. ······ (   )

① 2번　　② 3번
③ 4번　　④ 5번

G: What do you do in your _____ _____?

B: I play tennis.

G: Sounds interesting! _____ _____ do you play tennis?

B: I play _____ _____ a week.

G: Wow, that's a lot.

free time 여가시간 | **play tennis** 테니스를 치다 | **how often** 얼마나 자주 |
four times 네 번

TIPS How often을 이용해 질문하면, 다음과 같이 대답할 수 있습니다.
Three times a week. 일주일에 세 번.　Twice a week. 일주일에 두 번.

9

다음을 듣고, 남자 아이가 말한 내용과 일치하지 않는 것을 고르시오. ··········· (   )

① 형은 나보다 3살 많다.
② 형은 키가 크다.
③ 형은 야구하는 것을 좋아한다.
④ 형은 내가 숙제하는 것을 도와준다.

B: Hello, my name is Ben. I am 13 years old. I have an older brother. His name is Jim. He is _____ _____ older than me. He has big brown eyes, and he is _____ _____. He loves to play _____ and tennis. He often helps me do my _____. We have small fights, but I love him very much.

older brother 형 | **brown** 갈색의 | **basketball** 농구 | **tennis** 테니스 | **often** 종종 |
fight 싸움

TIPS 운동 종목 앞에는 관사를 쓰지 않습니다.
I like to play a volleyball. (x)　　I like to play volleyball. (o)

10

다음 대화를 듣고, 두 사람이 공원에 가기로 한
날짜를 고르시오. ·················· (   )

① 4월 3일　　　　② 4월 6일
③ 5월 6일　　　　④ 6월 6일

B: Jina, how about going to the park tomorrow?

G: It is going to rain tomorrow.

B: _____ _____ next Saturday?

G: You mean _____ 6?

B: Yes, April 6.

G: I'm free on that day.

B: Okay. _____ _____ to the park next
　　Saturday.

how about ~은 어때? | **tomorrow** 내일 | **next Saturday** 다음 주 토요일에 |
mean 의미하다

TIPS 날짜를 표시할 때 기수를 사용해서 쓰지만 읽을 때나 말할 때에는 서수를
이용합니다.

1월 January	2월 February	3월 March	4월 April
5월 May	6월 June	7월 July	8월 August
9월 September	10월 October	11월 November	12월 December

11

다음 대화를 듣고, 남자 아이가 좋아하는 운동
과 그 이유를 고르시오. ············ (   )

① 축구 – 활동적이고 재미있다.
② 탁구 – 누구나 할 수 있다.
③ 야구 – 활동적이고 흥미롭다.
④ 테니스 – 흥미롭다.

B: Susan, do you like sports?

G: No, I don't. But I'd like to play table tennis.

B: Table tennis?

G: Yes, it is a _____ for _____.
　　How about you? What is your favorite sport?

B: I like _____ because it's a very _____
　　and _____ sport.

sport 운동 | **table tennis** 탁구 | **everyone** 모두 | **active** 활동적인

TIPS 여자 아이는 탁구를 치고 싶어 하고, 남자 아이는 축구를 좋아합니다.

12

다음 대화를 듣고, 두 사람이 있는 장소를 고르
시오. ·················· (   )

① 식당　　　　②옷 가게
③ 호텔　　　　④ 가구점

W: May I help you?

M: Yes, I'm looking for a _____ for my daughter.

W: What size are you looking for?

M: I want a _____ _____.

W: How about this one?
　　It's _____ _____ now.

M: How much is it?

bed 침대 | **daughter** 딸 | **single bed** 1인용 침대 | **on sale** 할인 중

TIPS 남자가 딸의 침대를 구입하려는 대화이므로, 대화 장소가 가구점이라는 것을 알 수
있습니다.

13

다음 대화를 듣고, 대화가 자연스럽지 않은 것을 고르시오. ·················· (   )

①   ②   ③   ④

14

다음 대화를 듣고, 두 사람이 방과 후 할 일을 고르시오. ·················· (   )

①
②
③
④

15

다음 대화를 듣고, 두 사람이 어머니를 위해 할 일을 고르시오. ·················· (   )

① 청소하기   ② 쓰레기 버리기
③ 심부름하기   ④ 저녁식사 만들기

16

다음을 듣고, 여자의 직업을 고르시오. ·················· (   )

①
②
③
④

---

❶ B: This present is for you.

    G: Thank you very much.

❷ B: Hello. May I _____ _____ Sally?

    G: Speaking.

❸ B: _____ _____ sisters do you have?

    G: I _____ _____ my sisters.

❹ B: Where did you go last weekend?

    G: I went to the zoo with my family.

present 선물 | speak 말하다 | last weekend 지난 주말에

TIPS [How many + 복수명사 ~?]로 질문하면 구체적인 수를 이용하여 대답합니다.

B: Susie, how about _____ _____ after school?

G: Sorry, I _____ _____ like playing tennis today.

B: What would you like to do then?

G: Why don't we go to the _____ _____?

B: Sounds great.

play tennis 테니스를 치다 | swimming pool 수영장

TIPS [Why don't we + 동사원형~?] 은 '~하는 게 어때?'라고 제안할 때 사용하는 표현입니다.

B: Mom doesn't _____ _____ today.

G: Let's do something for her.

B: Sure. What can we do?

G: Let's _____ _____ for her.

B: That's a great idea. She will really _____ _____.

look good 좋아 보이다 | something 무언가 | make dinner 저녁을 만들다 | idea 생각

W: I work on a _____. My job is to make _____ comfortable for passengers. I _____ _____ and drinks to the passengers on the plane. I visit a lot of cities and countries every year.

plane 비행기 | flight 비행 | comfortable 편안한 | passenger 승객 | serve 제공하다 | country 나라 | every year 매년

17

다음 대화를 듣고, 두 아이가 만나서 할 일과 만나기로 한 시각을 고르시오. ······ (   )

① 청소하기 – 2시   ② 숙제하기 – 3시
③ 선물 사기 – 3시   ④ 생일파티 가기 – 3시

[Cellphone rings.]

G: Hello.

B: Hi, Sara. This is Ted. What are you doing?

G: I'm watching TV.

B: I will go to the mall to buy John's _____ _____. Will you join me?

G: Sure. What time?

B: Let's meet _____ _____ _____ the mall at _____ o'clock.

G: Okay.

mall 쇼핑몰 | birthday present 생일 선물 | join 함께하다 | in front of ~ 앞에서

18

다음 대화를 듣고, 이어질 말로 알맞은 것을 고르시오. ····················· (   )

G _____

① I like all kinds of books.
② I like action movies.
③ I want to be a writer.
④ I read books every day.

G: Steve, what do you do in your free time?

B: I _____ _____. How about you?

G: I _____ _____. I want to be an actor when I grow up.

B: Really? I didn't know that. _____ _____ of movie do you like to watch?

G: _____

free time 여가시간 | watch movies 영화 보다 | actor 배우 | grow up 자라다

19

다음 대화를 듣고, 이어질 말로 알맞은 것을 고르시오. ····················· (   )

G _____

① Yes, I want to go home.
② No, I don't like sports.
③ Thanks, but I'm full.
④ I'd love to, but I have to go home for dinner.

B: Do you have a favorite sport?

G: I enjoy _____ _____. How about you?

B: I like playing basketball, too! Do you want to _____ and _____ basketball with me right now?

G: _____

enjoy 즐기다 | too 또한, 역시 | right now 지금 당장

TIPS [enjoy + 동명사]는 '~하는 것을 즐기다'라는 의미입니다.

20

다음 대화를 듣고, 이어질 말로 알맞은 것을 고르시오. ····················· (   )

G _____

① I'm okay. Thank you.
② Oh, I'm sorry to hear that.
③ Don't worry. He will be all right.
④ When did you find it?

G: You look so sad. What's wrong?

B: I _____ _____ _____ on the bus.

G: Did you go to the Lost and Found?

B: Yes, I did. But I _____ _____ my bag there.

G: _____

wrong 잘못된 | Lost and Found 분실물 보관소

Word Check

● 다음 들려주는 단어와 그 의미를 쓰세요.

	단어	의미
01	leave	출발하다
02		
03		
04		
05		
06		
07		
08		
09		
10		
11		
12		
13		
14		
15		

8 회 Sentence Check

앞에 모의고사에 나오는 문장들을 잘 듣고, 빈칸을 완성하세요.

01 Can you _____give_____ me _____a_____ _____ride_____ to school today?

02 People are _____ _____ _____.

03 People are waiting for the _____ _____ to change.

04 I don't have any _____ _____.

05 I'm _____ _____ _____ on my phone.

06 I'm looking for _____ _____ for my husband.

07 I _____ my _____ at your restaurant yesterday.

08 I'll _____ _____ _____ this afternoon.

09 I play _____ _____ a week.

10 He _____ _____ me do my homework.

11 I like soccer because it's a very _____ and _____ sport.

12 May I _____ _____ Sally?

13 Why don't we go to the _____ _____?

14 My job is to make _____ _____ for passengers.

15 I want to be _____ _____ when I grow up.

보통 속도
 빠른 속도

| 학습일 | 월 일 | 부모님 확인 | 점수 |

1

다음 대화를 듣고, 여자 아이의 친구를 고르시오. ···························· (　　　)

① 　②

③ 　④

2

다음 대화를 듣고, 여자 아이가 전화 통화 직후에 할 일을 고르시오. ············· (　　　)

① 생일카드 보내기
② 이메일 확인하기
③ 생일카드 사기
④ 이메일 보내기

3

다음 대화를 듣고, 두 사람이 점심으로 먹을 음식을 고르시오. ····················· (　　　)

① 　②

③ 　④

4

다음 대화를 듣고, 여자 아이가 주말에 갈 곳과 이용할 교통수단을 고르시오. ······ (　　　)

① 해변 – 자동차
② 놀이공원 – 지하철
③ 놀이공원 – 버스
④ 동물원 – 버스

5

다음 대화를 듣고, 남자 아이가 어제 한 일을 고르시오. ···························· (　　　)

① 생일 파티 참석　　② 낚시하기
③ 그림 그리기　　④ 저녁 음식 만들기

6

다음 그림을 보고, 그림과 일치하는 대화를 고르시오. ·························· (   )

①   ②   ③   ④

7
중학기출 변형문제

다음 대화를 듣고, 남자 아이가 해변에 가는 이유를 고르시오. ····················· (   )

① 해변 축제에 참가하려고
② 친구들과 낚시하려고
③ 수영 대회에 참가하려고
④ 그림 그리기 대회에 참가하려고

8

다음 대화를 듣고, 두 사람이 내일 할 일을 고르시오. ·························· (   )

① TV 시청   ② 동물원 방문
③ 농구 경기 관람   ④ 체육관 청소

9

다음 대화를 듣고, 여자 아이가 아버지에게 부탁한 일을 고르시오. ·············· (   )

① 숙제 가져오기
② 우산 가져오기
③ 일기예보 확인하기
④ 버스 정류장까지 데려다 주기

10

다음 대화를 듣고, 여자가 찾는 물건이 있는 곳을 고르시오. ····················· (   )

①   ②   ③   ④

11

다음 대화를 듣고, Reo의 전화번호를 고르시오. ⋯⋯⋯⋯⋯⋯⋯⋯⋯⋯⋯⋯ ( )

① 1542-7856 ② 1542-7866
③ 1542-8855 ④ 1542-7855

12

다음 대화를 듣고, 대화 후 두 사람이 가려고 하는 장소를 고르시오. ⋯⋯⋯⋯⋯ ( )

① 도서관 ② 시장
③ 식당 ④ 편의점

13

다음을 듣고, 여자 아이가 말하는 내용과 일치하는 것을 고르시오. ⋯⋯⋯⋯⋯ ( )

① 7시 50분에 일어난다.
② 아침으로 빵과 과일을 먹는다.
③ 8시 30분까지 학교에 가야 한다.
④ 학교에서 새로운 것을 배우는 것이 좋아한다.

14

다음 대화를 듣고, 대화가 자연스럽지 <u>않은</u> 것을 고르시오. ⋯⋯⋯⋯⋯⋯⋯⋯ ( )

① ② ③ ④

15

다음 대화를 듣고, 두 아이가 사려는 선물을 고르시오. ⋯⋯⋯⋯⋯⋯⋯⋯⋯⋯⋯ ( )

① 여자 아이 –   남자 아이 –

② 여자 아이 –  남자 아이 –

③ 여자 아이 –   남자 아이 –

④ 여자 아이 –   남자 아이 –

16

다음 대화를 듣고, 두 사람이 무엇에 관해 이야기하고 있는지 고르시오. ·········· (   )

① 체육대회 연습   ② 중간고사 날짜
③ 현장학습 날짜 변경   ④ 교통수단 알아보기

17 중학기출 변형문제

다음 대화를 듣고, 이어질 말로 알맞은 것을 고르시오. ··························· (   )

B _____

① I'd be glad to. Anything else?
② I don't think so.
③ I feel better today.
④ I'll take it.

18

다음 대화를 듣고, 이어질 말로 알맞은 것을 고르시오. ··························· (   )

G _____

① It's on the second floor.
② I'll borrow the books.
③ Jane and Lisa.
④ I'll take the subway.

19

다음 대화를 듣고, 이어질 말로 알맞은 것을 고르시오. ··························· (   )

M _____

① I got up late.
② I have a cold.
③ Yes, it's too big for me.
④ Yes, I like that color.

20

다음 대화를 듣고, 이어질 말로 적절하지 <u>않은</u> 것을 고르시오. ··················· (   )

M _____

① No, that's all.
② I'm on a diet.
③ Do you have diet soda?
④ What do you have?

학습일 월 일 부모님 확인 점수

● 잘 듣고, 빈칸에 알맞은 말을 쓰세요.

1

다음 대화를 듣고, 여자 아이의 친구를 고르시오. ·························· (　)

① ② ③ ④

G: My friend Susan is over there.

B: Where is she?

G: Do you see the girl with _____ _____?

B: Is she wearing a skirt?

G: No, she's wearing a _____ blouse and _____.

B: Oh, I see her.

over there 저쪽에 | short hair 짧은 머리 | blouse 블라우스 | shorts 반바지

TIPS the girl with short hair는 '짧은 머리 소녀'라는 의미입니다. 여기서 전치사 with 는 '~을 가지고 있는, ~이 있는'이란 의미입니다.
the tall man with red hair 빨간 머리를 한 키 큰 남자

2

다음 대화를 듣고, 여자 아이가 전화 통화 직후에 할 일을 고르시오. ·············· (　)

① 생일카드 보내기
② 이메일 확인하기
③ 생일카드 사기
④ 이메일 보내기

[Cellphone rings.]

G: Hello.

B: Hello, Susie. This is John.

G: What's up, John?

B: I _____ you last night. Did you read it?

G: No, I didn't.

B: Please check your email. I _____ you a birthday card.

G: Okay. I _____ _____ it right away.

email 이메일을 보내다 | check 확인하다 | sent 보내다(send)의 과거형 | right away 바로

3

다음 대화를 듣고, 두 사람이 점심으로 먹을 음식을 고르시오. ·············· (　)

① ②

③ ④

W: James, where are you going?

M: I'm going to the cafeteria to _____ _____.

W: Can I join you?

M: Sure. What are you going to eat for lunch?

W: I'm having a _____ _____. How about you?

M: I'll have _____ _____. I'm on a diet.

cafeteria 구내식당 | join 함께하다 | chicken salad 치킨 샐러드 | same 같은 것 | be on a diet 다이어트 중이다

4

다음 대화를 듣고, 여자 아이가 주말에 갈 곳과 이용할 교통수단을 고르시오. …… (　　　)

① 해변 – 자동차
② 놀이공원 – 지하철
③ 놀이공원 – 버스
④ 동물원 – 버스

B: Jane, what are you going to do this weekend?

G: I will go to the amusement park with my cousins.

B: Sounds fun. _____ will you get there? Will your parents give you a _____?

G: No, we will _____ _____ _____.

B: Oh, I see. Have a nice weekend.

weekend 주말 | amusement park 놀이공원 | cousin 사촌 | ride 탈것 | subway 지하철

TIPS [give A a ride]는 'A(사람)를 차에 태워주다'라는 의미입니다.
동사 take은 '(교통수단 등을) 타다, 이용하다'라는 의미입니다.
take the bus 버스를 타다　　take the plane 비행기를 이용하다

5

다음 대화를 듣고, 남자 아이가 어제 한 일을 고르시오. ………………… (　　　)

① 생일 파티 참석　　② 낚시하기
③ 그림 그리기　　④ 저녁 음식 만들기

B: Lisa, what did you do yesterday?

G: I _____ _____ with my dad.

B: How was the fishing?

G: It was good. We caught a lot of fish. How about you?

B: It was my mom's birthday, so I _____ _____ for her.

G: Really? What did you cook for her?

B: I _____ pasta.

go fishing 낚시하러 가다 | caught 잡다(catch)의 과거형 | fish 물고기 | cook 요리하다

6

다음 그림을 보고, 그림과 일치하는 대화를 고르시오. …………… (　　　)

①　　②　　③　　④

❶ W: What do you think of _____ _____?
　 M: Wow, you're very _____ _____ painting.

❷ W: What's wrong?
　 M: I have a fever and a runny nose.

❸ W: I don't _____ _____.
　 I have a headache.
　 M: Sorry to hear that. Why don't you _____ some _____?

❹ W: I'm very hungry. What's for dinner?
　 M: Fried rice. It's on the table.

think 생각하다 | painting 그림 | fever 열 | runny nose 콧물 | headache 두통 | take some medicine 약을 먹다 | fried rice 볶음밥

7

다음 대화를 듣고, 남자 아이가 해변에 가는 이유를 고르시오. ·················· (   )

① 해변 축제에 참가하려고
② 친구들과 낚시하려고
③ 수영 대회에 참가하려고
④ 그림 그리기 대회에 참가하려고

G: Donovan, what are you going to do tomorrow?

B: I will go to the _____.

G: Are you going to swim there?

B: No, there is a _____ _____ at the beach. I'm going to _____ _____ in the contest.

G: Really? Good luck.

beach 해변 | **drawing contest** 사생대회 | **take part in** ~에 참가하다 | **luck** 행운

TIPS take part in the contest은 '대회에 참여하다'라는 의미입니다.

8

다음 대화를 듣고, 두 사람이 내일 할 일을 고르시오. ·················· (   )

① TV 시청   ② 동물원 방문
③ 농구 경기 관람   ④ 체육관 청소

W: What sports do you like?

M: I like _____.

W: I like basketball, too. I especially _____ _____ basketball games.

M: Really? Why don't we go to the _____ tomorrow? There will be a basketball _____ the Tigers against the Bears.

W: Okay. That's so exciting!

basketball 농구 | **too** 역시 | **especially** 특히 | **gym** 체육관 | **exciting** 흥미진진한

TIPS [Why don't we + 동사원형]은 '~하는 게 어때?'라는 의미로 제안할 때 사용합니다.
Why don't we go out to[for] dinner tonight?
오늘 밤에 저녁 나가서 먹는 게 어때?

9

다음 대화를 듣고, 여자 아이가 아버지에게 부탁한 일을 고르시오. ·············· (   )

① 숙제 가져오기
② 우산 가져오기
③ 일기예보 확인하기
④ 버스 정류장까지 데려다 주기

[Cellphone rings.]

G: Hello.

M: Hello, Ellen. What's up?

G: Dad, where are you?

M: I'm at home. Why?

G: It's _____ a lot now. Can you _____ me an _____?

M: Where are you now?

G: I'm at the _____ _____.

a lot 많이 | **bring** 가져오다 | **umbrella** 우산 | **bus stop** 버스 정류장

10

다음 대화를 듣고, 여자가 찾는 물건이 있는 곳을 고르시오. ·················· (   )

① ② ③ ④

W: Tony, can you bring me my sunglasses?
   They are on the sofa.
B: Okay. *[Pause]* Mom, they are not here.
   Didn't you leave them _____ _____
   _____?
W: I don't think so. Please check _____ the table.
B: Oh, I found them. They are _____ the table.

bring 가져오다 | **sunglasses** 선글라스 | **pause** 멈춤, 중단 | **leave** 두다 | **check** 확인하다 | **found** 찾다(find)의 과거형 | **under** ~ 아래에

TIPS around 전치사로 '둘레에, 주위에'라는 의미입니다.
around the table 책상 주위   around the Sun 태양 주위

11

다음 대화를 듣고, Reo의 전화번호를 고르시오. ·················· (   )

① 1542-7856   ② 1542-7866
③ 1542-8855   ④ 1542-7855

[Cellphone rings.]
B: Hello?
G: Hi, Jack!
B: Hi, Sue. How is it going?
G: Good! I called because I lost Leo's _____
   _____. Do you mind telling me his number?
B: Not at all. It's _____-7855.
G: 1542-8855?
B: No, it's 1542-_____. It's not 88, it's 78.
G: Okay. Thank you so much.

call 전화하다 | **because** ~ 때문에 | **phone number** 전화번호 | **mind** 꺼리다

TIPS [Do you mind + 동명사 ?]는 상대방에게 뭔가를 부탁할 때 사용하는 표현입니다.
Do you mind closing the window? 문 좀 닫아 주시겠어요?

12

다음 대화를 듣고, 대화 후 두 사람이 가려고 하는 장소를 고르시오. ·············· (   )

① 도서관   ② 시장
③ 식당   ④ 편의점

G: When is our science homework due?
B: Next Monday.
G: Do you want to _____ _____ to my
   house and do the homework together?
B: Sure, but I'm _____ right now.
   Let's _____ a sandwich at the food court.
G: Good idea. _____ _____.

be due 예정이다 | **come over** ~에 들르다 | **house** 집 | **right now** 지금 당장 | **grab** 먹다

TIPS 바쁠 때 급하게 잠깐 뭔가를 후딱 할 때 동사 grab을 씁니다. 예를 들어, 여유롭게 긴 시간은 없지만 잠깐이라도 틈이 있을 때 뭐라도 좀 먹자고 할 때도 eat 대신 grab을 써서 eat을 대신할 수 있습니다.
Let's grab a cup of coffee! 잠깐 커피 한 잔 하자!

13

다음을 듣고, 여자 아이가 말하는 내용과 일치하는 것을 고르시오. ·············· (　　)

① 7시 50분에 일어난다.
② 아침으로 빵과 과일을 먹는다.
③ 8시 30분까지 학교에 가야 한다.
④ 학교에서 새로운 것을 배우는 것이 좋아한다.

G: My name is Annie. I usually wake up at 7:30. After taking a shower, I eat breakfast. I usually eat some _____ _____ _____ for breakfast. I go to school _____ _____ o'clock. I like going to school because I like learning _____ _____.

take a shower 샤워하다 | usually 보통, 주로 | in the morning 아침에 | learn 배우다

14

다음 대화를 듣고, 대화가 자연스럽지 않은 것을 고르시오. ·············· (　　)

①　　②　　③　　④

❶ B: Hi, Claire. Are you free tomorrow?
　G: Yes, I'm free after school. Why?
❷ B: Can you do me a favor, Jennie?
　G: Sure. What is it?
❸ G: _____ _____, Sam?
　B: Okay, I'll take it.
❹ G: Let's go to the shopping mall.
　B: _____ _____ to me.

free 한가한 | favor 부탁 | wrong 잘못된 | shopping mall 쇼핑몰

15

다음 대화를 듣고, 두 아이가 사려는 선물을 고르시오. ·············· (　　)

① 여자 아이 – 　　　남자 아이 –
② 여자 아이 – 　　　남자 아이 –
③ 여자 아이 – 　　　남자 아이 –
④ 여자 아이 – 　　　남자 아이 –

G: Jack's birthday is coming up.
B: Did you buy a gift for him?
G: No, _____ _____. I'm going to buy a _____ _____. How about you?
B: I'm going to buy a _____ _____. His glove is very old.
G: That's a good idea.

come up 다가오다 | yet 아직 | baseball cap 야구모자 | glove 장갑 | idea 생각

16

다음 대화를 듣고, 두 사람이 무엇에 관해 이야기하고 있는지 고르시오. ·············· (　　)

① 체육대회 연습　　② 중간고사 날짜
③ 현장학습 날짜 변경　④ 교통수단 알아보기

B: Your school's _____ _____ is this Friday, right?
G: No, it was _____ because it'll be windy and rainy this Friday.
B: Really? So _____ is the field trip?
G: It's next Monday.

field trip 현장학습 | change 바뀌다 | windy 바람 부는
TIPS field trip은 '수학여행', '현장학습' 등의 의미입니다.

17

다음 대화를 듣고, 이어질 말로 알맞은 것을 고르시오. .... (   )

B _____

① I'd be glad to. Anything else?
② I don't think so.
③ I feel better today.
④ I'll take it.

W: Mike, can you _____ _____?
B: Sure, Ms. Brown. _____ can I do for you?
W: Can you help me _____ these _____ to the car?
B: _____

carry 옮기다 | box 상자 | glad 기쁜 | think 생각하다 | feel better 더 나아지다

TIPS I'd be glad to. / I'd be happy to.는 '그럴게요.'라는 의미로 상대방의 부탁을 기꺼이 들어 주어 상대방이 부담을 안 느끼도록 하는 표현입니다.

18

다음 대화를 듣고, 이어질 말로 알맞은 것을 고르시오. .... (   )

G _____

① It's on the second floor.
② I'll borrow the books.
③ Jane and Lisa.
④ I'll take the subway.

B: What are you going to do _____ _____?
G: I will go to the library.
B: _____ _____?
G: _____

library 도서관 | second floor 2층 | borrow 빌리다 | subway 지하철

TIPS With who?는 With who will you go to the library?의 줄임말입니다. 의문사 who로 물었으므로, 구체적인 사람에 대한 정보로 대답해야 합니다.

19

다음 대화를 듣고, 이어질 말로 알맞은 것을 고르시오. .... (   )

M _____

① I got up late.
② I have a cold.
③ Yes, it's too big for me.
④ Yes, I like that color.

W: Hello, can I help you?
M: Yes, I want to _____ this _____.
W: Okay. Is there _____ _____ with it?
M: _____

return 환불하다 | sweater 스웨터 | something 무언가 | late 늦은 | too 너무

TIPS something, anything, nothing과 같은 대명사는 형용사가 뒤에서 수식을 합니다.

20

다음 대화를 듣고, 이어질 말로 적절하지 <u>않은</u> 것을 고르시오. .... (   )

M _____

① No, that's all.
② I'm on a diet.
③ Do you have diet soda?
④ What do you have?

W: Hi, how can I help you?
M: Can I get a hamburger, please?
W: _____ _____ of hamburger would you like?
M: I will have a cheeseburger.
W: Okay, and _____ _____ _____?
M: _____

hamburger 햄버거 | cheeseburger 치즈버거 | be on a diet 다이어트 중이다

TIPS Anything to drink?는 '어떤 것을 마시겠어요?'라는 의미로 Would you like anything to drink?의 줄임말입니다.

9 회 Word Check

● 다음 들려주는 단어와 그 의미를 쓰세요.

	단어	의미
01	blouse	블라우스
02		
03		
04		
05		
06		
07		
08		
09		
10		
11		
12		
13		
14		
15		

● 앞에 모의고사에 나오는 문장들을 잘 듣고, 빈칸을 완성하세요.

01 She's wearing a pink ___blouse___ and ___shorts___.

02 I _____ _____ last night.

03 I'm _____ _____ _____.

04 Have a _____ _____.

05 It was my mom's birthday, so I _____ _____ for her.

06 Why don't you _____ _____ _____?

07 I'm going to _____ _____ _____ the contest.

08 I _____ _____ watching basketball games.

09 Can you _____ me an _____?

10 I called because I lost Leo's _____ _____.

11 Let's _____ _____ _____ at the food court.

12 Can you _____ _____ carry these boxes to the car?

13 I want to _____ _____ _____.

14 Is there _____ _____ with it?

15 Okay, and _____ _____ _____?

학습일   월   일   부모님 확인   점수

1

다음 대화를 듣고, 여자 아이의 장래 희망을 고르시오. ································ (   )

①  ②

③  ④

2

중학기출 변형문제

다음 대화를 듣고, 남자 아이가 엄마에게 부탁한 일을 고르시오. ················ (   )

① 집안 청소하기   ② 전등 끄기

③ 숙제 대신하기   ④ 숙제 함께하기

3

다음 대화를 듣고, 남자 아이가 겨울방학에 할 일을 고르시오. ····················· (   )

4

다음 대화를 듣고, 여자 아이가 살 케이크 가격과 누구를 위한 것인지를 고르시오.

································ (   )

① 25달러 – 남동생

② 24달러 – 아버지

③ 24달러 – 여동생

④ 25달러 – 어머니

5

다음 대화를 듣고, 대화와 일치하는 그림을 고르시오. ·························· (   )

①

②

③

④

8

다음 대화를 듣고, 여자가 찾는 물건이 있는 곳을 고르시오. ················· (   )

① ② ③ ④

6

다음 대화를 듣고, 두 사람이 대화 후 가장 먼저 할 일을 고르시오. ·············· (   )

① 수영하기   ② 쇼핑센터 가기
③ 시험공부하기   ④ 청소하기

7

다음 대화를 듣고, 현재의 날씨를 고르시오.
··· (   )

①

②

③

④

9

다음 그림을 보고, 그림과 일치하는 대화를 고르시오. ····························· (   )

① ② ③ ④

10 중학기출 변형문제

다음 대화를 듣고, 여자가 지불해야 할 금액을 고르시오. ·········· ( )

4 dollars Hamburger	2 dollars Coke
3 dollars Hotdog	1 dollars Ice Cream

① 3달러   ② 4달러

③ 5달러   ④ 6달러

11

다음을 듣고, 내용과 일치하지 <u>않는</u> 것을 고르시오. ···························· ( )

① 어제는 나의 12번째 생일이었다.

② 친구들을 파티에 초대했다.

③ 엄마가 생일 케이크를 사오셨다.

④ 친구들이 내게 생일 선물을 줬다.

12

다음 대화를 듣고, 대화가 자연스럽지 <u>않은</u> 것을 고르시오. ···················· ( )

①   ②   ③   ④

13

다음 대화를 듣고, 오늘의 요일과 남자 아이가 대화 직후 할 일을 고르시오. ······ ( )

① 목요일 – 전화하기

② 목요일 – 선물 사기

③ 금요일 – 선물 사기

④ 금요일 – 선물 포장하기

14

다음 대화를 듣고, 여자가 보고 있는 사진으로 알맞은 것을 고르시오. ·············· ( )

①    ②

③    ④

15 중학기출 변형문제

다음 대화를 듣고, 남자가 소풍에 필요하지 <u>않</u>은 물건을 고르시오. ················· ( )

① 음식   ② 음료수

③ 배낭   ④ 소풍 바구니

16

다음 대화를 듣고, 여자가 여행이 즐겁지 <u>않았</u>던 이유를 고르시오. ·················· (   )

① 음식이 맛이 없어서
② 잠을 잘 못 자서
③ 날씨가 좋지 않아서
④ 몸이 아파서

17

다음 대화를 듣고, 이어질 말로 알맞은 것을 고르시오. ····················· (   )

W _____

① How much is it?
② Sure. No problem.
③ Okay. Here you are.
④ No. Thank you.

18

다음 대화를 듣고, 이어질 말로 알맞은 것을 고르시오. ····················· (   )

B _____

① I'm reading a book.
② Yes, I feel like eating a sandwich.
③ No, I didn't take the medicine.
④ Yes, thank you for asking.

19

다음 대화를 듣고, 이어질 말로 알맞은 것을 고르시오. ····················· (   )

W _____

① Thank you. Let's go.
② I can't drive a car.
③ It is 20 dollars.
④ It took about two hours.

20

다음 대화를 듣고, 이어질 말로 적절하지 <u>않은</u> 것을 고르시오. ····················· (   )

W _____

① That's a good idea.
② What is your favorite food?
③ Okay. It's my favorite.
④ What kind of pizza do you want?

10회 Dictation 영어 듣기 모의고사

| 학습일 | 월 일 | 부모님 확인 | 점수 |

● 잘 듣고, 빈칸에 알맞은 말을 쓰세요.

1

다음 대화를 듣고, 여자 아이의 장래 희망을 고르시오. ·················· (　　)

① ② ③ ④

G: James, do you still want to be a movie director?

B: Yes, I do. How about you, Amy?

G: I want to be _____ _____ like my uncle.

B: Really? I thought you wanted to be a teacher.

G: I did, but I _____ my _____.

movie director 영화감독 | thought 생각하다(think)의 과거형 | change 바꾸다 | mind 마음

TIPS 여자 아이의 장래 희망이 선생님에서 의사로 마음을 바뀌었습니다.

2

다음 대화를 듣고, 남자 아이가 엄마에게 부탁한 일을 고르시오. ·················· (　　)

① 집안 청소하기　　② 전등 끄기
③ 숙제 대신하기　　④ 숙제 함께하기

[Cellphone rings.]

B: Hello.

W: Hello, Ted? What's up?

B: Mom, where are you?

W: I'm _____ _____. Why?

B: I forgot to turn off _____ _____ in my room. Could you _____ it _____?

W: Okay.

forgot 잊어버리다(forget)의 과거형 | turn off (불 등을) 끄다 | light 전등

TIPS [forget to + 동사원형]은 '~ 할 것을 잊다'라는 의미입니다.
I forgot to close the window. 창문 닫는 걸 깜박했다.

3

다음 대화를 듣고, 남자 아이가 겨울방학에 할 일을 고르시오. ·················· (　　)

G: Winter vacation is coming soon.

B: What are you planning to do?

G: I will learn Chinese. What is _____ _____?

B: I will take _____ _____.

G: Cooking classes?

B: Yes, I want to be _____ _____ when I grow up.

vacation 휴가, 방학 | plan 계획하다 | learn 배우다 | cooking class 요리 수업 | chef 주방장 | grow up 자라다

4

다음 대화를 듣고, 여자 아이가 살 케이크 가격과 누구를 위한 것인지를 고르시오. ·················· ( )

① 25달러 – 남동생
② 24달러 – 아버지
③ 24달러 – 여동생
④ 25달러 – 어머니

M: May I help you?

G: Yes, I'm looking for a cake for my younger sister.

M: _____ _____ of cake do you want?

G: I want a cheesecake.

M: Sorry, we only have a _____ _____ today.

G: Okay. I will _____ _____. How much is it?

M: It's _____ dollars.

younger sister 여동생 | kind 종류 | cheesecake 치즈케이크 | chocolate 초콜릿 | take 사다

TIPS younger sister 여동생　　younger brother 남동생
older sister 언니, 누나　　older brother 형, 오빠

5

다음 대화를 듣고, 대화와 일치하는 그림을 고르시오. ·················· ( )

① ② ③ ④

W: Excuse me.

M: Yes?

W: You _____ your _____.

M: Oh, I didn't notice. Thank you.

W: No problem.

drop 떨어뜨리다 | cellphone 휴대전화 | notice 알아차리다

TIPS 떨어트린 휴대전화를 찾아주는 대화이므로 ④번의 그림이 대화의 상황과 가장 어울립니다.

6

다음 대화를 듣고, 두 사람이 대화 후 가장 먼저 할 일을 고르시오. ·················· ( )

① 수영하기 ② 쇼핑센터 가기
③ 시험공부하기 ④ 청소하기

B: I'm happy that _____ _____ are over.

G: Me, too. How about going swimming?

B: Sure! The weather is very nice. But before we go, can we go to the _____ _____?

G: Why?

B: I lost my _____ _____, so I need a new one.

G: Okay. Let's go.

final exam 기말고사 | be over 끝나다 | weather 날씨 | before ~ 전에 | swimming cap 수영 모자

TIPS [I'm happy (that) + 주어 + 동사]는 '~해서 기쁘다'라는 의미입니다.
I'm happy (that) you came here. 네가 여기에 와서 기쁘다.

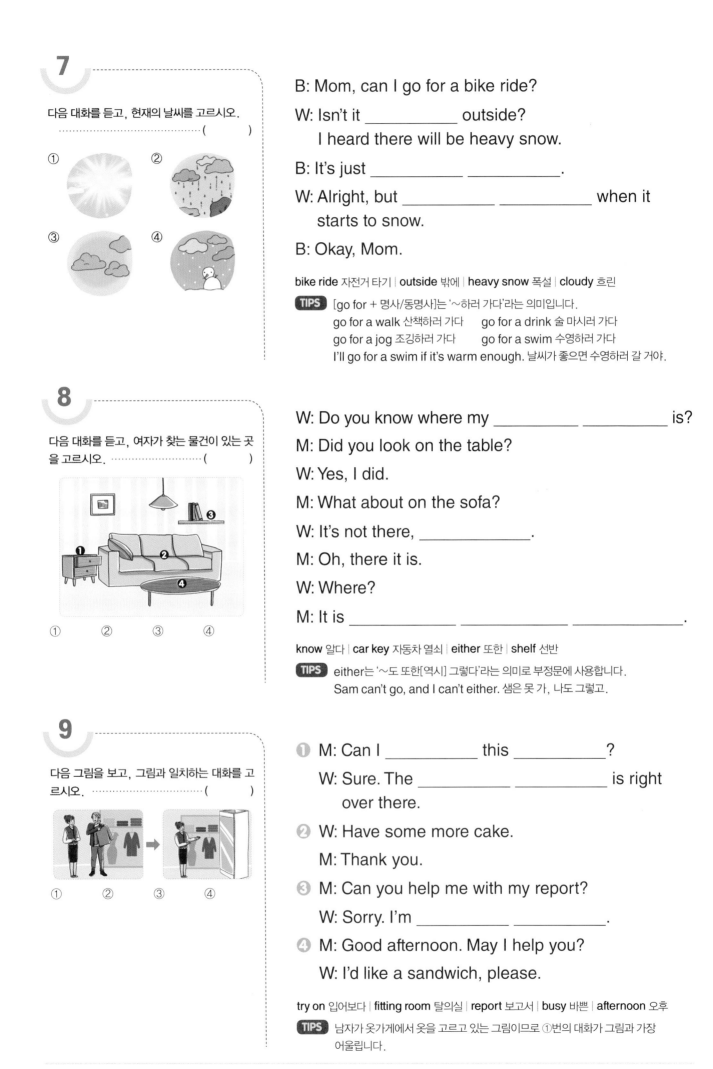

7

다음 대화를 듣고, 현재의 날씨를 고르시오.
·····( )

① ② ③ ④

B: Mom, can I go for a bike ride?

W: Isn't it _____ outside?
I heard there will be heavy snow.

B: It's just _____ _____.

W: Alright, but _____ _____ when it
starts to snow.

B: Okay, Mom.

bike ride 자전거 타기 | **outside** 밖에 | **heavy snow** 폭설 | **cloudy** 흐린

TIPS [go for + 명사/동명사]는 '~하러 가다'라는 의미입니다.
go for a walk 산책하러 가다　go for a drink 술 마시러 가다
go for a jog 조깅하러 가다　go for a swim 수영하러 가다
I'll go for a swim if it's warm enough. 날씨가 좋으면 수영하러 갈 거야.

8

다음 대화를 듣고, 여자가 찾는 물건이 있는 곳
을 고르시오. ·····( )

① ② ③ ④

W: Do you know where my _____ _____ is?

M: Did you look on the table?

W: Yes, I did.

M: What about on the sofa?

W: It's not there, _____.

M: Oh, there it is.

W: Where?

M: It is _____ _____ _____.

know 알다 | **car key** 자동차 열쇠 | **either** 또한 | **shelf** 선반

TIPS either는 '~도 또한[역시] 그렇다'라는 의미로 부정문에 사용합니다.
Sam can't go, and I can't either. 샘은 못 가, 나도 그렇고.

9

다음 그림을 보고, 그림과 일치하는 대화를 고
르시오. ·····( )

① ② ③ ④

❶ M: Can I _____ this _____?

W: Sure. The _____ _____ is right
over there.

❷ W: Have some more cake.

M: Thank you.

❸ M: Can you help me with my report?

W: Sorry. I'm _____ _____.

❹ M: Good afternoon. May I help you?

W: I'd like a sandwich, please.

try on 입어보다 | **fitting room** 탈의실 | **report** 보고서 | **busy** 바쁜 | **afternoon** 오후

TIPS 남자가 옷가게에서 옷을 고르고 있는 그림이므로 ①번의 대화가 그림과 가장
어울립니다.

10

다음 대화를 듣고, 여자가 지불해야 할 금액을 고르시오. ·················· ( )

| 4 dollars Hamburger | 2 dollars Coke |
| 3 dollars Hotdog | 1 dollars Ice Cream |

① 3달러   ② 4달러
③ 5달러   ④ 6달러

M: Good afternoon. May I help you?

W: I'd like a _____, please.

M: Anything to drink?

W: _____, please.

hamburger 햄버거 | anything 무언가

11

다음을 듣고, 내용과 일치하지 <u>않는</u> 것을 고르시오. ·················· ( )

① 어제는 나의 12번째 생일이었다.
② 친구들을 파티에 초대했다.
③ 엄마가 생일 케이크를 사오셨다.
④ 친구들이 내게 생일 선물을 줬다.

G: Yesterday was my twelfth birthday. I had a party at my house. I _____ my friends to the party. My mom _____ _____ _____ for me. My friends gave me _____. We played many games. The party was a lot of fun.

party 파티 | house 집 | invite 초대하다 | present 선물 | a lot of 많은

TIPS 엄마가 생일 케이크를 만들어 줬다고 했으므로, ③번이 내용과 일치하지 않습니다.

12

다음 대화를 듣고, 대화가 자연스럽지 <u>않은</u> 것을 고르시오. ·················· ( )

①   ②   ③   ④

❶ B: Alice, how was the movie last night?
   G: It was great.
❷ B: Did you finish the math homework?
   G: Not yet, but I did half of it.
❸ B: Hi, Lina! Can I talk to you now?
   G: Sure, Kevin. _____ _____?
❹ B: What do you do in your _____ _____?
   G: I played tennis _____.

movie 영화 | finish 끝나다 | half 절반 | now 지금 | free time 여가시간

TIPS I played tennis yesterday.에 대한 올바른 질문은 What did you do yesterday?입니다.

13

다음 대화를 듣고, 오늘의 요일과 남자 아이가 대화 직후 할 일을 고르시오. ······ ( )

① 목요일 – 전화하기
② 목요일 – 선물 사기
③ 금요일 – 선물 사기
④ 금요일 – 선물 포장하기

B: What are you going to do today?

G: I'm going to Jim's birthday party.

B: What? I thought Jim's birthday is on _____.

G: Yes. Today is Friday.

B: Oh, my gosh! I thought today was _____. I didn't buy a gift for him yet. _____ _____ to the mall now.

G: Okay.

birthday party 생일 파티 | thought 생각하다(think)의 과거형 | gift 선물

14

다음 대화를 듣고, 여자가 보고 있는 사진으로 알맞은 것을 고르시오. ·············· (   )

① ② ③ ④

W: Where did you get this photo?

M: I took the photo in the _____ last week.

W: Wow. The _____ on the _____ are very beautiful. You are _____ _____ taking photos.

M: Thank you.

photo 사진 | garden 정원 | last week 지난주에 | butterfly 나비 | take pictures 사진 찍다

TIPS the butterflies on the flowers은 '꽃 위에 나비들'이란 의미입니다. 전치사 on은 '~ 위에'라는 의미로 '물건이 책상이나 벽' 등의 표면에 닿아 있을 때 사용합니다.

15

다음 대화를 듣고, 남자가 소풍에 필요하지 않은 물건을 고르시오. ·············· (   )

① 음식   ② 음료수
③ 배낭   ④ 소풍 바구니

W: What do you need for the picnic?

M: I need some _____ and _____.

W: What about a backpack?

M: Yes, I need a _____ to put food and drinks in.

W: Do you need a _____ _____?

M: No, I don't need it.

need 필요하다 | picnic 소풍 | drink 음료 | backpack 배낭 | basket 바구니

16

다음 대화를 듣고, 여자가 여행이 즐겁지 않았던 이유를 고르시오. ·············· (   )

① 음식이 맛이 없어서
② 잠을 잘 못 자서
③ 날씨가 좋지 않아서
④ 몸이 아파서

M: Susan, what did you do during the vacation?

W: I took a trip to Busan.

M: How was it?

W: It was _____ _____.

M: Why?

W: It _____ _____ throughout the vacation, so we stayed at a hotel.

M: Oh, I'm sorry to _____ _____.

during ~ 동안 | vacation 휴가 | take a trip 여행하다 | throughout 내내 | sorry 미안한

TIPS throughout the vacation은 '휴가 내내'라는 의미입니다. [take a trip to + 장소]는 '어디로 여행가다'라는 의미입니다.

17

다음 대화를 듣고, 이어질 말로 알맞은 것을 고르시오. ·············· (　　)

W _____

① How much is it?
② Sure. No problem.
③ Okay. Here you are.
④ No. Thank you.

W: How may I help you?
B: Can I get three red pens?
W: Sure. Is that all you need?
B: Do you have blue pens _____ _____?
W: Of course. _____ _____ blue ones do you need?
B: _____, please.
W: _____

need 필요하다 | as well 역시 | of course 물론 | problem 문제 | here you are 여기 있다

18

다음 대화를 듣고, 이어질 말로 알맞은 것을 고르시오. ·············· (　　)

B _____

① I'm reading a book.
② Yes, I feel like eating a sandwich.
③ No, I didn't take the medicine.
④ Yes, thank you for asking.

G: Leo! What did you do yesterday?
B: I stayed home _____ _____.
G: Why?
B: I didn't _____ _____.
G: Are you feeling _____ now?
B: _____

stay 머무르다 | all day 하루 종일 | feel good 기분이 좋다 | better 더 나은 | take medicine 약을 먹다

TIPS better은 good의 비교급입니다.

19

다음 대화를 듣고, 이어질 말로 알맞은 것을 고르시오. ·············· (　　)

W _____

① Thank you. Let's go.
② I can't drive a car.
③ It is 20 dollars.
④ It took about two hours.

W: I went to Incheon with my family yesterday.
M: Did you take the _____?
W: No, I _____ an express bus.
M: _____ _____ did it take?
W: _____

yesterday 어제 | family 가족 | take the subway 지하철을 타다 | express bus 고속버스

TIPS How long으로 묻고 있으므로, 구체적인 수치로 답을 해야 합니다.
It is 20 dollars.에 알맞은 질문은 How much is it?입니다.

20

다음 대화를 듣고, 이어질 말로 적절하지 않은 것을 고르시오. ·············· (　　)

W _____

① That's a good idea.
② What is your favorite food?
③ Okay. It's my favorite.
④ What kind of pizza do you want?

W: What do you want for lunch?
M: I'd like to have noodles.
W: Well, I _____ _____ for lunch yesterday.
M: Then, _____ _____ pizza.
W: _____

noodles 국수 | idea 생각 | favorite 좋아하는 | kind 종류

● 다음 들려주는 단어와 그 의미를 쓰세요.

단어	의미
01 mind	마음
02	
03	
04	
05	
06	
07	
08	
09	
10	
11	
12	
13	
14	
15	

● 앞에 모의고사에 나오는 문장들을 잘 듣고, 빈칸을 완성하세요.

01 ____I____ ____thought____ you wanted to be a teacher.

02 I forgot to _____ _____ the light in my room.

03 Winter vacation is _____ _____.

04 I'm happy that final exams _____ _____.

05 I heard there will be _____ _____.

06 _____ _____ when it starts to snow.

07 Do you _____ _____ my car key is?

08 The _____ _____ is right over there.

09 I _____ _____ _____ to the party.

10 What do you do in your _____ _____?

11 The butterflies on the flowers are _____ _____.

12 I need a backpack _____ _____ _____ and drinks in.

13 It _____ _____ throughout the vacation.

14 I _____ _____ all day.

15 I _____ _____ for lunch yesterday.

보통 속도

빠른 속도

학습일 월 일 부모님 확인 점수

1

다음 대화를 듣고, 여자가 찾는 물건이 있는 곳을 고르시오. ························· (   )

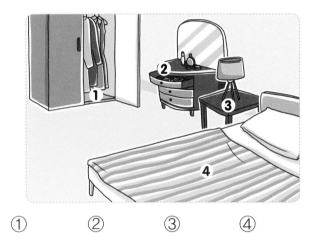

① ② ③ ④

2

다음 대화를 듣고, 두 사람이 대화 후 바로 할 일을 고르시오. ····················· (   )

① 집안 청소하기
② 아버지에게 전화하기
③ 콘서트 티켓 구매하기
④ 여자 아이 집 방문하기

3

다음 대화를 듣고, 대화가 이루어지는 장소를 고르시오. ························· (   )

① 서점   ② 도서관
③ 편의점   ④ 우체국

4

다음 대화를 듣고, 두 아이가 보고 있는 사진으로 알맞은 것을 고르시오. ········ (   )

①  ②

③  ④

5

다음 대화를 듣고, 여자 아이가 좋아하는 운동을 고르시오. ························· (   )

① 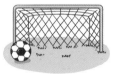 ②

③  ④

정답 및 해석 p. 42

6

다음 대화를 듣고, John의 전화번호를 고르시오. ···························· (   )

① 983-1149   ② 973-1149

③ 963-1149   ④ 783-1149

7

다음 대화를 듣고, 두 사람이 금요일에 하려는 일과 만나는 시각을 고르시오. ··· (   )

① 영화 관람 – 7시 30분

② 영화 관람 – 8시

③ 뮤지컬 공연 관람 – 7시 30분

④ 뮤지컬 공연 관람 – 8시

8

다음 대화를 듣고, 대화와 일치하는 그림을 고르시오. ································· (   )

①    ②

③    ④

9

다음 대화를 듣고, 여자 아이가 연주할 수 <u>없는</u> 악기를 고르시오. ················ (   )

①    ②

③   ④

10

다음 대화를 듣고, 두 사람의 대화가 <u>어색한</u> 것을 고르시오. ························ (   )

①   ②   ③   ④

11

다음을 듣고, 남자 아이가 말한 내용과 일치하지 <u>않는</u> 것을 고르시오. ·········· (　　　)

① 부모님은 일주일에 2번 테니스를 친다.
② 형은 농구를 좋아한다.
③ 형은 매일 방과 후 농구를 한다.
④ 여동생은 탁구선수가 되고 싶어 한다.

12

다음 대화를 듣고, 남자가 여자에게 부탁한 것을 고르시오. ····················· (　　　)

① 지갑 빌리기　　② 책 빌리기
③ 숙제 도와주기　④ 돈 빌리기

13

다음 그림을 보고, 그림과 일치하는 설명을 고르시오. ······························ (　　　)

①　　②　　③　　④

14

다음 대화를 듣고, 대화에 알맞은 표지판을 고르시오. ····························· (　　　)

① 　　②

③　　　④

15

다음 대화를 듣고, 남자 아이가 읽는 책과 책의 내용을 고르시오. ····················· (　　　)

① 과학잡지 – 공룡
② 과학잡지 – 우주
③ 영화잡지 – 공룡영화
④ 동물잡지 – 바다동물

16

다음 대화를 듣고, 여자 아이가 남자 아이에게 제안한 것을 고르시오. ·············· (   )

① 독서 동아리 가입
② 배드민턴 경기 관람
③ 함께 시험공부 하기
④ 농구 동아리 가입

17

다음 대화를 듣고, 이어질 말로 알맞은 것을 고르시오. ····························· (   )

M _____

① Here you are.
② Okay, I will take three mangos.
③ Where did you get them?
④ How many mangos do you want?

18

다음 대화를 듣고, 이어질 말로 알맞은 것을 고르시오. ····························· (   )

G _____

① It will rain soon.
② I was busy yesterday.
③ I have a swimming lesson.
④ Sure, I'll do it after school.

19

다음 대화를 듣고, 이어질 말로 알맞은 것을 고르시오. ····························· (   )

M _____

① Two weeks!
② Twenty dollars.
③ We went there by plane.
④ We stayed at a hotel.

20

다음 대화를 듣고, 이어질 말로 적절하지 <u>않은</u> 것을 고르시오. ····················· (   )

W _____

① It's October 5.
② Next Tuesday.
③ It want a new bike.
④ My birthday is the same as yours.

11회 Dictation 영어 듣기 모의고사

| 학습일 | 월 일 | 부모님 확인 | 점수 |

● 잘 듣고, 빈칸에 알맞은 말을 쓰세요.

1

다음 대화를 듣고, 여자가 찾는 물건이 있는 곳을 고르시오. ·············· (   )

① ② ③ ④

W: John, did you see my necklace?

B: No, Mom. Where did you _____ _____?

W: I don't know, but maybe I put it on the bed.

B: Nothing's there, Mom. Didn't you put it in the drawer?

W: Maybe? Please look for it in the drawer or

_____ _____ _____.

B: Oh, here it is. It's _____ the _____.

necklace 목걸이 | leave 두다 | know 알다 | maybe 아마 | drawer 서랍 | near 근처에 | lamp 전등

2

다음 대화를 듣고, 두 사람이 대화 후 바로 할 일을 고르시오. ·············· (   )

① 집안 청소하기
② 아버지에게 전화하기
③ 콘서트 티켓 구매하기
④ 여자 아이 집 방문하기

G: What's up? You look excited.

B: Guess what! My mom said I can go to the K-pop concert.

G: Wow, good for you.

B: Will you _____ _____?

G: I wish I could, but I have to _____ my dad _____.

B: Okay, let's go to _____ _____. I will help you.

excited 신이 난 | concert 콘서트 | join 함께하다 | wish 바라다 | first 먼저

TIPS Guess what.은 '있잖아.'라는 의미로 상대방에게 뭔가를 말하기 전에 하는 말이고 I wish I could ~는 '~라면 정말 좋을 텐데'라는 뜻을 가지고 있습니다.
I wish I could play an instrument. 악기를 연주할 수 있으면 좋을 텐데.

3

다음 대화를 듣고, 대화가 이루어지는 장소를 고르시오. ·············· (   )

① 서점
② 도서관
③ 편의점
④ 우체국

M: I would like to _____ _____ these books.

W: Okay. Do you have your library card?

M: Yes. Here you are. Can I borrow these books for a month?

W: Sorry. You can only _____ the _____ for two weeks.

check out 대출하다 | here you are 여기 있다 | borrow 빌리다 | month 달

4

다음 대화를 듣고, 두 아이가 보고 있는 사진으로 알맞은 것을 고르시오. ········· (   )

① ② ③ ④

B: Alice, did you take this photo?

G: Yes, I took it at the park last month.

B: Wow, the tree is very big. By the way, who is the boy _____ _____ the tree?

G: The boy _____ a balloon?

B: Yes, he is.

G: He's _____ _____, Minsu.

last month 지난달에 | by the way 그런데 | next to ~ 옆에 | hold 들다 | balloon 풍선

TIPS by the way는 대화에서 화제를 바꿀 때 사용하는 표현으로 '그런데', '그건 그렇고'라는 의미입니다.

5

다음 대화를 듣고, 여자 아이가 좋아하는 운동을 고르시오. ························ (   )

① ② ③ ④

G: You are a great football player, Chris.

B: Thanks. Do you enjoy football, Jen?

G: I do, but my favorite sport is _____ _____.

B: Really? Why?

G: I like _____ _____ _____.

B: Will you teach me how to skate one day?

G: _____ _____, I can!

football 미식축구 | hockey 하키 | because 때문에 | ice hockey 아이스하키 | ice 얼음 | of course 물론

TIPS ice hockey, skating on ice(얼음에서 스케이트 타기)가 문제 해결의 열쇠입니다.

6

다음 대화를 듣고, John의 전화번호를 고르시오. ····························· (   )

① 983-1149 ② 973-1149
③ 963-1149 ④ 783-1149

G: Hey, Albert! How is it going?

B: I'm good, thanks for asking. How about you?

G: I'm doing well. Do you have John's phone number by any chance?

B: Yes. _____ _____.

G: Okay.

B: His phone number is _____-1149.

G: 973-_____?

B: No, it's 983.

ask 묻다 | do well 잘하다 | phone number 전화번호

7

다음 대화를 듣고, 두 사람이 금요일에 하려는 일과 만나는 시각을 고르시오. … (   )

① 영화 관람 – 7시 30분
② 영화 관람 – 8시
③ 뮤지컬 공연 관람 – 7시 30분
④ 뮤지컬 공연 관람 – 8시

B: Hi, Stephanie. Do you want to go _____ _____ _____ with me?
G: I would love to, but when?
B: Friday night.
G: I'm free that day. _____ _____ shall we meet?
B: The musical starts at 8 o'clock. Let's meet in front of the theater at _____.
G: Okay. See you then.

musical 뮤지컬 | free 한가한 | meet 만나다 | in front of ~ 앞에서 | theater 극장

TIPS go see a musical은 '뮤지컬을 보러 가다'라는 뜻으로 go와 see 사이에 and가 생략되었습니다.

8

다음 대화를 듣고, 대화와 일치하는 그림을 고르시오. ……………… (   )

① ② ③ ④

G: Look at the _____ over there. He's _____ on the street.
B: I don't really understand people smoking in _____ _____.
G: Me, either.
B: Smoking is bad for _____ smokers _____ nonsmokers.

smoke 담배 피우다 | street 길, 거리 | understand 이해하다 | people 사람들 | public place 공공장소 | either 역시 | both A and B A와 B 둘 다 | nonsmoker 담배 안 피우는 사람

9

다음 대화를 듣고, 여자 아이가 연주할 수 없는 악기를 고르시오. ……………… (   )

① ② ③ ④

B: Alice, what's your favorite subject?
G: My favorite subject is music. I like playing musical instruments.
B: What instruments can you play?
G: I can play the _____, the harmonica, and the _____.
B: That's cool. What about the _____? Can you play it?
G: No, I can't, but I want to learn _____ _____ _____ it.

subject 과목 | musical instrument 악기 | guitar 기타 | harmonica 하모니카 | trumpet 트럼펫

TIPS [의문사 how + to 동사원형]은 '어떻게 할 것인가'라는 의미로 how to play는 '어떻게 (연주) 할 것인가, 연주하는 방법'이란 뜻입니다.

10

다음 대화를 듣고, 두 사람의 대화가 <u>어색한</u> 것을 고르시오. ······· ( )

① ② ③ ④

❶ W: Can you come to my birthday party?

M: Sure, I can.

❷ W: _____ _____ do you go swimming?

M: I go almost every day.

❸ W: _____ does the movie start?

M: It starts at my _____.

❹ W: Who's that girl over there?

M: She's my sister.

birthday party 생일 파티 | almost 거의 | every day 매일 | movie 영화 | over there 저쪽에

TIPS 의문사 when으로 물어보면, 구체적인 시각이나 연도 등으로 답해야 합니다.
A: When does the movie start? 영화 언제 시작해?
B: It starts at 11 o'clock. 11시에 시작해.

11

다음을 듣고, 남자 아이가 말한 내용과 일치하지 <u>않는</u> 것을 고르시오. ······· ( )

① 부모님은 일주일에 2번 테니스를 친다.
② 형은 농구를 좋아한다.
③ 형은 매일 방과 후 농구를 한다.
④ 여동생은 탁구선수가 되고 싶어 한다.

B: My family like sports. My parents like playing tennis. They play tennis _____ a week. My older brother likes playing basketball. He _____ _____ basketball after school. My younger sister likes playing _____ _____. She wants to be a table tennis player.

parents 부모 | twice a week 일주일에 두 번 | older brother 형 | often 종종 | table tennis 탁구

TIPS He often plays basketball after school.(형은 자주 방과 후 농구를 한다.)고 했으므로 ③번이 내용과 일치하지 않습니다.

12

다음 대화를 듣고, 남자가 여자에게 부탁한 것을 고르시오. ······· ( )

① 지갑 빌리기　　② 책 빌리기
③ 숙제 도와주기　　④ 돈 빌리기

M: Would you do me a _____?

W: Sure. What can I do for you?

M: Can I _____ some _____? I left my wallet at home.

W: Okay. How much do you want?

M: Thanks. Five dollars is good _____.

favor 부탁, 요청 | borrow 빌리다 | money 돈 | wallet 지갑 | enough 충분한

TIPS Can I borrow some money? 대신 Can you lend me some money? (돈 좀 꿔줄래요?)로 바꿔 쓸 수 있습니다.
lend는 '빌려주다', borrow는 '빌리다'라는 의미입니다.

13

다음 그림을 보고, 그림과 일치하는 설명을 고르시오. ·················· (　　)

① ② ③ ④

M: ❶ A woman is drinking milk at a café.

　❷ A woman is _____ groceries _____ a cart.

　❸ A woman is selling vegetables at a market.

　❹ A woman is _____ a book in her hand.

grocery 식료품 | sell 팔다 | vegetable 야채 | hold 들다

14

다음 대화를 듣고, 대화에 알맞은 표지판을 고르시오. ·················· (　　)

① ② ③ ④

M: Alice, what are you doing here?

W: I'm _____ _____ _____.

M: Did you see the _____ over there?

W: Oh, I didn't see that.

M: The flea market opens here every Saturday, so you can't ride your bike _____ this _____ today.

ride one's bike 자전거를 타다 | sign 표지판 | flea market 벼룩시장 | around ~ 주위에 | area 지역

15

다음 대화를 듣고, 남자 아이가 읽는 책과 책의 내용을 고르시오. ·················· (　　)

① 과학잡지 – 공룡
② 과학잡지 – 우주
③ 영화잡지 – 공룡영화
④ 동물잡지 – 바다동물

G: Ted, what are you reading?

B: I am reading a _____ _____ about dinosaurs.

G: Dinosaurs?

B: Yes, I'm interested in _____.

G: Can I _____ the magazine when you finish reading it?

B: Sure. You should read this book, too.

science magazine 과학 잡지 | dinosaur 공룡 | be interested in ~에 흥미가 있다 | borrow 빌리다

16

다음 대화를 듣고, 여자 아이가 남자 아이에게 제안한 것을 고르시오. ·················· (　　)

① 독서 동아리 가입
② 배드민턴 경기 관람
③ 함께 시험공부 하기
④ 농구 동아리 가입

B: Amy, which club are you in?

G: I'm in the reading club. How about you?

B: I'm still thinking.

G: You like basketball. What about joining the _____ _____?

B: I'd like to. But first, I have to pass the test.

G: Don't worry about that. Just _____ _____ for it.

club 동아리 | reading club 독서 동아리 | still 여전히 | pass 통과하다 | try out 시도하다

17

다음 대화를 듣고, 이어질 말로 알맞은 것을 고르시오. ················ (   )

M _____

① Here you are.
② Okay, I will take three mangos.
③ Where did you get them?
④ How many mangos do you want?

W: Good morning. How can I help you?

M: How much are these oranges?

W: It's 12 dollars for one box.

M: Oh, it's _____ _____. How much are theses mangos?

W: It's one dollar _____.

M: _____

expensive 비싼 | mango 망고 | take 사다 | get 얻다

18

다음 대화를 듣고, 이어질 말로 알맞은 것을 고르시오. ················ (   )

G _____

① It will rain soon.
② I was busy yesterday.
③ I have a swimming lesson.
④ Sure, I'll do it after school.

G: What time do you have lunch?

B: I have lunch at 12:30. After lunch, I usually

_____ _____.

G: Soccer is a lot of fun.

B: _____ _____ you do after lunch?

G: _____

usually 보통 | fun 재미 | soon 곧 | busy 바쁜 | lesson 수업

TIPS 운동종목이나 식사 앞에는 관사를 붙이지 않습니다.
I play soccer. 나는 축구를 한다.
I had dinner a few minutes ago. 나는 몇 분 전에 저녁을 먹었다.

19

다음 대화를 듣고, 이어질 말로 알맞은 것을 고르시오. ················ (   )

M _____

① Two weeks!
② Twenty dollars.
③ We went there by plane.
④ We stayed at a hotel.

W: Kevin, how was your vacation?

M: It was great. I _____ _____ _____ to Hawaii with my family.

W: Wow, that's cool. _____ _____ did you stay there?

M: _____

vacation 휴가 | take a trip 여행하다 | how long 얼마동안

TIPS How long did you stay there?로 질문하고 있으므로 구체적인 기간으로 답해야 합니다. 따라서 Two weeks!가 가장 어울립니다. 여기서 Two weeks!는 We stayed there for two weeks.를 줄여서 표현한 것입니다.

20

다음 대화를 듣고, 이어질 말로 적절하지 <u>않은</u> 것을 고르시오. ················ (   )

W _____

① It's October 5.
② Next Tuesday.
③ It want a new bike.
④ My birthday is the same as yours.

W: What's the _____ _____?

M: It's September 18.

W: My birthday is coming up.

M: Oh, _____ _____ _____?

W: _____

date 날짜 | come up 다가오다 | same 같은 것

● 다음 들려주는 단어와 그 의미를 쓰세요.

단어	의미
01 necklace	목걸이
02	
03	
04	
05	
06	
07	
08	
09	
10	
11	
12	
13	
14	
15	

● 앞에 모의고사에 나오는 문장들을 잘 듣고, 빈칸을 완성하세요.

01 Please ___look___ ___for___ ___it___ in the drawer.

02 _____ _____ I could, but I have to ask my dad first.

03 I _____ _____ _____ check out these books.

04 You can only borrow the books _____ _____ _____.

05 My _____ _____ is ice hockey.

06 I'm free _____ _____.

07 Smoking is bad for _____ smokers _____ nonsmokers.

08 I want to learn _____ _____ _____ it.

09 They _____ _____ twice a week.

10 I left _____ _____ at home.

11 A woman is _____ groceries _____ a cart.

12 The _____ _____ opens here every Saturday.

13 I am reading a _____ _____ about dinosaurs.

14 I _____ _____ _____ to Hawaii with my family.

15 My birthday is _____ _____.

보통 속도   빠른 속도

| 학습일 | 월 일 | 부모님 확인 | 점수 |

1

다음 대화를 듣고, 대화가 일어나는 장소를 고르시오. ·················· (   )

① 식당   ② 서점
③ 옷 가게   ④ 신발 가게

2

다음 대화를 듣고, 대화 직후 두 사람이 할 일을 고르시오. ····················· (   )

① 공원에 간다.   ② 약국에 간다.
③ 물을 마신다.   ④ 학교에 간다.

3

다음 대화를 듣고, 남자 아이가 내일 할 일을 고르시오. ····················· (   )

① 놀이공원에 가기   ② 음식 만들기
③ 집에서 숙제하기   ④ 아버지와 야구하기

4

다음 대화를 듣고, 여자가 찾는 물건이 있는 곳을 고르시오. ·················· (   )

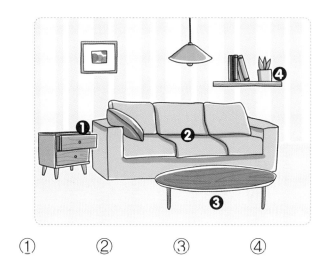

①   ②   ③   ④

5 중학기출 변형문제

다음 대화를 듣고, 남자 아이의 나이를 고르시오. ····················· (   )

① 12살   ② 13살
③ 14살   ④ 15살

6

다음 대화를 듣고, 대화와 일치하는 그림을 고르시오. ……………………………… (   )

8

다음 대화를 듣고, 여자 아이의 남동생 모습을 고르시오. ……………………………… (   )

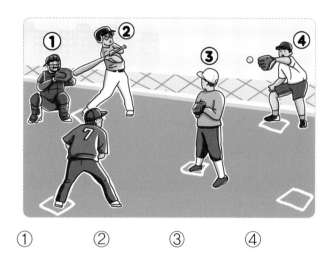

①   ②   ③   ④

7

다음 대화를 듣고, 남자 아이가 어제 한 일을 고르시오. ……………………………… (   )

9

다음 대화를 듣고, 남자 아이가 생일 선물로 받은 것을 고르시오. ……………………… (   )

10

다음 대화를 듣고, 두 사람이 만날 요일과 시각을 고르시오. ·························· (   )

① 화요일 – 6시   ② 화요일 – 7시

③ 수요일 – 6시   ④ 수요일 – 7시

11

다음 그림을 보고, 그림과 일치하는 대화를 고르시오. ····················· (   )

①   ②   ③   ④

12

다음 대화를 듣고, 여자가 베트남 음식을 좋아하는 이유를 고르시오. ············ (   )

① 맛이 있어서

② 국수를 좋아해서

③ 요리하기 쉬워서

④ 가격이 싸고 건강에 좋아서

13

다음 대화를 듣고, 현장 학습 가는 날짜와 장소를 고르시오. ···················· (   )

① 10월 15일 – 동물원

② 10월 11일 – 박물관

③ 11월 15일 – 박물관

④ 11월 11일 – 동물원

14

다음 대화를 듣고, 대화가 자연스럽지 않은 것을 고르시오. ···················· (   )

①   ②   ③   ④

15

다음을 듣고, 남자 아이가 말한 내용과 일치하지 않는 것을 고르시오. ············ (   )

① 어머니는 은행에서 일하신다.

② 어머니는 5시에 집에 오신다.

③ 어머니는 머리 길이가 짧다.

④ 어머니는 피아노 치는 것을 좋아하신다.

16

다음 대화를 듣고, 남자가 부탁한 일을 고르시오. ····················· (   )

① 강아지 돌보기　　② 강아지 산책시키기
③ 강아지 찾기　　　④ 강아지와 놀아주기

17 중학기출 변형문제

다음 대화를 듣고, 이어질 말로 알맞은 것을 고르시오. ····················· (   )

M _____

① It's at 3 p.m.
② Congratulations.
③ She's 27 years old.
④ It's far from here.

18

다음 대화를 듣고, 이어질 말로 알맞은 것을 고르시오. ····················· (   )

G _____

① Yes, she is.
② I was busy yesterday.
③ Yes, my mom is a doctor.
④ I had a cold, but I'm better now.

19

다음 대화를 듣고, 이어질 말로 알맞은 것을 고르시오. ····················· (   )

B _____

① She likes reading books.
② She wants to be a writer.
③ I like reading science magazines.
④ She bought some comic books.

20

다음 대화를 듣고, 이어질 말로 적절하지 <u>않은</u> 것을 고르시오. ····················· (   )

G _____

① I had pizza.
② I ate fried rice.
③ I'd like to have some coffee.
④ I'm on a diet, so I don't eat lunch.

● 잘 듣고, 빈칸에 알맞은 말을 쓰세요.

1

다음 대화를 듣고, 대화가 일어나는 장소를 고르시오. ·············· (　)

① 식당　　　　② 서점
③ 옷 가게　　　④ 신발 가게

W: May I help you?

B: Yes, I'm looking for ＿＿＿＿＿＿ ＿＿＿＿＿＿.

W: How about these ones? These are very popular among teens.

B: They look nice. ＿＿＿＿＿ ＿＿＿＿＿ are they?

W: These are 100 dollars, but you can get a 20% discount.

running shoes 운동화 | popular 인기 있는 | teens 십대 | discount 할인

2

다음 대화를 듣고, 대화 직후 두 사람이 할 일을 고르시오. ·············· (　)

① 공원에 간다.　　② 약국에 간다.
③ 물을 마신다.　　④ 학교에 간다.

W: Kevin, where are you going?

M: I'm going to the park to take a walk. Will you come with me?

W: Sure. But can we go to the ＿＿＿＿＿ first.
　 I need some ＿＿＿＿＿ for my headache.

M: Is it far from here?

W: No, it's just around the corner.

M: Okay. Let's ＿＿＿＿＿ there ＿＿＿＿＿.

take a walk 산책하다 | drugstore 약국 | first 먼저 | medicine 약 | headache 두통 | far 먼 | around 근처에 | corner 모퉁이

TIPS drugstore는 처방전 없이도 살 수 있는 의약품을 살 수 있는 곳으로 기타 잡화들도 판매합니다.

3

다음 대화를 듣고, 남자 아이가 내일 할 일을 고르시오. ·············· (　)

① 놀이공원에 가기　② 음식 만들기
③ 집에서 숙제하기　④ 아버지와 야구하기

B: Did you hear tomorrow's weather?

G: They said it would ＿＿＿＿＿ ＿＿＿＿＿.
　 Do you have any special plans?

B: I'm going to the ＿＿＿＿＿ ＿＿＿＿＿ tomorrow.

G: That sounds exciting. Who are you going with?

B: ＿＿＿＿＿ ＿＿＿＿＿.

G: Have a great time!

hear 듣다 | weather 날씨 | special 특별한 | plan 계획 | amusement park 놀이공원

TIPS '가다, 오다, 출발하다, 돌아오다' 등과 같은 갔다왔다하는(왕래발착) 동사와 가까운 미래를 나타내는 부사(구)를 쓰면 현재진행형이 미래시제를 대신할 수 있습니다.
I'm moving to Seoul tomorrow. 나 내일 서울로 이사 가.

4

다음 대화를 듣고, 여자가 찾는 물건이 있는 곳을 고르시오. ····················· ( )

① ② ③ ④

5

다음 대화를 듣고, 남자 아이의 나이를 고르시오. ····················· ( )

① 12살 ② 13살
③ 14살 ④ 15살

6

다음 대화를 듣고, 대화와 일치하는 그림을 고르시오. ····················· ( )

① ② ③ ④

7

다음 대화를 듣고, 남자 아이가 어제 한 일을 고르시오. ····················· ( )

① ② ③ ④

B: Mom, what are you looking for?

W: I can't find _____ _____.

B: Where did you put it?

W: I thought I put it on the table, but it's _____ _____.

B: Oh, there it is. It's in the _____ _____ of the side table.

ring 반지 | thought 생각하다(think)의 과거형 | top 맨 위 | drawer 서랍 | side table 협탁

TIPS the top drawer는 '맨 위 서랍'이란 의미입니다. 동사 put의 과거형은 put으로 모양이 바뀌지 않습니다.

G: Who is this girl in the picture?

B: That's my _____ _____, Amy.

G: How old is she?

B: She's _____ _____ older than me.

G: Then, she's _____ years old, isn't she?

B: You're right.

picture 사진 | older sister 누나 | older than ~보다 나이 든 | right 올바른

TIPS 누나가 15살로 남자 아이보다 3살 많으므로 남자 아이는 12살입니다.

B: It's very _____ _____.

G: Do you want me to _____ the _____?

B: That will be nice.

G: Sure, not a problem.

cold 추운 | window 창문 | nice 좋은 | problem 문제

TIPS [Do you want me to + 동사원형?]은 '내가 ~을 해줄까?'라는 의미입니다.
Do you want me to help? 내가 도와주기를 바라니[내가 도와줄까]?

B: Christine, what did you do yesterday?

G: I went to my cousin's birthday party.

B: How was the party?

G: It was a lot of fun. How about you, Paul?

B: I stayed home _____ _____.

G: Why? Were you _____?

B: No, I helped my mom _____ the _____.

yesterday 어제 | cousin 사촌 | a lot of 많은 | fun 재미 | all day 하루 종일 | sick 아픈 | clean 청소하다

8

다음 대화를 듣고, 여자 아이의 남동생 모습을
고르시오. ·················· (   )

①   ②   ③   ④

B: Where is your brother?

G: He's playing baseball with his friends over there.
   He is _____ _____.

B: Is he wearing glasses?

G: No, he isn't. He is _____ _____
   _____ right now.

B: Oh, I found him.

play baseball 야구하다 | **over there** 저쪽에 | **shorts** 반바지 | **glasses** 안경 |
right now 지금

9

다음 대화를 듣고, 남자 아이가 생일 선물로 받
은 것을 고르시오. ·················· (   )

①   ②

③   ④

G: What did you get for your birthday?

B: I got something I needed from my mom.

G: What did you get from your mom?

B: I got a new _____.

G: Wow! You got a big _____. Can I see it?

B: I put it on the desk. I'll _____ _____
   _____ it.

smartphone 스마트폰 | **gift** 선물 | **bring** 가져오다

TIPS I got something I needed.는 '내가 필요한 것을 받았어.'라는 의미로
something과 I needed 사이에 that이 생략되었습니다.

10

다음 대화를 듣고, 두 사람이 만날 요일과 시각
을 고르시오. ·················· (   )

① 화요일 – 6시   ② 화요일 – 7시
③ 수요일 – 6시   ④ 수요일 – 7시

[Cellphone rings.]

G: Hello?

B: Hello, Susan. This is Mike. Are you free this
   _____?

G: Well, I have a piano lesson, but it finishes at 3.
   I will be free after that. Why?

B: I got two K-pop concert tickets. Do you want to
   _____ _____ me?

G: Of course.

B: The concert starts at 7. Let's meet at the subway
   station _____ _____.

G: Okay. See you then.

free 한가한 | **lesson** 수업 | **concert** 콘서트 | **ticket** 표 | **subway station** 지하철역

TIPS 형용사 free는 '할 일이 없는, 한가한'이란 의미 이외에 '무료의, 공짜의'란 의미도
있습니다.
It's free for children. 어린이들에게는 무료입니다.

11

다음 그림을 보고, 그림과 일치하는 대화를 고르시오. ·························· (   )

① ② ③ ④

① W: Excuse me. _____ _____ goes to the beach?

M: Please take the bus number 17.

② W: Can I help you?

M: Could you please open the door?

③ W: Would you like to order?

M: _____ _____. I'm looking at the menu.

④ M: I have a cold.

W: You should go _____ a _____.

bus number 버스 번호 | order 주문하다 | yet 아직 | menu 메뉴
see a doctor 병원에 가다

TIPS 조동사 should '하는 것이 좋겠다'로 의미로 충고하거나 의견을 말할 때 사용됩니다.
You should dress for cold weather today.
오늘 추운 날씨에 맞는 옷차림을 해야 한다.

12

다음 대화를 듣고, 여자가 베트남 음식을 좋아하는 이유를 고르시오. ············· (   )

① 맛이 있어서
② 국수를 좋아해서
③ 요리하기 쉬워서
④ 가격이 싸고 건강에 좋아서

W: Let's eat out for dinner.

M: Okay. Do you have any place _____ _____?

W: No, I don't.

M: Then, how about going to the Vietnamese _____?

W: All right. I like Vietnamese food because it is _____ and _____.

eat out 외식하다 | have A in mind A를 염두에 두다 | noodle 국수 | cheap 싼 |
healthy 건강한

TIPS cheap and healthy은 '가격이 저렴하고 몸에 좋은'이라는 의미입니다.

13

다음 대화를 듣고, 현장 학습 가는 날짜와 장소를 고르시오. ·················· (   )

① 10월 15일 – 동물원
② 10월 11일 – 박물관
③ 11월 15일 – 박물관
④ 11월 11일 – 동물원

B: I'd like to tell you some good news.

G: What is it?

B: We are going on a _____ _____ next month _____ _____ 15.

G: Do you know where we are going?

B: We are going to _____ _____.

G: Great.

news 소식 | field trip 현장학습 | next month 다음 달에 | zoo 동물원

14

다음 대화를 듣고, 대화가 자연스럽지 <u>않은</u> 것을 고르시오. ·················· (   )

① ② ③ ④

❶ B: Jessica, how was Christmas?

G: It was great.

❷ B: I am sorry. I'm late.

G: _____ _____. Thanks.

❸ B: Hi, Linda. How are you doing?

G: I'm doing very well.

❹ B: _____ _____ please?

G: This is Amy.

Christmas 크리스마스 | late 늦은 | do well 잘하다 | call 전화하다

TIPS Sounds good. '그게 좋겠네요.'라는 의미로 어떤 생각이나 의견 또는 일에 대해 긍정적인 동의 표현을 할 때 쓰는 표현입니다.

15

다음을 듣고, 남자 아이가 말한 내용과 일치하지 <u>않는</u> 것을 고르시오. ·········· (   )

① 어머니는 은행에서 일하신다.
② 어머니는 5시에 집에 오신다.
③ 어머니는 머리 길이가 짧다.
④ 어머니는 피아노 치는 것을 좋아하신다.

B: I'd like to introduce my mom to you. She works at a _____. My mom goes to work early in the morning and comes home _____ 5 p.m. She has _____, black _____ and wears glasses. She likes playing the piano in her _____ _____.

introduce 소개하다 | around 대략 | long hair 긴 머리 | glasses 안경 | free time 여가시간

TIPS go to work는 '출근하다'라는 의미로 여기서 work는 동사가 아니고 '(자기가 근무하는) 직장'이란 의미의 명사입니다.

16

다음 대화를 듣고, 남자가 부탁한 일을 고르시오. ·················· (   )

① 강아지 돌보기 ② 강아지 산책시키기
③ 강아지 찾기 ④ 강아지와 놀아주기

W: Dennis, what are you doing here?

M: I'm looking for _____ _____. When I was talking on the phone, it _____ _____.

W: What does it look like?

M: It's small and black. Can you help me _____ _____?

W: Sure.

here 여기 | puppy 강아지 | run away 달아나다 | look like ~처럼 보이다

TIPS talk on the phone은 '전화 통화하다'라는 의미입니다.
[help + A + 동사]는 'A가 ~하는 것을 돕다'라는 의미입니다.
Can you help me do my homework? 제 숙제 좀 도와주시겠어요?

17

다음 대화를 듣고, 이어질 말로 알맞은 것을 고르시오. ································ (   )

M _____

① It's at 3 p.m.
② Congratulations.
③ She's 27 years old.
④ It's far from here.

M: I have something to tell you.

W: What is that?

M: My older sister is going to _____ _____ this Saturday.

W: Wow, that's surprising! _____ _____ is the wedding?

M: _____

something 무언가 | older sister 누나 | get married 결혼하다 | surprising 놀라운 | wedding 결혼

TIPS What time으로 묻고 있으므로 구체적인 시각으로 대답을 해야 합니다.

18

다음 대화를 듣고, 이어질 말로 알맞은 것을 고르시오. ································ (   )

G _____

① Yes, she is.
② I was busy yesterday.
③ Yes, my mom is a doctor.
④ I had a cold, but I'm better now.

B: I didn't see you at school yesterday. What happened?

G: Oh, I went to _____ _____ _____ with my mom.

B: Why? _____ you _____?

G: _____

happen 일어나다 | see the doctor 병원에 가다 | sick 아픈

19

다음 대화를 듣고, 이어질 말로 알맞은 것을 고르시오. ································ (   )

B _____

① She likes reading books.
② She wants to be a writer.
③ I like reading science magazines.
④ She bought some comic books.

G: Bob, were you at the _____ yesterday?

B: Yes, I was there with my _____ _____.

G: Oh, it was you! I saw you there.

B: Really? My sister wanted to buy a book, so I took her there.

G: _____ kind of _____ did she get?

B: _____

bookstore 서점 | younger sister 여동생 | take 데리고 가다 | kind 종류

TIPS What kind of book ~?으로 묻고 있으므로 구체적인 책의 종류로 대답해야 합니다.

20

다음 대화를 듣고, 이어질 말로 적절하지 <u>않은</u> 것을 고르시오. ································ (   )

G _____

① I had pizza.
② I ate fried rice.
③ I'd like to have some coffee.
④ I'm on a diet, so I don't eat lunch.

G: What did you have _____ _____?

B: I had pasta and bread.

G: Was it delicious?

B: Yes, it was good. _____ _____ you?

G: _____

pasta 파스타 | bread 빵 | delicious 맛있는

TIPS What about you?는 What did you have for lunch?라는 의미입니다.

● 다음 들려주는 단어와 그 의미를 쓰세요.

단어	의미
01 popular	인기 있는
02	
03	
04	
05	
06	
07	
08	
09	
10	
11	
12	
13	
14	
15	

● 앞에 모의고사에 나오는 문장들을 잘 듣고, 빈칸을 완성하세요.

01 These are very popular ___among___ ___teens___.

02 I need _____ _____ for my headache.

03 It's just _____ _____ _____.

04 It's in the _____ _____ of the side table.

05 I helped my mom _____ _____ _____.

06 He is _____ _____ _____ right now.

07 Let's meet at the _____ _____ at 6.

08 You should go _____ _____ _____.

09 We are going on a _____ _____ next month.

10 I'd like to _____ _____ _____ to you.

11 I have _____ _____ _____ you.

12 _____ _____ is the wedding?

13 My older sister is going to _____ _____ this Saturday.

14 I went to see a doctor _____ _____ _____.

15 I was there with _____ _____ _____.

보통 속도 빠른 속도

| 학습일 | 월 일 | 부모님 확인 | 점수 |

1

다음 그림을 보고, 그림과 일치하는 설명을 고르시오. ····································· (   )

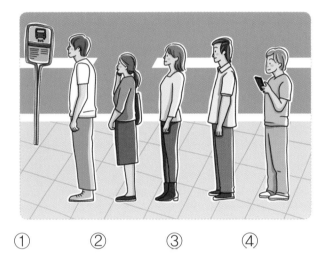

①   ②   ③   ④

2

다음 대화를 듣고, 남자가 가장 좋아하는 과일을 고르시오. ····························· (   )

① 사과   ② 바나나

③ 딸기   ④ 수박

3

다음 그림을 보고, 그림과 일치하는 대화를 고르시오. ····························· (   )

①   ②   ③   ④

4

다음 대화를 듣고, 여자 아이가 대화 직후 할 일로 알맞은 것을 고르시오. ······ (   )

① 노래 부르기

② 동아리 가입하기

③ 콘서트 표 예매하기

④ 인터넷으로 쇼핑하기

5

다음 대화를 듣고, 과학 선생님의 모습을 고르시오. ······························ (   )

①  ②

③  ④

6

다음 대화를 듣고, 대화가 이루어지는 장소를 고르시오. ···························· (   )

① 동물원   ② 놀이공원
③ 도서관   ④ 수족관

7 중학기출 변형문제

다음 대화를 듣고, 대화의 내용과 <u>다른</u> 것을 고르시오. ···························· (   )

① 박물관은 아직 열리지 않았다.
② 박물관은 9시 30분에 열린다.
③ 지금은 9시 20분이다.
④ 박물관은 6시에 닫는다.

8

다음을 듣고, 무엇에 대해 설명하고 있는지 고르시오. ···························· (   )

①  ②

③  ④

9

다음 대화를 듣고, 두 아이가 말하고 있는 운동을 고르시오. ···························· (   )

①  ②

③  ④

10

다음 대화를 듣고, 남자 아이가 전화한 이유를 고르시오. ····················· (   )

① 약속 장소를 바꾸려고

② 약속을 취소하려고

③ 자전거를 빌리려고

④ 병문 진료 예약을 하려고

11

다음 대화를 듣고, 여자 아이가 좋아하는 월을 고르시오. ····················· (   )

① 5월   ② 6월   ③ 7월   ④ 8월

12

다음 대화를 듣고, 두 사람이 오늘 오후 할 일을 고르시오. ····················· (   )

① 개 산책시키기

② 숙제하기

③ 친구 집 방문하기

④ 공원에서 사진 찍기

13

다음 대화를 듣고, 영화가 시작하는 시각을 고르시오. ····················· (   )

① 3시 15분   ② 4시 15분

③ 5시 15분   ④ 6시 15분

14

다음 대화를 듣고, 두 아이가 토요일에 한 일을 고르시오. ····················· (   )

여아 아이	남자 아이

①

②

③

④

15

다음 대화를 듣고, 대화가 자연스럽지 <u>않은</u> 것을 고르시오. ····················· (   )

①   ②   ③   ④

16

다음 대화를 듣고, 남자가 사려는 사과의 수와 지불할 금액을 고르시오. ·········· (   )

① 3개 – 3달러   ② 4개 – 4달러
③ 5개 – 5달러   ④ 6개 – 6달러

17 중학기출 변형문제

다음 대화를 듣고, 이어질 말로 알맞은 것을 고르시오. ····················· (   )

W _____

① I'll be there by bus.
② I'm going to buy some food.
③ I don't have a car.
④ I'll stay at the Sunny Hotel.

18

다음 대화를 듣고, 이어질 말로 알맞은 것을 고르시오. ····················· (   )

M _____

① It's okay.
② It's very fresh.
③ It's five dollars for one box.
④ I'd like to, but I can't.

19 중학기출 변형문제

다음 대화를 듣고, 이어질 말로 알맞은 것을 고르시오. ····················· (   )

G _____

① It's Thursday.
② It will be sunny.
③ It's not far from here.
④ I'm busy every Monday.

20

다음 대화를 듣고, 이어질 말로 적절하지 않은 것을 고르시오. ····················· (   )

M _____

① No problem.
② What do you have?
③ I would like a Coke, please.
④ Can I have some water please?

학습일	월	일	부모님 확인		점수

● 잘 듣고, 빈칸에 알맞은 말을 쓰세요.

1

다음 그림을 보고, 그림과 일치하는 설명을 고르시오. ·························· (   )

① ② ③ ④

M: ❶ People are eating at the restaurant.

❷ People are _____ _____ _____ at the bus stop.

❸ The children are waiting for their teacher.

❹ People are _____ _____ the bus at the bus stop.

restaurant 식당 | stand in line 줄을 서고 있다 | get on ~에 타다

TIPS stand in line은 '줄 서 있다'라는 의미로 ②번이 그림과 가장 어울리는 설명입니다.

2

다음 대화를 듣고, 남자가 가장 좋아하는 과일을 고르시오. ·························· (   )

① 사과　　　　② 바나나
③ 딸기　　　　④ 수박

W: Mike, what do you have for breakfast?

M: I _____ have bread and milk. How about you?

W: I have salad and fruit.

M: Fruit? What kind of fruit do you have for breakfast?

W: Apples or bananas. Do you _____ _____?

M: Yes, I like _____.

usually 보통 | bread 빵 | salad 샐러드 | fruit 과일 | strawberry 딸기

3

다음 그림을 보고, 그림과 일치하는 대화를 고르시오. ·························· (   )

① ② ③ ④

❶ B: Why are you so _____?

G: Someone broke my bike.

❷ B: What did you do last night?

G: I watched a movie with my dad.

❸ B: What's your favorite subject?

G: I like math.

❹ B: Why are you _____?

G: The _____ is so _____.

upset 화난 | someone 누군가 | break 고장 내다 | movie 영화 | cry 울다 | sad 슬픈

TIPS 여자 아이가 TV를 보면서 울고 있으므로 ④번의 대화가 가장 그림과 일치합니다.

4

다음 대화를 듣고, 여자 아이가 대화 직후 할
일로 알맞은 것을 고르시오. ⋯⋯ (   )

① 노래 부르기
② 동아리 가입하기
③ 콘서트 표 예매하기
④ 인터넷으로 쇼핑하기

B: Jenny, are you interested in K-pop?

G: Yes, I am. Why?

B: Why don't you _____ the K-pop _____?

G: What is the K-pop club?

B: The K-pop club is a space for students to learn more about Korean pop music, dance, and culture.

G: That's cool. _____ _____ I join the club?

B: You can do it _____.

G: Okay. _____ _____ it now.

be interested in ~에 관심 있다 | club 동아리 | space 공간 | culture 문화 | online 온라인으로

TIPS [why don't you+ 동사원형]은 '~하는 게 어때?'라는 의미로 제안할 때 사용하는 표현입니다.
Why don't you go to the movies? 영화 보러 가는 게 어때?

5

다음 대화를 듣고, 과학 선생님의 모습을 고르
시오. ⋯⋯⋯⋯⋯⋯⋯⋯ (   )

① ② ③ ④

B: Did you see the new science teacher?

G: Not yet. What does she _____ _____?

B: She is _____ and _____.

G: Is she the woman wearing a _____ blouse and a _____ skirt over there?

B: Yes, that's her.

new 새로운 | science 과학 | slim 날씬한 | blouse 블라우스 | over there 저쪽에

TIPS 새로운 과학 선생님은 마르고 키가 크며, 파란 블라우스에 빨간 치마를 입고 있습니다.

6

다음 대화를 듣고, 대화가 이루어지는 장소를
고르시오. ⋯⋯⋯⋯⋯⋯⋯⋯⋯⋯ (   )

① 동물원   ② 놀이공원
③ 도서관   ④ 수족관

B: Cathy, there are _____ in the _____.

G: Yes, they are very big.

B: Where are the penguins? I want to see them.

G: There aren't any penguins in this _____.

B: Then, let's go look at the _____.

G: Okay. They are just around the corner.

shark 상어 | tank 탱크 | penguin 펭귄 | aquarium 수족관, 아쿠아리움 | dolphin 돌고래

7

다음 대화를 듣고, 대화의 내용과 다른 것을 고르시오. ·························· ( )

① 박물관은 아직 열리지 않았다.
② 박물관은 9시 30분에 열린다.
③ 지금은 9시 20분이다.
④ 박물관은 6시에 닫는다.

8

다음을 듣고, 무엇에 대해 설명하고 있는지 고르시오. ·························· ( )

① ② ③ ④

9

다음 대화를 듣고, 두 아이가 말하고 있는 운동을 고르시오. ·················· ( )

① ② ③ ④

10

다음 대화를 듣고, 남자 아이가 전화한 이유를 고르시오. ·················· ( )

① 약속 장소를 바꾸려고
② 약속을 취소하려고
③ 자전거를 빌리려고
④ 병문 진료 예약을 하려고

B: The history museum is _____ _____ yet.
G: What time is it now?
B: It's _____.
G: It opens at 9:30, so we have to wait for 20 minutes.
B: I wonder what time it closes.
G: It closes _____ _____ in the afternoon.

history museum 역사박물관 | yet 아직 | wonder 궁금하다 | afternoon 오후

TIPS yet은 '아직'이란 의미로 부정문이나 의문문에서 사용합니다.
Don't go yet. 아직 가지 마.

W: This is an animal. It _____ _____ the sea. It doesn't have a _____.
It has a soft, rounded body, and large eyes.
It also has _____ _____ arms.
It can change the color of its skin quickly.

animal 동물 | spine 척추 | body 몸 | large 커다란 | arm 팔 | change 바꾸다 | skin 피부 | quickly 빨리

B: Where are you going?
G: I'm going to the gym to _____ _____.
B: Do you know that our national volleyball team won the _____ _____ at the Olympic Games?
G: Yeah! That game was _____ _____.
B: They are great players, and I like them.
G: I like them, too. I want to be a volleyball player.

volleyball 배구 | national volleyball team 국가대표 배구팀 | silver medal 은메달

TIPS volleyball 배구   basketball 농구   baseball 야구   soccer 축구
football 축구, 미식축구   bowling 볼링   boxing 권투   wrestling 레슬링

[Cellphone rings.]
G: Hello?
B: Hello, Susan. This is Kevin. I'm sorry, but I _____ _____ you today.
G: What happened?
B: I _____ _____ while riding my bicycle yesterday. I hurt my leg.
G: I'm sorry to hear that. I hope you get well soon.

happen 일어나다 | fall down 넘어지다 | hurt 다치다 | hope 바라다 | get well 나아지다

11

다음 대화를 듣고, 여자 아이가 좋아하는 월을 고르시오. ·························· (　　)

① 5월　　② 6월　　③ 7월　　④ 8월

G: Can you believe tomorrow will be the last day of June?

B: Yes, it's going to be _____ _____!

G: July is my _____ _____ of the year.

B: Why?

G: Every July we go on a _____ _____.

B: Where are you going this year?

G: We are going to Jeju Island.

believe 믿다 | **last day** 마지막 날 | **already** 이미, 벌써 | **year** 해, 연 |
family trip 가족여행 | **island** 섬

TIPS 여자 아이는 매년 7월에 가족여행을 가서 7월을 좋아한다고 합니다.

12

다음 대화를 듣고, 두 사람이 오늘 오후 할 일을 고르시오. ·················· (　　)

① 개 산책시키기
② 숙제하기
③ 친구 집 방문하기
④ 공원에서 사진 찍기

M: What are you going to do this afternoon?

W: I will go to the park.

M: What for?

W: I will _____ _____ _____ there.

M: Can I _____ you? I miss your dog Blackie.

W: Of course. _____ _____ at 3 in front of the park.

this afternoon 오늘 오후에 | **walk** 산책시키다 | **miss** 보고 싶다 | **in front of** ~ 앞에서

TIPS What for?는 '무엇 때문에?, 왜?'라는 의미로 Why?로 바꿔 쓸 수 있습니다.

13

다음 대화를 듣고, 영화가 시작하는 시각을 고르시오. ·················· (　　)

① 3시 15분　　② 4시 15분
③ 5시 15분　　④ 6시 15분

M: Hi, can I get _____ _____ for *Spiderman*.

W: Sure. What about the time?

M: When does the _____ _____ start?

W: It starts at 5:15.

M: Okay. That sounds fine. How much is it?

W: Your total is 18 dollars. You can enter the _____ 10 minutes before the movie starts.

ticket 표 | **next movie** 다음 영화 | **total** 모두, 전체 | **enter** 들어가다 | **theater** 영화관

14

다음 대화를 듣고, 두 아이가 토요일에 한 일을 고르시오. ·························· (   )

여아 아이	남자 아이
①	
②	
③	
④	

B: Gina, what did you do last Saturday?

G: I _____ _____ with my family. How about you?

B: I went to the amusement park.

G: Really? Did you ride the _____ _____.

B: Yes, I rode it _____.

G: Wow, you must have had a lot of fun.

go skiing 스키 타러 가다 | **amusement park** 놀이공원 | **roller coaster** 롤러코스터 | **fun** 재미

TIPS have a lot of fun은 '재미있게 지내다'라는 의미입니다.
[must + have + 과거분사]는 '~했음에 틀림없다'라는 의미입니다.
I must have made a mistake. 내가 실수를 한 게 틀림없다.

15

다음 대화를 듣고, 대화가 자연스럽지 <u>않은</u> 것을 고르시오. ·················· (   )

①   ②   ③   ④

❶ G: What are you doing?

B: I am preparing for the English test.

❷ G: Did you finish the science homework?

B: No, I'm doing it now.

❸ G: You look sad. _____ the matter?

B: I _____ Korean food.

❹ G: Let's _____ _____ ice cream.

B: Sounds good to me.

prepare 준비하다 | **finish** 마치다 | **matter** 일 | **Korean food** 한국 음식 | **ice cream** 아이스크림

TIPS I like Korean food.의 대답에 대한 올바른 질문은 What kind of food do you like?입니다.

16

다음 대화를 듣고, 남자가 사려는 사과의 수와 지불할 금액을 고르시오. ············ (   )

① 3개 – 3달러   ② 4개 – 4달러
③ 5개 – 5달러   ④ 6개 – 6달러

W: May I help you?

M: Yes, I'm _____ _____ apples. Where can I find them?

W: They're here.

M: How much are these apples?

W: They are _____ dollar _____.

M: Okay. I'll _____ _____.

look for ~을 찾다 | **here** 여기에 | **each** 각각

TIPS 사과는 1개에 1달러이고, 남자는 5개를 산다고 했습니다.

17

다음 대화를 듣고, 이어질 말로 알맞은 것을 고르시오. ……………… (   )

W _____

① I'll be there by bus.
② I'm going to buy some food.
③ I don't have a car.
④ I'll stay at the Sunny Hotel.

M: Can I see your passport, please?
W: Here you are.
M: _____ _____ will you stay in Hawaii?
W: About two weeks.
M: _____ are you going to _____?
W: _____

passport 여권 | here you are 여기 있다 | about 대략 | stay 머무르다

18

다음 대화를 듣고, 이어질 말로 알맞은 것을 고르시오. ……………… (   )

M _____

① It's okay.
② It's very fresh.
③ It's five dollars for one box.
④ I'd like to, but I can't.

M: Good morning, ma'am. May I help you?
W: I want to buy some strawberries.
M: The strawberries are _____ _____.
W: I like these strawberries. _____ _____ are they?
M: _____

strawberry 딸기 | over there 저쪽에 | how much 얼마 | fresh 신선한

TIPS How much are they?로 질문하고 있으므로 구체적인 가격으로 대답하고 있는 It's five dollars for one box.가 가장 어울립니다.

19

다음 대화를 듣고, 이어질 말로 알맞은 것을 고르시오. ……………… (   )

G _____

① It's Thursday.
② It will be sunny.
③ It's not far from here.
④ I'm busy every Monday.

G: Sam, can you come with us to the _____ _____ between Korea and Japan?
B: Sure. When is it?
G: It's on April 4 at 6 p.m.
B: _____ _____ is it?
G: _____

baseball game 야구경기 | when 언제 | what day 무슨 요일 | far 먼 | every 매, 모두

20

다음 대화를 듣고, 이어질 말로 적절하지 <u>않은</u> 것을 고르시오. ……………… (   )

M _____

① No problem.
② What do you have?
③ I would like a Coke, please.
④ Can I have some water please?

W: Are you ready to _____?
M: Yes. The mushroom pasta, please.
W: _____ would you like to _____?
M: _____

ready 준비된 | order 주문하다 | mushroom 버섯 | pasta 파스타 | problem 문제

TIPS No problem.(문제없어.)은 상대방의 요구에 긍정으로 대답할 때나 감사의 표현에 대한 대답으로 사용합니다.
A: Thanks a lot. 감사합니다.   B: No, problem. 천만에요.

● 다음 들려주는 단어와 그 의미를 쓰세요.

단어	의미
01 prepare	준비하다
02	
03	
04	
05	
06	
07	
08	
09	
10	
11	
12	
13	
14	
15	

● 앞에 모의고사에 나오는 문장들을 잘 듣고, 빈칸을 완성하세요.

01 People are ___standing___ ___in___ ___line___ at the bus stop.

02 I _____ _____ bread and milk.

03 Someone _____ _____ _____.

04 You can do it _____.

05 She is _____ _____ _____.

06 _____ _____ any penguins in this aquarium.

07 The _____ _____ is not open yet.

08 _____ _____ what time it closes.

09 It can _____ _____ _____ of its skin quickly.

10 I _____ _____ while riding my bicycle yesterday.

11 I hope you _____ _____ soon.

12 I am _____ _____ the English test.

13 They are one _____ _____.

14 Can I _____ _____, please?

15 _____ would you like to _____?

보통 속도

빠른 속도

학습일   월   일   부모님 확인   점수

1

다음 대화를 듣고, 여자 아이가 어제 한 일을 고르시오. ·····························( )

①  ②

③  ④

2

다음 대화를 듣고, 여자 아이의 취미와 취미를 하는 횟수를 고르시오. ············( )

① 낚시하기 – 한 달에 3~4번
② 영화 보러 가기 – 한 달에 3~4번
③ 음악 감상 – 일주일에 3~4번
④ 캠핑하기 – 한 달에 4번

3

다음 대화를 듣고, 여자 아이의 장래 희망을 고르시오. ·····························( )

① 화가   ② 기타리스트
③ 피아니스트   ④ 선생님

4 중학기출 변형문제

다음 대화를 듣고, 남자 아이가 대화 직후 할 일을 고르시오. ·····················( )

① 전화하기   ② 노래하기
③ 숙제 하기   ④ 이메일 보내기

5

다음 대화를 듣고, 남자 아이가 생일 선물로 살 물건을 고르시오. ····················( )

①  ②

③  ④

6

다음 대화를 듣고, 두 아이가 이용할 교통수단을 고르시오. ························ (　　　)

① 버스　　　　　② 자전거
③ 지하철　　　　④ 택시

7

다음 대화를 듣고, 여자 아이가 구입할 지갑을 고르시오. ························ (　　　)

① 　　②
③ 　　④

8

중학기출 변형문제

다음을 듣고, 내일의 날씨를 고르시오. ························ (　　　)

① 　　②

③ 　　④

9

다음 대화를 듣고, 대화가 자연스럽지 않은 것을 고르시오. ····················· (　　　)

①　　　②　　　③　　　④

10

다음 대화를 듣고, 두 아이가 무엇에 관해 이야기하고 있는지 고르시오. ········ (　　　)

① 장래 희망　　　② 아버지 직업
③ 좋아하는 과목　④ 과학 숙제

11

다음 대화를 듣고, 여자 아이가 생일 파티에 참석하지 못하는 이유를 고르시오. ··· (   )

① 개를 돌봐야 해서
② 공부를 해야 해서
③ 부모님과 함께 외출을 해야 해서
④ 부모님이 아파서

12 중학기출 변형문제

다음 대화를 듣고, 두 사람이 내일 할 일과 만날 시각을 고르시오. ················ (   )

① 파티 참석 – 12시 30분
② 선물 구매 – 12시 30분
③ 과학 숙제 – 11시
④ 선물 구매 – 11시

13

다음 대화를 듣고, 대화가 일어나는 장소를 고르시오. ····························· (   )

① 도서관   ② 꽃 가게
③ 영화관   ④ 공원

14

다음 대화를 듣고, 대화의 내용과 일치하지 <u>않</u>는 것을 고르시오. ····················· (   )

① 여자 아이는 생일 선물로 개를 받았다.
② 개는 2살이다.
③ 개의 귀가 짧다.
④ 개의 이름은 Happy이다.

15

다음 대화를 듣고, 남자 아이가 그리는 그림으로 알맞은 것을 고르시오. ········ (   )

①    ②

③    ④

16 중학기출 변형문제

다음 대화를 듣고, 남자 아이가 여자 아이를 도와줄 수 없는 이유를 고르시오. ··· (   )

① 치과에 가야 해서
② 동생을 돌봐야 해서
③ 도서관에 가야 해서
④ 수영 수업이 있어서

17

다음 대화를 듣고, 이어질 말로 알맞은 것을 고르시오. ···························· (   )

B _____

① I like Korean food.
② Pizza is my favorite food.
③ I'd like to eat Chinese food.
④ We ate chicken, pizza, and ice cream.

18

다음 대화를 듣고, 이어질 말로 알맞은 것을 고르시오. ···························· (   )

G _____

① Of course. Let's go.
② No, I can't play tennis.
③ No, I don't want to watch it.
④ No, I don't like tennis.

19

다음 대화를 듣고, 이어질 말로 알맞은 것을 고르시오. ···························· (   )

M _____

① Let's take a taxi.
② It will be sunny tomorrow.
③ Okay. Here we are.
④ Okay. See you there at eleven.

20

다음 대화를 듣고, 이어질 말로 적절하지 않은 것을 고르시오. ···················· (   )

G _____

① A little bit.
② Yes, she can.
③ No, she can't.
④ Yes, she will study English.

14회

보통 속도　빠른 속도

Dictation 영어 듣기 모의고사

학습일　월　일　부모님 확인　점수

● 잘 듣고, 빈칸에 알맞은 말을 쓰세요.

1

다음 대화를 듣고, 여자 아이가 어제 한 일을 고르시오. ·························· (　)

① ②

③ ④

B: Catherine! What did you do yesterday?

G: Yesterday? I _____ _____.

B: Why didn't you go to the library?

G: My parents went out, so I _____ _____ _____ my younger brother.

B: You're a very good older sister.

stay 머무르다 | go out 외출하다 | babysit 아이를 돌봐주다 | younger brother 남동생

TIPS [had to + 동사원형]은 '~해야 했다'라는 의미로 [have to + 동사원형]의 과거형입니다.

2

다음 대화를 듣고, 여자 아이의 취미와 취미를 하는 횟수를 고르시오. ············ (　)

① 낚시하기 – 한 달에 3~4번
② 영화 보러 가기 – 한 달에 3~4번
③ 음악 감상 – 일주일에 3~4번
④ 캠핑하기 – 한 달에 4번

B: What do you do when you are free?

G: I enjoy _____ to the _____.

B: Sounds interesting! _____ _____ do you go to the movies?

G: I go three or _____ _____ a month.

B: Wow, that's a lot.

free 한가한 | enjoy 즐기다 | movie 영화 | often 자주 | three or four times 서너 번

TIPS go to the movies는 '영화 보러 가다'라는 의미입니다.
three or four times a month는 '한 달에 서너 번 정도'라는 의미입니다.

3

다음 대화를 듣고, 여자 아이의 장래 희망을 고르시오. ·························· (　)

① 화가　　　② 기타리스트
③ 피아니스트　④ 선생님

B: Jina, who is the man in this picture?

G: He's my _____ _____ Alfred Brendel.

B: Do you want to be a musician _____ _____ in the future?

G: Yes. I want to be a _____ _____ someday.

B: That's cool.

picture 사진 | pianist 피아니스트 | musician 음악가 | in the future 장래에 | someday 언젠가 | cool 멋진

TIPS 악기명에 -ist를 붙여서 악기를 연주하는 사람을 만들 수 있습니다.
guitar – guitarist 기타 연주자　　piano – pianist 피아노 연주자
violin – violinist 바이올린 연주자

4

다음 대화를 듣고, 남자 아이가 대화 직후 할 일을 고르시오. ·················· (　　)

① 전화하기　　　② 노래하기
③ 숙제 하기　　　④ 이메일 보내기

[Cellphone rings.]

G: Hello.

B: Hello, Jessie.

G: Hi, Daniel. What's up?

B: I'm calling to ask you a favor. My _____ isn't working. Can you print out my _____ _____ for me?

G: Sure. Just email me your file.

B: Okay. I will _____ _____ to you in a minute.

call 전화하다 | **ask** 묻다 | **favor** 부탁 | **printer** 프린터 | **file** 파일 | **in a minute** 곧

TIPS ask you a favor는 '부탁하다'라는 의미로 ask a favor of you로 바꿔 말할 수 있습니다.

5

다음 대화를 듣고, 남자 아이가 생일 선물로 살 물건을 고르시오. ·················· (　　)

① ② ③ ④

B: Mike's birthday is next week.

G: Right. What birthday _____ will you get for him?

B: I'll buy him a baseball cap.

G: He already has _____ _____ caps.

B: How about a _____ _____?

G: That's a good idea. He'll love it.

next week 다음 주 | **right** 맞아 | **present** 선물 | **baseball cap** 야구모자 | **a few** 조금

TIPS few에는 셀 수 있는 명사, little에는 셀 수 없는 명사가 옵니다. a가 있으면 긍정의 의미로 '조금'이라고 해석하고, a가 없으면 '거의 없는'이라는 부정으로 해석하면 됩니다.
He has a few friends. 그는 친구가 조금 있다.
He has few friends. 그는 친구가 거의 없다.

6

다음 대화를 듣고, 두 아이가 이용할 교통수단을 고르시오. ·················· (　　)

① 버스　　　② 자전거
③ 지하철　　　④ 택시

G: Billy, how about going to the flower festival after school?

B: Okay. How do we _____ _____?

G: We can take the subway.

B: But the subway station is too _____ _____ here.

G: Right. Then, what about _____ our _____?

B: Sounds good.

flower festival 꽃 박람회 | **subway** 지하철 | **far** 먼 | **ride one's bike** 자전거를 타다

TIPS 동사 ride는 올라타서 움직이는 느낌으로 특히 말, 자전거, 오토바이를 이용할 때 사용하고, get on은 올라타는 행동 자체를 가리키는 느낌입니다.
He got on the subway. 지하철에 탔다.

7

다음 대화를 듣고, 여자 아이가 구입할 지갑을
고르시오. ························ (   )

① ② ③ ④

M: May I help you?

G: Yes. I'm looking for a _____ for my mom.

M: What about this one _____ _____
_____ on it? It's our most popular one.

G: I like the ribbon, but it's not my mom's favorite color.
Do you have one _____ _____?

M: Yes, here it is.

G: Great! I'll _____ _____.

purse 지갑 | ribbon 리본 | popular 인기 있는 | great 멋진 | take 사다

8

다음을 듣고, 내일의 날씨를 고르시오.
························ (   )

① ② ③ ④

M: Good morning, everybody! This is the weather
report. It's _____ _____ _____.
So don't forget to take your umbrella. The rain will
stop tonight. Tomorrow will be _____ and
very _____. Be careful not to catch a cold.

everybody 모두 | outside 밖에 | forget 잊다 | tonight 오늘 저녁 | careful 조심스러운

TIPS catch a cold는 '감기에 걸리다'라는 의미입니다.

9

다음 대화를 듣고, 대화가 자연스럽지 <u>않은</u> 것
을 고르시오. ········· (   )

① ② ③ ④

❶ B: Is something wrong, Jenny?

G: I don't feel good. My stomach hurts.

❷ B: Did you make this pizza, Susan?

G: Yes, I did. Do you like it?

❸ B: Alice! How are you doing _____ _____?

G: Hi, Jio. I'm doing well.

❹ B: Jina, _____ _____ is it now?

G: It _____ at 9 o'clock.

something 무언가 | feel good 몸이 좋다 | stomach 위 | hurt 아프다 |
these days 요즘 | do well 잘하다

10

다음 대화를 듣고, 두 아이가 무엇에 관해 이야
기하고 있는지 고르시오. ········· (   )

① 장래 희망   ② 아버지 직업
③ 좋아하는 과목   ④ 과학 숙제

G: Jack, what does _____ _____ do?

B: My dad is a teacher.

G: I never knew that. What subject does he teach?

B: He _____ _____ at a middle school.

G: No way! My dad is _____ a science teacher!

B: Really? What a coincidence!

never 결코 ~ 아닌 | subject 과목 | middle school 중학교 | also 역시 | coincidence 우연

11

다음 대화를 듣고, 여자 아이가 생일 파티에 참석하지 못하는 이유를 고르시오. ··· (   )

① 개를 돌봐야 해서
② 공부를 해야 해서
③ 부모님과 함께 외출을 해야 해서
④ 부모님이 아파서

[Cellphone rings.]

B: Hello.

G: Hello, Sam. This is Susan.

B: Hi, Susan. What's up?

G: I'm sorry, but I can't go to your _____ _____.

B: Why?

G: My dog _____ _____, so I have to take care of it.

B: Oh, I see. I hope your dog _____ _____ soon.

birthday party 생일 파티 | sick 아픈 | take care of ~을 돌보다 | get better 좋아지다

12

다음 대화를 듣고, 두 사람이 내일 할 일과 만날 시각을 고르시오. ················ (   )

① 파티 참석 – 12시 30분
② 선물 구매 – 12시 30분
③ 과학 숙제 – 11시
④ 선물 구매 – 11시

W: Sam, did you _____ _____ _____ for Jim's birthday?

M: No. What about you?

W: I didn't, either. Why don't we _____ to the _____ together?

M: Okay. Let's meet tomorrow morning at 11.

W: Umm... That's a little early for me. How about _____?

M: No problem. See you tomorrow.

gift 선물 | either 역시 | mall 쇼핑몰 | together 함께 | a little 조금 | early 이른

TIPS I didn't, either.는 '나도 사지 않았어.'라는 의미로 either는 '(부정문에서) ~도 또한/역시 그렇다'라는 의미입니다.

13

다음 대화를 듣고, 대화가 일어나는 장소를 고르시오. ·························· (   )

① 도서관   ② 꽃 가게
③ 영화관   ④ 공원

B: Look at these _____ here.

G: Wow! They're really beautiful.

B: There are so many kinds of flowers in this _____ _____.

G: I like those yellow _____.

B: Me, too. _____ _____ those yellow tulips for Mom.

G: Okay. That's a good idea.

really 정말 | flower shop 꽃 가게 | too 역시 | tulip 튤립

14

다음 대화를 듣고, 대화의 내용과 일치하지 않는 것을 고르시오. ·················· (　)

① 여자 아이는 생일 선물로 개를 받았다.
② 개는 2살이다.
③ 개의 귀가 짧다.
④ 개의 이름은 Happy이다.

B: Alice, is this your dog?

G: Yes, my dad gave it to me for _____ _____.

B: Oh, he has _____ _____.
How old is he?

G: He is _____ _____ old.

B: What's his name?

G: His name is Happy.

long ear 긴 귀 | name 이름

TIPS 개는 두 살이고, 귀가 길다고 했으므로 ③번이 대화 내용과 일치하지 않습니다.

15

다음 대화를 듣고, 남자 아이가 그리는 그림으로 알맞은 것을 고르시오. ········· (　)

① ② ③ ④

W: Jake, what are you doing?

B: I'm drawing my future job, Mom.

W: Your future job?

B: Yes, I want to be _____ _____.

W: Oh, that's nice. Are they _____?

B: Yes! I want to work _____ _____ _____ as a veterinarian.

W: Cool!

draw 그리다 | future job 미래 직업 | veterinarian 수의사 | zebra 얼룩말 | zoo 동물원

TIPS 남자 아이는 동물원에서 수의사로 일하고 싶다고 했으며, 얼룩말을 그리고 있으므로 ① 번 그림이 대화의 내용과 일치합니다.

16

다음 대화를 듣고, 남자 아이가 여자 아이를 도와줄 수 없는 이유를 고르시오. ··· (　)

① 치과에 가야 해서
② 동생을 돌봐야 해서
③ 도서관에 가야 해서
④ 수영 수업이 있어서

G: Can you do me a _____?

B: What is it?

G: Could you help me with my _____ _____ after school?

B: I'd love to, but I can't.
I have a _____ _____ today.

G: Oh, I see.

B: Why don't you ask David for help?

G: Okay, I will. Thanks.

favor 부탁 | homework 숙제 | dentist appointment 치과 약속

TIPS appointment는 '시간 약속'으로, '(시간) 예약'이라는 뜻으로 쓰입니다. 주로 일과 관련된 시간 약속을 나타냅니다. promise는 '특정한 행동을 하겠다는 약속'입니다. He kept his promise to stop smoking. 그는 금연한다는 약속을 지켰다.

17

다음 대화를 듣고, 이어질 말로 알맞은 것을 고르시오. ·················· (   )

B _____

① I like Korean food.
② Pizza is my favorite food.
③ I'd like to eat Chinese food.
④ We ate chicken, pizza, and ice cream.

G: How was Jim's birthday party?

B: It was a lot of fun. We ate a lot of delicious food.

G: What _____ _____ _____ did you eat?

B: _____

fun 재미 | delicious 맛있는 | kind 종류 | Korean food 한국 음식

TIPS What kind of food did you eat?에서 did로 질문하고 있으므로 과거형을 이용해서 대답해야 합니다.

18

다음 대화를 듣고, 이어질 말로 알맞은 것을 고르시오. ·················· (   )

G _____

① Of course. Let's go.
② No, I can't play tennis.
③ No, I don't want to watch it.
④ No, I don't like tennis.

B: Kelly, where are you going?

G: Oh, hi, John. I'm _____ _____ _____ to tennis practice right now.

B: I didn't know you _____ _____.

G: I have been playing tennis for 3 years.

B: _____ _____ go and watch you play?

G: _____

on one's way 도중에 | tennis practice 테니스 연습 | right now 지금

19

다음 대화를 듣고, 이어질 말로 알맞은 것을 고르시오. ·················· (   )

M _____

① Let's take a taxi.
② It will be sunny tomorrow.
③ Okay. Here we are.
④ Okay. See you there at eleven.

M: Let's go to the _____ _____ tomorrow.

W: Great! What time does it open?

M: It opens at 9:30.

W: Then, _____ _____ at the entrance of the museum at 11 o'clock.

M: _____

science museum 과학박물관 | entrance 입구 | take a taxi 택시를 타다

20

다음 대화를 듣고, 이어질 말로 적절하지 않은 것을 고르시오. ·················· (   )

G _____

① A little bit.
② Yes, she can.
③ No, she can't.
④ Yes, she will study English.

B: Is that your sister by the window?

G: No, that is _____ _____. She came from South Korea.

B: Wow! She's very tall.

G: Yes, she is _____ than me.

B: Can she _____ _____?

G: _____

window 창문 | cousin 사촌 | South Korea 대한민국 | speak 말하다 |
a little bit 아주 조금

Word Check

● 다음 들려주는 단어와 그 의미를 쓰세요.

단어	의미
01 babysit	아이를 돌봐주다
02	
03	
04	
05	
06	
07	
08	
09	
10	
11	
12	
13	
14	
15	

● 앞에 모의고사에 나오는 문장들을 잘 듣고, 빈칸을 완성하세요.

01 I had to babysit my ___younger___ ___brother___ .

02 I _____ going to the _____ .

03 I want to be a _____ _____ someday.

04 _____ _____ to ask you a favor.

05 The subway station is too _____ _____ _____ .

06 Be careful not to _____ _____ _____ .

07 He teaches science at a _____ _____ .

08 Why don't we _____ to the _____ together?

09 My dad gave it to me for _____ _____ .

10 I want to work at a zoo _____ _____ _____ .

11 I have a _____ _____ today.

12 We ate a lot of _____ _____ .

13 I have been _____ _____ for 3 years.

14 Let's meet at the _____ of the _____ .

15 She _____ _____ South Korea.

보통 속도
 빠른 속도

학습일 월 일 | 부모님 확인 | 점수

1

다음 대화를 듣고, 두 사람이 만날 시각을 고르시오. ················· (   )

① 12시   ② 12시 30분
③ 1시   ④ 1시 30분

2

다음 대화를 듣고, 여자 아이의 삼촌을 고르시오. ···················· (   )

①    ②

③    ④

3

다음 대화를 듣고, 여자 아이가 부탁한 것을 고르시오. ···················· (   )

① 책 반납하기
② 자전거 빌리기
③ 숙제 함께하기
④ 피아노 수업 함께 가기

4

다음을 듣고, 무엇에 관해 설명하고 있는지 고르시오. ···················· (   )

①    ②

③    ④

5

다음 대화를 듣고, 대화가 끝난 직후 두 사람이 할 일을 고르시오. ···················· (   )

① 컴퓨터 끄기   ② 인터넷 검색
③ 피자 주문   ④ 컴퓨터 게임

6

다음 대화를 듣고, 남자 아이가 지난 주말에 한 일을 고르시오. ……………………… (   )

①

②

③

④

7

다음 그림을 보고, 질문에 알맞은 대답을 고르시오. ……………………………… (   )

①　　　②　　　③　　　④

8

다음 대화를 듣고, 여자 아이가 좋아하는 음식과 이유를 고르시오. …………… (   )

① 비빔밥 – 건강에 좋다.

② 비빔밥 – 만들기 쉽다.

③ 피자 – 건강에 좋다.

④ 피자 – 가격이 저렴하다.

9

다음을 듣고, 여자 아이가 말한 내용과 일치하지 <u>않는</u> 것을 고르시오. ………… (   )

① 할머니와 함께 산다.

② 아버지는 소방관이다.

③ 어머니는 요리사이다.

④ 여동생은 초등학교에 다닌다.

10

다음 대화를 듣고, 두 아이가 무엇에 관해 이야기하고 있는지 고르시오. ……… (   )

① 생일 파티　　　　② 쇼핑

③ 생일 선물　　　　④ 좋아하는 운동

11

다음 대화를 듣고, 대화가 자연스럽지 <u>않은</u> 것을 고르시오. ····················· (　　　)

① 　　② 　　③ 　　④

14

다음 대화를 듣고, 두 아이가 내일 할 일과 만날 시각을 고르시오. ················· (　　　)

① 공연 관람 – 5시
② 생일 파티 참석 – 4시
③ 생일 파티 참석 – 5시
④ 생일 선물 구입 – 5시

12

다음 대화를 듣고, 남자 아이가 찾는 물건이 있는 곳을 고르시오. ·············· (　　　)

① 　　② 　　③ 　　④

15

다음 대화를 듣고, 여자가 구입하려는 컵과 가격을 고르시오. ····················· (　　　)

① 　　　　　　　　②
– 2달러 　　　　　– 2달러

③ 　　　　　　　　④
– 3달러 　　　　　– 3달러

16

다음 그림을 보고, 그림과 일치하는 대화를 고르시오. ························· (　　　)

① 　　② 　　③ 　　④

13 　중학기출 변형문제

다음 대화를 듣고, 남자 아이가 여자 아이에게 제안한 것을 고르시오. ·············· (　　　)

① 기타 구입하기
② 함께 기타 연주하기
③ 공연 함께 관람하기
④ 음악동아리 가입하기

17

다음 대화를 듣고, 이어질 말로 알맞은 것을 고르시오. ····························· (   )

W _____

① Look over there,
② I don't have money.
③ Yes, that's all. Thank you.
④ Here you are. Anything else?

18

다음 대화를 듣고, 이어질 말로 알맞은 것을 고르시오. ····························· (   )

G _____

① I went shopping with my mom.
② It was very cold yesterday.
③ I don't feel good today.
④ That's too bad.

19 중학기출 변형문제

다음 대화를 듣고, 이어질 말로 알맞은 것을 고르시오. ····························· (   )

W _____

① I'm sorry to hear that.
② I'm going to eat pizza.
③ Really? It sounds good.
④ Oh, I went there last year.

20

다음 대화를 듣고, 이어질 말로 적절하지 <u>않은</u> 것을 고르시오. ····················· (   )

M _____

① I have a chicken salad.
② I don't eat breakfast.
③ I don't like eggs.
④ I usually have some cereal and fruit.

● 잘 듣고, 빈칸에 알맞은 말을 쓰세요.

1

다음 대화를 듣고, 두 사람이 만날 시각을 고르시오. ……………………………… (   )

① 12시
② 12시 30분
③ 1시
④ 1시 30분

B: Amy, are you going to the _____ _____ tomorrow?

G: Yes, I am. What about you?

B: Me, too. Let's go together.

G: Sure. _____ _____ we meet at 2 at the bus stop?

B: I want to get there early. _____ _____ 12:30?

G: Okay. See you then.

book festival 도서 박람회 | together 함께 | bus stop 버스 정류장 | early 이른

TIPS [Why don't we ~?]는 '~하는 게 어때?'라는 의미로 제안할 때 하는 표현입니다.

2

다음 대화를 듣고, 여자 아이의 삼촌을 고르시오. ……………………………… (   )

①
②
③
④

B: Is your uncle in this room?

G: Of course. He's _____ on the sofa.

B: You mean the man wearing the blue T-shirt?

G: No, he's wearing a _____ T-shirt. He is _____ _____ now.

B: Oh, I see him.

uncle 삼촌 | sit 앉다 | sofa 소파 | mean 의미하다 | drink 마시다

3

다음 대화를 듣고, 여자 아이가 부탁한 것을 고르시오. ……………………………… (   )

① 책 반납하기
② 자전거 빌리기
③ 숙제 함께하기
④ 피아노 수업 함께 가기

G: Mike, could you do me a favor?

B: What is it?

G: Can I _____ _____ _____? I'm late for my piano lesson.

B: Sure. Go ahead.

G: Thank you. I will _____ _____ by 6 o'clock.

favor 부탁 | borrow 빌리다 | be late 늦다 | go ahead 계속하다 | return 돌려주다

TIPS Can I borrow your bike? 대신 Can you lend me your bike?라고 표현할 수 있습니다.

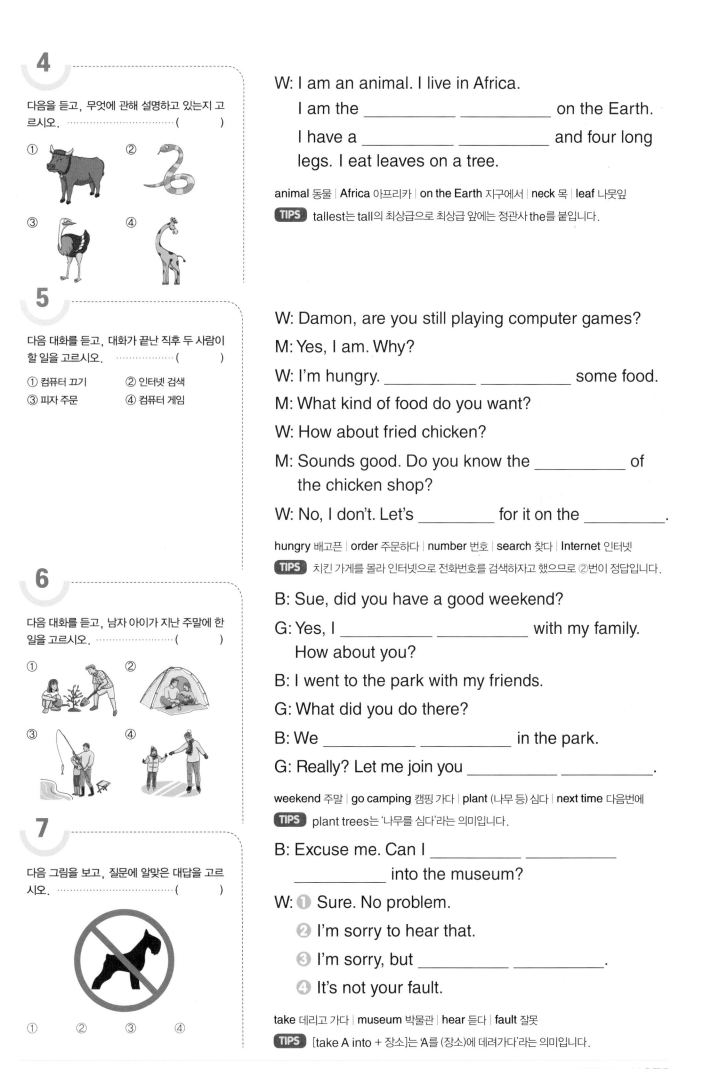

4

다음을 듣고, 무엇에 관해 설명하고 있는지 고르시오. ·············· (　　)

① ② ③ ④

W: I am an animal. I live in Africa.
I am the ＿＿＿＿＿ ＿＿＿＿＿ on the Earth.
I have a ＿＿＿＿＿ ＿＿＿＿＿ and four long legs. I eat leaves on a tree.

animal 동물 | Africa 아프리카 | on the Earth 지구에서 | neck 목 | leaf 나뭇잎
TIPS tallest는 tall의 최상급으로 최상급 앞에는 정관사 the를 붙입니다.

5

다음 대화를 듣고, 대화가 끝난 직후 두 사람이 할 일을 고르시오. ·············· (　　)

① 컴퓨터 끄기　② 인터넷 검색
③ 피자 주문　④ 컴퓨터 게임

W: Damon, are you still playing computer games?
M: Yes, I am. Why?
W: I'm hungry. ＿＿＿＿＿ ＿＿＿＿＿ some food.
M: What kind of food do you want?
W: How about fried chicken?
M: Sounds good. Do you know the ＿＿＿＿＿ of the chicken shop?
W: No, I don't. Let's ＿＿＿＿＿ for it on the ＿＿＿＿＿.

hungry 배고픈 | order 주문하다 | number 번호 | search 찾다 | Internet 인터넷
TIPS 치킨 가게를 몰라 인터넷으로 전화번호를 검색하자고 했으므로 ②번이 정답입니다.

6

다음 대화를 듣고, 남자 아이가 지난 주말에 한 일을 고르시오. ·············· (　　)

① ② ③ ④

B: Sue, did you have a good weekend?
G: Yes, I ＿＿＿＿＿ ＿＿＿＿＿ with my family. How about you?
B: I went to the park with my friends.
G: What did you do there?
B: We ＿＿＿＿＿ ＿＿＿＿＿ in the park.
G: Really? Let me join you ＿＿＿＿＿ ＿＿＿＿＿.

weekend 주말 | go camping 캠핑 가다 | plant (나무 등) 심다 | next time 다음번에
TIPS plant trees는 '나무를 심다'라는 의미입니다.

7

다음 그림을 보고, 질문에 알맞은 대답을 고르시오. ·············· (　　)

① ② ③ ④

B: Excuse me. Can I ＿＿＿＿＿ ＿＿＿＿＿ ＿＿＿＿＿ into the museum?
W: ❶ Sure. No problem.
❷ I'm sorry to hear that.
❸ I'm sorry, but ＿＿＿＿＿ ＿＿＿＿＿.
❹ It's not your fault.

take 데리고 가다 | museum 박물관 | hear 듣다 | fault 잘못
TIPS [take A into + 장소]는 'A를 (장소에) 데려가다'라는 의미입니다.

8

다음 대화를 듣고, 여자 아이가 좋아하는 음식과 이유를 고르시오. ………… (   )

① 비빔밥 – 건강에 좋다.
② 비빔밥 – 만들기 쉽다.
③ 피자 – 건강에 좋다.
④ 피자 – 가격이 저렴하다.

G: Jim, what are you eating?
B: I'm eating pizza. You _____ _____?
G: No, I don't like pizza.
B: Then, what's your _____ _____?
G: I like bibimbap.
B: Why do you like it?
G: It's _____.

eat 먹다 | some 약간 | favorite 좋아하는 | healthy 건강에 좋은

9

다음을 듣고, 여자 아이가 말한 내용과 일치하지 않는 것을 고르시오. ………… (   )

① 할머니와 함께 산다.
② 아버지는 소방관이다.
③ 어머니는 요리사이다.
④ 여동생은 초등학교에 다닌다.

G: I'll introduce my family to you. There are five people in my family. They are my _____, my father, my mother, my younger sister, and me. My father is a _____. He is very brave. My mother is a _____. She works at a restaurant. My younger sister is 6 years old. She goes to _____.

introduce 소개하다 | grandmother 할머니 | younger sister 여동생 | firefighter 소방관 | cook 요리사 | kindergarten 유치원

TIPS 여동생은 6살이며, 유치원에 다니고 있습니다.

10

다음 대화를 듣고, 두 아이가 무엇에 관해 이야기하고 있는지 고르시오. ……… (   )

① 생일 파티   ② 쇼핑
③ 생일 선물   ④ 좋아하는 운동

B: Christine. I have something to ask you.
G: What is that?
B: What are you going to _____ for Jim's _____?
G: I'm thinking of buying him a backpack. How about you?
B: I haven't _____ _____.
G: Why don't you buy him _____ _____? His shoes are very old.
B: Oh, that's a good idea.

something 무언가 | ask 묻다 | think 생각하다 | backpack 가방 | decide 결정하다 | yet 아직 | running shoes 운동화 | old 낡은

TIPS [I'm thinking of -ing + A]는 '나는 A를 ～할까 생각 중이야.'라는 의미입니다.
I'm thinking of going to Canada to study next year.
나는 내년에 공부하러 캐나다에 갈 생각이야.

11

다음 대화를 듣고, 대화가 자연스럽지 않은 것을 고르시오. ····················(   )

①   ②   ③   ④

❶ M: What can I do for you?

   G: I'm looking for a bag.

❷ M: Where is your cellphone?

   G: It's on the table.

❸ M: Excuse me, _____ _____ goes to the airport?

   G: It will _____ 20 minutes.

❹ M: What a pretty scarf! It _____ so _____ on you.

   G: Thank you, Dad.

cellphone 휴대전화 | airport 공항 | pretty 예쁜 | scarf 스카프

TIPS It will take 20 minutes.에 알맞은 질문은 How long will it take from here to the airport?입니다.

12

다음 대화를 듣고, 남자 아이가 찾는 물건이 있는 곳을 고르시오. ·················(   )

①   ②   ③   ④

B: Do you know where my science _____ is?

W: I think I saw it on the desk in the morning.

B: No, it's not there.

W: Then, check your backpack.

B: It's not there, _____.

W: Hmm. Did you look _____ _____ _____?

B: Oh, there it is! It's on the _____ shelf.

magazine 잡지 | think 생각하다 | check 확인하다 | either 역시 | shelf 선반

13

다음 대화를 듣고, 남자 아이가 여자 아이에게 제안한 것을 고르시오. ·················(   )

① 기타 구입하기
② 함께 기타 연주하기
③ 공연 함께 관람하기
④ 음악동아리 가입하기

G: Wow! John, you're _____ _____ playing the guitar.

B: Thank you for saying that.

G: Where did you learn to play?

B: I joined the school music club last year.

G: I want to learn _____ _____ _____ the guitar.

B: Then, how about _____ our _____?

G: That sounds good.

be good at ~을 잘하다 | guitar 기타 | learn 배우다 | join 가입하다 | club 동아리

TIPS How about joining our club? 대신 Why don't you join our club?(우리 동아리에 가입하는 게 어때?)이라고 표현할 수 있습니다.

14

다음 대화를 듣고, 두 아이가 내일 할 일과 만날 시각을 고르시오. ·············· (   )

① 공연 관람 – 5시
② 생일 파티 참석 – 4시
③ 생일 파티 참석 – 5시
④ 생일 선물 구입 – 5시

G: Jack, are you going to Tony's _____
_____ tomorrow?
B: Yes, I am.
G: I don't know where his house is.
Can we _____ _____?
B: Sure. Let's meet at 4 o'clock at the bus stop.
G: Well, that's too early.
How about _____ _____?
B: No problem.

tomorrow 내일 | know 알다 | together 함께 | meet 만나다 | too 너무 | early 이른
TIPS 두 사람은 내일 생일파티에 가기 위해 5시에 만나기로 했습니다.

15

다음 대화를 듣고, 여자가 구입하려는 컵과 가격을 고르시오. ·············· (   )

① [cup with cat] – 2달러   ② [cup with flower] – 2달러
③ [cup with cat] – 3달러   ④ [cup with flower] – 3달러

M: May I help you?
W: I'm looking for a cup.
M: How about the cup with a cat on it?
W: Hmm... It _____ _____, but I don't like cats.
M: Then, how about this cup _____ _____ _____?
W: Oh, that's good. How much is it?
M: It's _____ _____.

look good 좋아 보이다 | flower 꽃
TIPS the cup with a flower은 '꽃이 있는 컵'이란 의미입니다.
전치사 with는 '~을 가지고 있는, ~이 있는' 등의 의미를 가지고 있습니다.
the man with a hat 모자를 쓴 남자
the tall woman with yellow hair 노란 머리를 한 키 큰 여자

16

다음 그림을 보고, 그림과 일치하는 대화를 고르시오. ·············· (   )

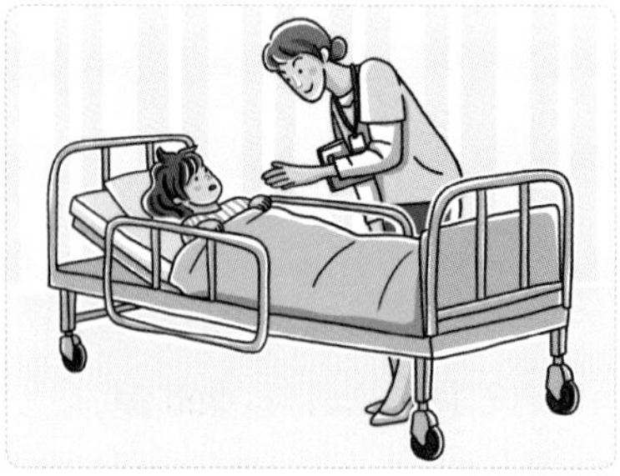

① ② ③ ④

M: ❶ A man is _____ _____ _____ a girl.
❷ A nurse is looking out the window.
❸ A doctor is sitting on the sofa.
❹ A _____ is taking care of a _____.

take care of ~을 돌보다 | look out 밖을 보다 | sit 앉다 | patient 환자
TIPS 간호가가 환자를 돌보고 있으므로 ④ 번의 표현이 그림과 가장 어울립니다.

17

다음 대화를 듣고, 이어질 말로 알맞은 것을 고르시오. ·········· (   )

W _____

① Look over there.
② I don't have money.
③ Yes, that's all. Thank you.
④ Here you are. Anything else?

W: May I help you?

M: Yes, I'm looking for apples.

W: _____ _____ apples do you want?

M: I want _____.

W: _____

want 원하다 | look over 검토하다 | money 돈 | anything else 그밖에 다른 것

TIPS Anything else?는 Would you like anything else? '뭐 더 필요한 거 있어요?'의 줄임말입니다.

18

다음 대화를 듣고, 이어질 말로 알맞은 것을 고르시오. ·········· (   )

G _____

① I went shopping with my mom.
② It was very cold yesterday.
③ I don't feel good today.
④ That's too bad.

G: Jack, what did you do yesterday?

B: I _____ _____ at home.

G: Oh, did you? What program did you watch?

B: I watched a soccer game. _____ _____ you?

G: _____

watch 보다 | program 프로그램 | go shopping 쇼핑 가다 | feel good 몸이 좋다

TIPS What about you?는 '너는 어제 뭐했니?'라는 의미이므로 과거시제를 이용해 대답해야 합니다. 따라서 I went shopping with my mom.이 올바른 대답입니다.

19

다음 대화를 듣고, 이어질 말로 알맞은 것을 고르시오. ·········· (   )

W _____

① I'm sorry to hear that.
② I'm going to eat pizza.
③ Really? It sounds good.
④ Oh, I went there last year.

W: What are you going to do this weekend?

M: I'm going to _____ _____ with my cousins. Do you have any special plans?

W: No, I don't. I will just _____ _____.

M: Why don't you _____ _____ _____?

W: _____

weekend 주말 | go camping 캠핑 가다 | cousin 사촌 | special 특별한 | last year 작년에

20

다음 대화를 듣고, 이어질 말로 적절하지 <u>않은</u> 것을 고르시오. ·········· (   )

M _____

① I have a chicken salad.
② I don't eat breakfast.
③ I don't like eggs.
④ I usually have some cereal and fruit.

M: Do you have breakfast every day?

W: Yes, I do.

M: What do you have _____ _____?

W: I usually have bread and eggs. _____ _____ you?

M: _____

every day 매일 | usually 보통 | cereal 시리얼 | fruit 과일

TIPS How about you?는 What do you have for breakfast?라는 의미이므로 I don't like eggs.는 대답으로 어울리지 않습니다.

● 다음 들려주는 단어와 그 의미를 쓰세요.

	단어	의미
01	together	함께
02		
03		
04		
05		
06		
07		
08		
09		
10		
11		
12		
13		
14		
15		

● 앞에 모의고사에 나오는 문장들을 잘 듣고, 빈칸을 완성하세요.

01 I want to _____<u>get</u>_____ _____<u>there</u>_____ early.

02 I will _____ _____ by 6 o'clock.

03 I am the _____ _____ on the Earth.

04 _____ _____ for it on the Internet.

05 We _____ _____ in the park.

06 Let me join you _____ _____.

07 There are _____ _____ in my family.

08 _____ _____ _____ buy him running shoes?

09 It looks _____ _____ on you.

10 I think I saw it on the desk _____ _____ _____.

11 I want to learn _____ _____ _____ the guitar.

12 I don't know _____ his house _____.

13 A nurse is _____ _____ of a patient.

14 I'm going to _____ _____ with my cousins.

15 I usually have _____ _____ _____.

 **Vocabulary**

● 다음 단어들을 듣고, 뜻을 미리 알아보세요.

01	bookshelf	책장	16	practice	연습하다
02	bottom	밑바닥	17	anything	무언가
03	town	도시, 시내	18	pleasure	즐거움
04	know	알다	19	introduce	소개하다
05	change	바꾸다	20	often	종종
06	mind	마음, ~을 꺼리다	21	healthy	건강한
07	trip	여행	22	exercise	운동하다
08	flight	비행	23	aquarium	수족관
09	anymore	더 이상	24	next door	옆집
10	maybe	아마	25	grow up	자라다
11	safe	안전한	26	fall off	~에서 떨어지다
12	favor	부탁	27	jump rope	줄넘기하다
13	return	반납하다	28	baseball glove	야구 글러브
14	arm	팔	29	go on vacation	휴가를 가다
15	soon	곧	30	clean up	청소하다

2^회 Vocabulary

● 다음 단어들을 듣고, 뜻을 미리 알아보세요.

01	clothes	옷	16	straight	곧장
02	stick	막대기	17	sunglasses	선글라스
03	bamboo	대나무	18	chocolate	초콜릿
04	metal	금속	19	Christmas	크리스마스
05	especially	특별히	20	lend	빌려주다
06	people	사람들	21	deadline	마감일
07	still	여전히	22	yet	아직
08	delicious	맛있는	23	just	방금
09	market	시장	24	pick up	～을 들다
10	onion	양파	25	of course	물론
11	appointment	약속	26	art museum	미술관
12	call	전화하다	27	after-school activity	방과 후 활동
13	difficult	어려운	28	for a minute	잠시 동안
14	park	공원, 주차하다	29	go ahead	계속하다
15	vacation	휴가, 방학	30	be interested in	～에 관심 있다

● 다음 단어들을 듣고, 뜻을 미리 알아보세요.

01	daughter	딸		16	change	잔돈
02	choice	선택		17	perfect	완벽한
03	finish	끝내다		18	pretty	꽤
04	enough	충분한		19	wallet	(남자용) 지갑
05	check	확인하다		20	grapes	포도
06	adult	어른		21	special	특별한
07	scared	무서워하는		22	blanket	담요
08	stand	서 있다		23	documentary	다큐멘터리
09	designer	디자이너		24	awesome	멋진
10	style	스타일		25	give it a try	시도해 보다
11	around	~ 주위에		26	go camping	캠핑 가다
12	envy	부러워하다		27	be back	돌아오다
13	package	소포		28	give a call	전화하다
14	send	보내다		29	picnic basket	소풍 바구니
15	young	어린		30	clothing company	의류 회사

4 ^회 **Voca**bulary

● 다음 단어들을 듣고, 뜻을 미리 알아보세요.

01	sweater	스웨터	16	subway	지하철
02	show	보여주다	17	warm	따뜻한
03	festival	축제	18	unfortunately	불행하게도
04	lesson	수업	19	interesting	재미있는
05	forget	잊다	20	wonderful	멋진
06	o'clock	시	21	fell	넘어지다
07	return	환불하다	22	be in hospital	입원해 있다
08	add	첨가하다	23	leave for	～을 향해 떠나다
09	bacon	베이컨	24	be from	～ 출신이다
10	delicious	맛있는	25	would like to	～하고 싶다
11	bookstore	서점	26	action movie	액션 영화
12	already	이마, 벌써	27	make sure	확실히 ～하다
13	happen	(일이) 일어나다	28	classical music	고전음악
14	cartoon	만화	29	speech contest	말하기 대회
15	character	캐릭터	30	by the way	그런데

5 Vocabulary

● 다음 단어들을 듣고, 뜻을 미리 알아보세요.

01	online	온라인으로	16	heavy	많은, 심한
02	church	교회	17	tulip	튤립
03	poem	시	18	favor	부탁, 요청
04	dream	꿈	19	homework	숙제
05	something	무언가	20	wrong	잘못된
06	know	알다	21	problem	문제
07	drawer	서랍	22	post office	우체국
08	believe	믿다	23	sweet potato	고구마
09	hold	들다, 잡다	24	come up soon	곧 다가오다
10	present	선물	25	here you are	여기 있다
11	concert	콘서트	26	be late for	～에 늦다
12	weekend	주말	27	curly hair	곱슬머리
13	begin	시작하다	28	anything else	그밖에 다른 것
14	donut	도넛	29	convenience store	편의점
15	traffic	교통	30	which one	어느 것

● 다음 단어들을 듣고, 뜻을 미리 알아보세요.

01	dress	원피스	16	musical	뮤지컬
02	noon	정오	17	extra	여분의
03	awesome	멋진	18	carrot	당근
04	aunt	고모, 이모	19	market	시장
05	message	메시지	20	artist	예술가
06	repeat	반복하다	21	become	～이 되다
07	beach	해변	22	slice	조각
08	later	나중에	23	curly hair	곱슬머리
09	drop	떨어뜨리다	24	phone number	전화번호
10	screen	화면	25	next time	다음 번에
11	crack	금이 가다	26	come true	실현되다
12	dream	꿈	27	try on	～을 입어보다
13	campfire	캠프파이어, 모닥불	28	return books	책을 반납하다
14	smoke	담배 피우다	29	anything else	그밖에 다른 것
15	first	먼저	30	so much	무척

● 다음 단어들을 듣고, 뜻을 미리 알아보세요.

01	try	노력하다	16	plan	계획
02	always	항상, 언제나	17	sandcastle	모래성
03	early	일찍	18	forget	잊다
04	basket	바구니	19	really	정말
05	front	앞	20	vacation	방학, 휴가
06	percent	퍼센트	21	somewhere	어딘가
07	competition	대회	22	talk on the phone	전화통화하다
08	nervous	긴장한	23	be in (the) hospital	입원하다
09	soon	곧	24	see a doctor	병원에 가다
10	still	여전히	25	right now	지금 당장
11	drawer	서랍	26	best friend	가장 친한 친구
12	same	같은	27	a little	조금
13	ask	요청하다	28	department store	백화점
14	loud	시끄러운	29	at the moment	지금
15	yet	아직	30	weather report	일기예보

● 다음 단어들을 듣고, 뜻을 미리 알아보세요.

01	leave	출발하다
02	about	대략
03	people	사람들
04	street	길, 거리
05	cross	건너다
06	road	도로
07	exciting	흥미진진한
08	mean	의미하다
09	husband	남편
10	rainbow	무지개
11	purse	지갑
12	vacuum	진공청소하다
13	rule	규칙
14	country	나라
15	daughter	딸

16	everyone	모두
17	active	활동적인
18	flight	비행
19	comfortable	편안한
20	passenger	승객
21	serve	제공하다
22	table tennis	탁구
23	give me a ride	나를 태워주다
24	pick up	태워주다, 가지러 가다
25	traffic light	교통신호
26	running shoes	운동화
27	free time	여가시간
28	how often	얼마나 자주
29	swimming pool	수영장
30	watch movies	영화 보다

9 ^회 **Voca**bulary

● 다음 단어들을 듣고, 뜻을 미리 알아보세요.

01	blouse	블라우스	16	grab	먹다
02	email	이메일을 보내다	17	carry	옮기다
03	cafeteria	구내식당	18	glad	기쁜
04	ride	탈것	19	wake up	일어나다
05	subway	지하철	20	feel better	더 나아지다
06	catch	잡다	21	short hair	짧은 머리
07	painting	그림	22	right away	바로
08	headache	두통	23	be on a diet	다이어트 중이다
09	luck	행운	24	amusement park	놀이공원
10	especially	특히	25	take some medicine	약을 먹다
11	gym	체육관	26	drawing contest	사생대회
12	bring	가져오다	27	take part in	～에 참가하다
13	return	환불하다	28	be due	예정이다
14	because	～ 때문에	29	come over	～에 들르다
15	mind	꺼리다	30	field trip	현장학습

● 다음 단어들을 듣고, 뜻을 미리 알아보세요.

01	mind	마음	16	garden	정원
02	forget	잊어버리다	17	picnic	소풍
03	light	빛, 전등	18	during	~ 동안
04	kind	종류	19	through	내내
05	chocolate	초콜릿	20	problem	문제
06	notice	알아차리다	21	better	더 나은
07	before	~ 전에	22	movie director	영화감독
08	outside	밖에	23	cooking class	요리 수업
09	either	또한	24	final exam	기말고사
10	shelf	선반	25	express bus	고속버스
11	hamburger	햄버거	26	heavy snow	폭설
12	anything	무언가	27	fitting room	탈의실
13	invite	초대하다	28	take a trip	여행하다
14	half	절반	29	as well	역시
15	butterfly	나비	30	all day	하루 종일

Vocabulary

● 다음 단어들을 듣고, 뜻을 미리 알아보세요.

01	necklace	목걸이	16	nonsmoker	담배 안 피우는 사람
02	maybe	아마	17	harmonica	하모니카
03	grocery	식료품	18	trumpet	트럼펫
04	near	근처에	19	almost	거의
05	wish	바라다	20	area	지역
06	borrow	빌리다	21	dinosaur	공룡
07	enough	충분한	22	club	동아리
08	hold	들다	23	check out	대출하다
09	balloon	풍선	24	by the way	그런데
10	vegetable	야채	25	do well	잘하다
11	ice hockey	아이스하키	26	public place	공공장소
12	musical	뮤지컬	27	both A and B	A와 B 모두
13	theater	극장	28	musical instrument	악기
14	understand	이해하다	29	flea market	벼룩시장
15	person	사람	30	come up	다가오다

● 다음 단어들을 듣고, 뜻을 미리 알아보세요.

01	popular	인기 있는	16	puppy	강아지
02	teens	십대	17	surprising	놀라운
03	discount	할인	18	wedding	결혼
04	drugstore	약국	19	happen	일어나다
05	around	근처에, 대략	20	get married	결혼하다
06	corner	모퉁이	21	run away	달아나다
07	right	올바른	22	free time	여가시간
08	gift	선물	23	side table	협탁
09	menu	메뉴	24	older than	~보다 나이 든
10	yet	아직	25	right now	지금
11	cheap	싼	26	subway station	지하철역
12	healthy	건강한	27	bus number	버스 번호
13	news	소식	28	see a doctor	병원에 가다
14	Christmas	크리스마스	29	eat out	외식하다
15	call	전화하다	30	have A in mind	A를 마음에 두다

● 다음 단어들을 듣고, 뜻을 미리 알아보세요.

01	restaurant	식당	16	skin	피부
02	prepare	준비하다	17	hurt	다치다
03	upset	화난	18	believe	믿다
04	someone	누군가	19	miss	보고 싶다
05	space	공간	20	total	모두, 전체
06	culture	문화	21	enter	들어가다
07	online	온라인으로	22	passport	여권
08	slim	날씬한	23	stand in line	줄을 서고 있다
09	shark	상어	24	get on	～에 타다
10	tank	탱크	25	be interested in	～에 관심 있다
11	dolphin	돌고래	26	history museum	역사박물관
12	penguin	펭귄	27	sliver medal	은메달
13	wonder	궁금하다	28	fall down	넘어지다
14	spine	척추	29	get well	나아지다
15	body	몸	30	family trip	가족 여행

● 다음 단어들을 듣고, 뜻을 미리 알아보세요.

01	babysit	아이를 돌봐주다	16	either	(부정문) ~도, 역시
02	someday	언젠가	17	a little	조금(셀 수 없는)
03	pianist	피아니스트	18	delicious	맛있는
04	printer	프린터	19	entrance	입구
05	file	파일	20	veterinarian	수의사
06	present	선물	21	on one's way	도중에
07	purse	지갑	22	dentist appointment	치과 약속
08	ribbon	리본	23	three or four times	서너 번
09	everybody	모두	24	in a minute	곧
10	forget	잊다	25	a few	조금(셀 수 있는)
11	careful	조심스러운	26	flower festival	꽃 박람회
12	stomach	위	27	feel good	기분이 좋다
13	never	결코 ~ 아닌	28	these days	요즘
14	coincidence	우연	29	middle school	중학교
15	also	역시, 또한	30	a little bit	아주 조금

15회 Vocabulary

● 다음 단어들을 듣고, 뜻을 미리 알아보세요.

01	together	함께	16	know	알다
02	mean	의미하다	17	patient	환자
03	return	돌려주다	18	program	프로그램
04	leaf	나뭇잎	19	money	돈
05	search	찾다	20	weekend	주말
06	Internet	인터넷	21	usually	보통
07	take	데리고 가다	22	book festival	도서 박람회
08	fault	잘못	23	go ahead	계속하다
09	health	건강	24	on Earth	지구에서
10	kindergarten	유치원	25	plant trees	나무를 심다
11	decide	결정하다	26	running shoes	운동화
12	introduce	소개하다	27	on the top shelf	맨 위 선반에
13	airport	공항	28	take care of	～을 돌보다
14	magazine	잡지	29	look out	밖을 보다
15	guitar	기타	30	look over	검토하다

Longman

Listening
mentor
joy

정답 및 해석

5
LEVEL

Pearson

1회 영어 듣기 모의고사

1 ③	2 ②	3 ③	4 ④	5 ①	6 ③	7 ①	8 ③	9 ④	10 ③
11 ②	12 ③	13 ④	14 ④	15 ④	16 ②	17 ④	18 ④	19 ②	20 ②

듣기 대본

1
B: Mom, have you seen my notebook?
W: Are you talking about the red one?
B: Yes.
W: I think I saw it on the bookshelf.
B: The bookshelf?
W: Yes, look on the bottom shelf.
B: Oh, I found it. Thank you, Mom.

2
M: Do you like Italian food?
W: Yes, I love pasta. How about you?
M: I like it, too. Do you know a new Italian restaurant opened in town?
W: Where?
M: Next to Hillside Park. How about eating pasta there this Saturday?
W: Sure, I'm free this weekend.

3
B: Do you still want to be a doctor when you grow up?
G: Yes, I do. How about you, John?
B: I want to be a police officer like my dad.
G: I thought you wanted to be an English teacher.
B: I did, but I changed my mind.
G: Oh, I see.

4
M: Melissa, how was your trip?
W: It was great. It was a long flight, but I was happy to see my family.
M: How long was the flight?
W: It took me 6 hours to get there

5
G: I think I lost my pencil case.
B: Where did you leave it?
G: I left it in the library, but it's not there anymore.
B: What does it look like?
G: It is blue, and it has stars on it.

해석

1
B: 엄마, 제 공책 보셨어요?
W: 그 빨간색 말하는 거니?
B: 예.
W: 책장에서 본 거 같은데.
B: 책장이요?
W: 응, 맨 아래 선반을 봐.
B: 오, 찾았어요. 감사합니다, 엄마.

2
M: 너 이탈리아 음식 좋아하니?
W: 응, 파스타를 무척 좋아해. 너는 어때?
M: 나도 그거 좋아해.
   시내에 새로운 이탈리아 식당이 오픈한 거 아니?
W: 어디?
M: 힐사이드 파크 옆에.
   이번 토요일 거기서 파스타 먹는 거 어때?
W: 좋아, 나 이번 주말 한가해.

3
B: 너는 커서 여전히 의사가 되고 싶니?
G: 응, 그래. 너는 어때, 존?
B: 나는 아빠처럼 경찰관이 되고 싶어.
G: 난 네가 영어 선생님이 되고 싶어한다고 생각했어.
B: 그랬는데, 마음이 바뀌었어.
G: 오, 알았어.

4
M: 멜리사, 여행 어땠어?
W: 멋졌어. 장거리 비행이었지만 가족을 볼 수 있어서 행복했어.
M: 비행이 얼마 동안이었어?
W: 거기 도착하는 데 6시간 걸렸어.

5
G: 나 필통을 잃어버린 거 같아.
B: 그거 어디에 나뒀는데?
G: 도서관에 나뒀는데 더 이상 거기에 없어.
B: 어떻게 생겼는데?
G: 파란색에 별들이 있어.

6 B: Look at my new watch.

G: Wow! Is that your birthday present?

B: Yes, my parents bought it for me.

G: You are so lucky. I want that same watch.

B: You should ask for it for your birthday.

G: Maybe I will.

6 B : 내 새 시계를 봐.

G : 와우! 그거 네 생일 선물이야?

B : 응, 부모님이 나를 위해 사주셨어.

G : 넌 정말 운도 좋아. 나 그거랑 똑같은 시계를 원해.

B : 네 생일에 사달라고 해.

G : 그럴 거야.

7 M: Are you going to Sue's birthday party this Saturday?

W: I don't think I can make it.
I am going on vacation with my family.

M: Where are you going?

W: We're going to Jeju Island.

M: Sounds fun. Have a safe trip.

7 M : 이번 주 토요일에 수의 생일 파티에 갈 거니?

W : 가지 못할 거 같아.
나 가족이랑 휴가를 가기로 했어.

M : 어디로 가는데?

W : 우리 제주도에 가.

M : 재미있겠다. 안전한 여행해.

8 B: Alice, did you buy a birthday present for Smith?

G: Yes, I bought a baseball cap. How about you?

B: I'm going to buy a backpack. What do you think?

G: He already has two backpacks.

B: Then, how about a baseball glove?

G: That's a good idea.

8 B : 앨리스, 너 스미스에게 줄 생일 선물 샀니?

G : 응, 야구모자를 샀어. 너는 어때?

B : 배낭을 사려고. 어떻게 생각해?

G : 스미스는 이미 배낭이 두 개나 있어.

B : 그러면, 야구 글러브는 어때?

G : 좋은 생각이야.

9 W: Mike, what are you going to do today?

M: I'm going to the library.

W: Can you do me a favor?

M: What is it?

W: Do you mind returning these books to the library?

M: No, that won't be a problem. I can do that.

9 W : 마이크, 오늘 뭐할 거야?

M : 나 도서관에 갈 거야.

W : 부탁 하나 해도 될까?

M : 뭔데?

W : 이 책들 도서관에 반납해 주지 않겠니?

M : 응, 문제없어. 할 수 있어.

10 ① M: Do you enjoy watching baseball games?

W: Yes, why?

② M: What happened to your arm?

W: I fell from a tree.

③ M: What's wrong? You look sick.

W: I have the flu.

④ M: Where are you going?

W: I'm going to the dentist.

10 ① M : 야구 경기 보는 거 즐기니?

W : 응, 왜?

② M : 너 팔 무슨 일이야?

W : 나무에서 떨어졌어.

③ M : 무슨 일이야? 아픈 거 같아.

W : 독감에 걸렸어.

④ M : 어디 가고 있어?

W : 나 치과에 가고 있어.

11 W: Jack, your piano teacher is coming soon.
Clean up your room.

B: I've already cleaned it.

W: Okay, go practice until your teacher gets here.

B: Alright, Mom.

11 W : 잭, 네 피아노 선생님이 곧 오실 거야.
방 청소를 해라.

B : 이미 청소했어요.

W : 좋아, 가서 선생님이 여기 오실 때까지 연습해.

B : 알겠어요, 엄마.

12 M: May I help you?
　　W: Yes, I'm looking for mangos.
　　M: They're here.
　　W: How much are these mangos?
　　M: It's one dollar each.
　　W: Okay. I'll take four.

12 M: 도와드릴까요?
　　W: 예, 망고를 찾고 있어요.
　　M: 그것들은 여기에 있어요.
　　W: 이 망고는 얼마예요?
　　M: 하나에 1달러예요.
　　W: 좋아요. 4개 살게요.

13 ① M: Would you like anything to drink?
　　　W: Yes, I'd like some orange juice.
　　② M: Thank you for helping me.
　　　W: It was my pleasure!
　　③ M: What are you doing now?
　　　W: I'm watching TV.
　　④ M: What's your favorite food?
　　　W: I like reading books.

13 ① M: 마실 거 드릴까요?
　　　W: 예, 오렌지 주스 주세요.
　　② M: 도와주셔서 감사합니다.
　　　W: 천만에요!
　　③ M: 지금 뭐하고 있어?
　　　W: TV 보고 있어.
　　④ M: 네가 좋아하는 음식은 뭐야?
　　　W: 난 책 읽는 것을 좋아해.

14 G: I'd like to introduce my friend Cathy to you. She is from Canada, and she lives next door. We often play together after school. She likes dancing. She sometimes dances to K-pop.

14 G: 내 친구 캐시를 여러분께 소개하고 싶어요. 그녀는 캐나다에서 왔고 옆집에 살아요. 우리는 종종 방과 후에 함께 놀아요. 그녀는 춤추는 것을 좋아해요. 그녀는 가끔 케이팝 음악에 맞춰 춤을 춰요.

15 [Cellphone rings.]
　　W: Hello.
　　M: Hello, Julia. What's up?
　　W: Ted and I are going to the aquarium tomorrow. Do you want to come with us?
　　M: Sure, what time shall we meet?
　　W: How about 11 o'clock?
　　M: That's too early. Let's meet at 11:30 at the subway station.
　　W: Okay.

15 [휴대폰이 울린다.]
　　W: 여보세요.
　　M: 안녕, 줄리아. 무슨 일이야?
　　W: 테드와 내가 내일 수족관에 갈 거야. 우리랑 같이 가고 싶니?
　　M: 물론, 우리 몇 시에 만날까?
　　W: 11시 어때?
　　M: 그거 너무 일러. 11시 30분에 지하철역에서 만나자.
　　W: 좋아.

16 M: Michelle, you look healthy these days.
　　W: Really? I exercise every day.
　　M: Do you go jogging every day?
　　W: No, I jump rope every day.
　　M: Jump rope?
　　W: Yes, jumping rope is good for health.

16 M: 미쉘, 너 요즘 건강해 보인다.
　　W: 정말? 매일 운동하고 있어.
　　M: 매일 조깅해?
　　W: 아니, 매일 줄넘기를 해.
　　M: 줄넘기?
　　W: 응, 줄넘기하는 것은 건강에 좋아.

17 G: Jim! Where are you going?
　　B: I'm going to the mall.
　　G: Why are you going to the mall?
　　B: It's my brother's birthday tomorrow, so I am getting his favorite toy.
　　G: Your brother will be so happy.
　　B: ① No, it's not my toy.
　　　② How much is it?
　　　③ No, he doesn't have a toy.
　　　④ Yes, I hope he likes it.

17 G: 짐! 어디 가고 있어?
　　B: 나 쇼핑몰에 가고 있어.
　　G: 쇼핑몰에는 왜 가는데?
　　B: 내 남동생 생일이 내일이어서, 그가 좋아하는 장난감을 사려고.
　　G: 네 남동생이 무척 행복해 할 거야.
　　B: ① 아니, 그것은 내 장난감이 아니야.
　　　② 그거 얼마예요?
　　　③ 아니, 그는 장난감을 가지고 있지 않아.
　　　④ 응, 그가 그걸 좋아하기를 바라.

18 [Cellphone rings.]

G: Hello.

B: Hi. Jessica! It's Nick.

G: Oh, hi, Nick.

B: If you are free this Sunday, do you want to go ice skating?

G: Sure, that sounds fun! What time shall we meet?

B: How about 2 o'clock in front of the gym?

G: ① Yes, I like spicy food.

　② I don't like ice skating.

　③ Yes, it's in front of the gym.

　④ Great. See you on Sunday.

19 G: Is this a picture of your family?

B: Yes, it is.

G: Is this your dad?

B: No, he's my uncle, Brian.

G: Your uncle is very tall. What does he do?

B: ① Yes, I like him.

　② He's a taxi driver.

　③ He lives in Seoul.

　④ He's from Italy.

20 W: Hi, Ted. Did you hear about Tony? He's in the hospital now.

M: What happened to him?

W: He fell off his bike and broke his leg.

M: ① It's my pleasure.

　② Oh, that's too bad.

　③ You're welcome.

　④ Long time no see.

18 [휴대폰이 울린다.]

G: 여보세요.

B: 안녕. 제시카! 나 닉이야.

G: 오, 안녕, 닉.

B: 네가 이번 주 일요일 시간 되면 스케이트 타러 갈래?

G: 물론이지, 재미있겠다! 우리 몇 시에 만날까?

B: 2시에 체육관 앞에서 보는 거 어때?

G: ① 응, 나 매운 음식을 좋아해.

　② 나는 스케이트 타는 거 좋아하지 않아.

　③ 응, 그것은 체육관 앞에 있어.

　④ 좋아. 일요일에 보자.

19 G: 이것이 네 가족사진이니?

B: 응, 그래.

G: 이 남자는 누구야?

B: 아니, 그는 내 삼촌 브라이언이야.

G: 삼촌이 키가 매우 크시구나. 무슨 일을 하셔?

　① 응, 나는 그를 좋아해.

　② 그는 택시 운전사야.

　③ 그는 서울에 살아.

　④ 그는 이탈리아에서 왔어.

20 W: 안녕, 테드. 토니에 대해 들었니? 그가 지금 병원에 있대.

M: 무슨 일이 있었니?

W: 자전거에서 떨어져서 다리가 부러졌어.

M: ① 별말씀을.

　② 오, 그거 너무 안됐다.

　③ 천만에요.

　④ 오랜만이야.

Word Check
본책 p. 16

01 bookshelf 책장

02 bottom 밑바닥

03 mind 마음, ~을 꺼리다

04 flight 비행

05 anymore 더 이상

06 maybe 아마

07 return 반납하다

08 soon 곧

09 practice 연습하다

10 anything 무언가

11 pleasure 즐거움

12 introduce 소개하다

13 healthy 건강한

14 exercise 운동하다

15 aquarium 수족관

Sentence Check
본책 p. 17

01 I think I saw it on the bookshelf.

02 There is a new Italian restaurant in town.

03 I want to be a police officer like my dad.

04 It took me 6 hours to get there.

05 You should ask for it for your birthday.

06 Have a safe trip.

07 I fell from a tree.

08 Go practice until your teacher gets here.

09 Thank you for helping me.

10 I'd like to introduce my friend Cathy to you.

11 Let's meet at 11:30 at the subway station.

12 You look healthy these days.

13 Your brother will be so happy.

14 What time shall we meet?

15 He fell off his bike and broke his leg.

2 회 영어 듣기 모의고사

1 ②	2 ②	3 ②	4 ④	5 ④	6 ④	7 ④	8 ②	9 ③	10 ④
11 ④	12 ②	13 ①	14 ③	15 ②	16 ②	17 ④	18 ①	19 ②	20 ②

듣기 대본

1 M: I'm looking for new clothes for my son.
W: How about this coat? This just came in.
M: How much is it?
W: It's 50 dollars.
M: Okay. I'll take it.

2 ① B: It smells so good in here. What are you doing?
G: I'm making some cookies for you.
② B: What a pretty scarf! It looks so nice on you.
G: Thank you, Kevin.
③ B: Can you be quiet, please?
G: Okay. I'm sorry.
④ B: Jane, what are you looking for?
G: I'm looking for my scarf.

3 W: They are long and thin sticks. They are made of wood, bamboo, or metal. We use these to pick up or eat food. These are used especially by Asians.

4 M: Are we still going to the shopping mall tomorrow?
W: Of course. Where and when should we meet?
M: The shopping mall opens at 10 a.m. Let's meet in front of the mall at 10:30.
W: That's too early. How about 12:30? Let's have pizza for lunch before shopping.
M: Great. See you then.

5 W: Chris! I'm thinking about cooking bulgogi tonight.
B: That sounds so delicious.
W: Can you do me a favor?
B: What is it?
W: Can you go to the market and get some onions?
B: Sure.

6 B: Amy, do you like science?
G: No, I don't. It's too hard.
B: What is your favorite subject?
G: I enjoy learning math. How about you?
B: I like English. I want to become an English teacher when I grow up.

해석

1 M: 아들을 위한 새 옷을 찾고 있어요.
W: 이 코트 어때요? 이것이 막 나왔어요.
M: 얼마예요?
W: 50달러예요.
M: 좋아요. 그걸로 살게요.

2 ① B: 여기 냄새가 무척 좋아. 뭐하고 있어?
G: 너를 위해서 쿠키를 좀 만들고 있어.
② B: 예쁜 스카프구나! 너한테 무척 잘 어울려.
G: 고마워, 케빈.
③ B: 조용히 해주시겠어요?
G: 알았어요. 미안해요.
④ B: 제인, 뭐 찾고 있어?
G: 나 내 스카프 찾고 있어.

3 W: 이것은 길고 얇은 막대기입니다. 이것은 나무, 대나무, 또는 금속으로 만들어집니다. 우리는 이것을 음식을 들거나 먹을 때 사용합니다. 이것은 특히 아시아 사람들이 사용합니다.

4 M: 우리 여전히 내일 쇼핑몰 가는 거지?
W: 물론. 어디서 언제 우리 만날까?
M: 쇼핑몰이 오전 10시에 열어.
몰 앞에서 10시 30분에 만나자.
W: 그거 너무 일러. 12시 30분은 어때?
쇼핑 전에 점심으로 피자 먹자.
M: 좋아. 그때 보자.

5 W: 크리스! 오늘 저녁에 불고기 요리를 할까 생각 중이야.
B: 너무 맛있을 거 같아요.
W: 나 부탁하나 들어줄 수 있니?
B: 뭔데요?
W: 시장에 가서 양파를 좀 사다줄래?
B: 물론이죠.

6 B: 에이미, 너 과학 좋아하니?
G: 아니, 그렇지 않아. 너무 어려워.
B: 네가 좋아하는 과목은 뭐야?
G: 나는 수학 배우는 게 좋아. 너는 어때?
B: 나는 영어가 좋아. 나는 커서 영어 선생님이 되고 싶어.

7
B: I lost my sister. Can you help me find her?
W: What does she look like?
B: She has long brown hair and she's <u>wearing glasses</u>.
W: Is she wearing a dress?
B: Yes, she's wearing a <u>red dress</u>.

7
B : 여동생을 잃어버렸어요. 찾는 거 도와주실 수 있나요?
W : 어떻게 생겼니?
B : 긴 갈색머리에 안경을 쓰고 있어요.
W : 원피스를 입고 있니?
B : 예, 빨간 원피스를 입고 있어요.

8
G: Jim, do you want to go to the <u>art museum</u> with me this Saturday?
B: I'm sorry, but I can't.
G: Do you have <u>any plans</u>?
B: Yes, I have an <u>appointment</u> with the <u>dentist</u> this Saturday.

8
G : 짐, 이번 주 토요일에 나랑 미술관 같이 갈래?
B : 미안한데 못 갈 거 같아.
G : 다른 계획 있어?
B : 응, 치과 예약이 이번 주 토요일에 있어.

9
B: Cindy, how do you go to school?
G: My school is near my house, so I <u>walk to school</u> every day.
B: What do you do after school?
G: I walk <u>my dog</u> on Monday and Thursday.
B: What after-school activities do you do?
G: I joined a <u>book club</u>.

9
B : 신디, 학교에 어떻게 가?
G : 학교에 집이랑 가까워서 매일 걸어서 가.
B : 방과 후에는 뭐해?
G : 난 월요일과 목요일에 개를 산책시켜.
B : 방과 후 활동으로 무엇을 하니?
G : 나는 독서 모임에 가입했어.

10 *[Cellphone rings.]*
G: Hello.
B: Hi, Susan. It's David.
G: Oh, hi, David. What's up?
B: I'm calling to ask you <u>a favor</u>.
G: What is it?
B: I have a <u>math quiz</u> tomorrow, but these math problems are <u>too difficult</u> for me. Can you help me?
G: Sure. Let's meet at the library.

10 *[휴대폰이 울린다.]*
G : 여보세요.
B : 안녕, 수잔. 나 데이비드야.
G : 오, 안녕, 데이비드. 무슨 일이야?
B : 너한테 부탁이 있어서 전화했어.
G : 뭔데?
G : 내일 수학 퀴즈가 있는데 이 수학 문제들이 나한테 너무 어려워서. 날 도와줄 수 있니?
B : 물론이지. 도서관에서 만나자.

11 ① W: Can I talk to you for a minute?
M: Sorry, I'm busy <u>right now</u>.
② W: Would you like something to drink?
M: No, thank you.
③ W: Can I use your computer for a minute?
M: Sure. Go ahead.
④ W: <u>When will</u> you come home?
M: Yes, I came back <u>last week</u>.

11 ① W : 잠시만 얘기할 수 있나요?
M : 미안한데, 지금 당장은 바빠요.
② W : 마실 것 좀 드릴까요?
M : 아니요, 감사해요.
③ W : 네 컴퓨터를 잠시 사용해도 되니?
M : 물론이지. 어서 써.
④ W : 넌 언제 집에 돌아올 거니?
M : 응, 나는 지난주에 돌아왔어.

12 ① M: Can I take your order?
W: Sure. I'd like the chicken curry, please.
② M: Excuse me. You <u>can't park</u> here.
W: Sorry, I didn't know that.
③ M: Where are you going?
W: I'm going to the bus stop.
④ M: How was your vacation?
W: It was <u>a lot of</u> fun.

12 ① M : 주문하시겠어요?
W : 예. 치킨 카레 주세요.
② M : 실례합니다. 여기에 주차할 수 없어요.
W : 죄송해요, 그걸 몰랐어요.
③ M : 어디 가고 있어?
W : 나 버스 정류장에 가고 있어.
④ M : 네 휴가가 어땠어?
W : 무척 재미있었어.

13 M: Excuse me, can I ask you something?

W: Sure. What is it?

M: Where is the bookstore?

W: Just go straight ahead for two blocks and turn left.

M: Go straight ahead for two blocks and turn left, and then?

W: It's on your right. It is next to the hospital.

13 M : 실례합니다, 무얼 여쭤 봐도 될까요?

W : 물론이죠. 뭔데요?

M : 서점이 어디에 있어요?

W : 그냥 앞으로 두 블록 곧장 가서 왼쪽으로 도세요.

M : 앞으로 두 블론 가서 왼쪽으로 돌고, 그 다음은요?

W : 오른쪽에 있어요. 병원 옆이에요.

---

14 W: Mike, did you see my sunglasses?

B: No, Mom. Where did you leave them?

W: I don't know, but maybe I put them on the sofa.

B: Nothing's there, Mom. Did you check the bookshelf?

W: Yes, I did.

B: Mom, I found your sunglasses. They are on the desk.

14 W : 마이크, 내 선글라스 봤니?

B : 아니요, 엄마. 어디에 두셨는데요?

W : 모르겠어, 하지만 아마 소파 위에 놓았을 거야.

B : 거기에는 아무것도 없어요, 엄마. 책꽂이는 확인해 보셨어요?

W : 응, 확인했어.

B : 엄마, 선글라스 찾았어요. 책상 위에 있어요.

---

15 M: Good morning, may I help you?

G: Yes, I want to buy a chocolate cake.

M: Sorry, we don't have any chocolate cake now. How about a cheesecake or a strawberry cake?

G: I'll take the cheesecake. How much is it?

M: The large one is 25 dollars, and the small one is 20 dollars.

G: I would like the large one, please.

15 M : 안녕하세요, 도와드릴까요?

G : 예, 초콜릿 케이크를 사고 싶어요.

M : 죄송해요, 지금 초콜릿 케이크가 하나도 없어요. 치즈케이크나 딸기 케이크는 어때요?

G : 치즈게이크로 살게요. 일마예요?

M : 큰 거는 25달려고, 작은 거는 20달러예요.

G : 큰 거로 주세요.

---

16 G: John, how was Christmas?

B: It was great. My parents gave me a baseball bat. What presents did you get?

G: I got some books about American history.

B: Really? I'm very interested in history. Can you lend them to me?

G: Sure.

16 G : 존, 크리스마스 어땠어?

B : 멋졌어. 부모님이 야구방망이를 주셨어. 너는 무슨 선물 받았어?

G : 나는 미국 역사에 관한 책을 몇 권 받았어.

B : 정말? 나 역사에 정말 관심 있는데. 그것들 나한테 빌려줄 수 있니?

G : 물론이지.

---

17 G: Hi, Minsu. What are you going to do after school?

B: I will play tennis with my friends.

G: Do you play any other sports?

B: I also play basketball.

G: How often do you play basketball?

B: ① I'm not good at basketball.

② I play basketball in the gym.

③ I play with my friends.

④ I play basketball once a week.

17 G : 안녕, 민수. 방과 후에 뭐할 거야?

B : 친구들이랑 테니스 칠 거야.

G : 너 다른 운동도 하니?

B : 나 농구도 해.

G : 얼마나 자주 농구를 하니?

B : ① 난 농구를 잘하지 못 해.

② 나는 체육관에서 농구를 해

③ 나는 친구들이랑 해.

④ 나는 일주일에 한 번 농구를 해.

18 G: Kevin, did you do the history homework?

B: Not yet. When is the deadline?

G: ① This Friday.

② It's on the desk.

③ I was busy yesterday.

④ History is my favorite subject.

19 M: Kelly, look at this beautiful painting!

W: Wow, it is very beautiful. Who drew it?

M: My cousin did. She wants to become an artist.

W: ① I think you will like her.

② I'm sure she will be a great artist.

③ Yes, I like drawing flowers.

④ I have art classes on Monday.

20 M: Amy, do you like watching baseball games?

W: Yes, why?

M: I have two tickets to tomorrow's game. Would you like to come with me?

W: ① Yes, I'd love to. Thank you,

② Yes, I like watching baseball on TV.

③ I'd like to, but I have another plan.

④ Sure. What time shall we meet?

18 G: 케빈, 역사 숙제했니?

B: 아니 아직. 마감일이 언제야?

G: ① 이번 주 금요일.

② 그것은 책상 위에 있어.

③ 나 어제 바빴어.

④ 역사는 내가 좋아하는 과목이야.

19 M: 켈리, 이 아름다운 그림을 봐!

W: 와우, 정말 아름다운 그림이야. 누가 그렸어?

M: 내 사촌이 그렸어. 그녀는 화가가 되고 싶어 해.

W: ① 네가 그녀를 좋아할 거 같아.

② 그녀는 훌륭한 화가가 될 거라고 확신해.

③ 응, 나는 꽃 그리는 것을 좋아해.

④ 나는 월요일에 미술 수업이 있어.

20 M: 에이미, 너 야구 경기 보는 거 좋아하니?

W: 응, 왜?

M: 내가 내일 경기 표가 두 장 있어. 같이 갈래?

W: ① 응, 그러고 싶어. 고마워,

② 응, 나는 TV로 야구 경기 보는 거 좋아해.

③ 그러고 싶은데 다른 계획이 있어.

④ 물론. 우리 몇 시에 만날까?

Word Check

본책 p. 28

01 stick 막대기

02 bamboo 대나무

03 metal 금속

04 especially 특별히

05 still 여전히

06 delicious 맛있는

07 appointment 약속

08 difficult 어려운

09 vacation 휴가

10 straight 곧장

11 sunglasses 선글라스

12 lend 빌려주다

13 deadline 마감일

14 yet 아직

15 history 역사

Sentence Check

본책 p. 29

01 This just came in.

02 It looks so nice on you.

03 They are made of wood bamboo, or metal.

04 Where and when should we meet?

05 That sounds so delicious.

06 I enjoy learning math.

07 I have an appointment with the dentist.

08 I walk to school every day.

09 I'm calling to ask you a favor.

10 Would you like something to drink?

11 I came back last week.

12 Just go straight ahead for two blocks and turn left.

13 I would like the large one, please.

14 I'm very interested in history.

15 She wants to become an artist.

1 ③	**2** ②	**3** ②	**4** ①	**5** ③	**6** ④	**7** ①	**8** ③	**9** ③	**10** ①
11 ④	**12** ①	**13** ④	**14** ②	**15** ②	**16** ④	**17** ②	**18** ①	**19** ④	**20** ②

듣기 대본   본책 p. 34

1
W: Hello. Can I help you?
M: Yes, I want a backpack for my daughter.
W: Okay. What about this one with the star on it?
M: It looks good, but it's not her favorite color. I want that <u>yellow</u> one with the <u>rose</u> on it. She likes flowers.
W: <u>Good</u> <u>choice</u>. Many girls like that backpack.

2
W: Damon, did you finish your homework?
B: Yes, I finished it last night.
W: When are you going to <u>clean</u> your room?
B: I'll do it <u>tomorrow</u>. I can't do it now.
W: Why?
B: I'm <u>going</u> <u>out</u> to play soccer now.

3
B: Am I <u>tall</u> <u>enough</u> to ride the roller coaster?
W: Let me check. Yes, you are!
B: Great!
W: But for <u>this</u> <u>ride</u>, you need an adult to ride with you.
B: Okay, my dad will ride the roller coaster with me.

4
B: Can you <u>ride</u> a <u>bike</u>?
G: No, I can't.
B: Do you want me to teach you?
G: I'm <u>scared</u> to ride a bike.
B: Don't be scared. I'll stand next to you.
G: Okay, I'll give it a <u>try</u>.

5
B: Amy, is your mom a chef?
G: No, she's a <u>nurse</u>. She works at a hospital in town.
B: What does your father do?
G: Are you asking for what my father's <u>job</u> is?
B: Yes.
G: He's a <u>firefighter</u>.

6
W: Are you planning to go to Australia during <u>this</u> <u>vacation</u>?
M: Yes, I'll visit my uncle and <u>travel</u> around Sydney.
W: I envy you.
M: How about you? Do you have any special plans?
W: I'm going to <u>go</u> <u>camping</u> for a week.

해석

1
W: 안녕하세요. 도와드릴까요?
M: 예, 딸을 위한 배낭을 찾고 있어요.
W: 알겠어요. 별 모양이 있는 이거 어때요?
M: 좋아 보이는데 딸이 좋아하는 색이 아니네요. 장미가 있는 저 노란 거 주세요. 꽃을 좋아해요.
W: 잘 선택하셨어요. 많은 소녀들이 그 배낭을 좋아해요.

2
W: 데이먼, 숙제 다했니?
B: 예, 어젯밤에 끝냈어요.
W: 네 방은 언제 청소할 거야?
B: 내일 할게요. 지금 할 수 없어요.
W: 왜?
B: 지금 축구하러 나갈 거예요.

3
B: 제가 롤러코스터 탈 수 있을 만큼 키가 큰 가요?
W: 확인해 볼게. 응, 그래!
B: 멋져요!
W: 하지만 이 탈것을 타려면 어른이 함께 타야 해.
B: 알겠어요. 아빠가 저랑 롤러코스터 함께 탈 거예요.

4
B: 너 자전거 탈 수 있니?
G: 아니, 못 타.
B: 내가 가르쳐줄까?
G: 난 자전거 타는 게 무서워.
B: 무서워하지 마. 내가 옆에 서 있을게.
G: 좋아, 한번 시도해 볼게.

5
B: 에이미, 네 엄마는 요리사니?
G: 아니, 간호사야. 시내에 있는 병원에서 일해서.
B: 아버지는 무슨 일을 하셔?
G: 아버지 직업을 묻는 거야?
B: 응.
G: 소방관이셔.

6
W: 이번 휴가에 호주에 갈 계획이니?
M: 응, 삼촌댁에 방문해서 시드니 주변을 여행할 거야.
W: 부럽다.
M: 너는 어때? 특별한 계획이 있니?
W: 일주일 동안 캠핑을 갈 거야.

7 ① M: May I help you?

　W: Yes, I'd like to send this package to London.

② M: What would you like to have?

　W: I'd like two donuts and an iced tea.

③ M: Could you please help me move this box?

　W: Sure.

④ M: Good afternoon. How may I help you?

　W: I need two tickets to Busan, please.

8 G: What do you want to be in the future?

B: I want to be a doctor. What about you?

G: When I was young, I wanted to be a pianist.
But now, I really want to be a chef like my dad.

B: Your dad's food is really good.

G: Thanks.

9 W: May I help you?

M: Yes, I'd like to order a tuna sandwich and a soda. How much is it?

W: The tuna sandwich is 4 dollars, and the soda is 2 dollars.

M: Here's 10 dollars.

W: Here's your change.

10 G: Mom, can I go to Jessica's house?

W: Sure, but what time would you be back?

G: I will be home for dinner.

W: Okay, do you want me to drive you there?

G: No, it's a perfect weather to walk.

W: Okay, give me a call when you get there.

11 G: Hello, everyone. My name is Jessica Brown.
I'm 12 years old. I'm from Germany. I live in
Incheon. My favorite food is fried chicken. I
like listening to music. I'm good at playing the
violin.

12 ① W: What is your favorite subject?

M: I like baseball.

② W: Is there a bank near here?

M: Yes, there is one at the corner.

③ W: How are you doing?

M: Pretty good.

④ W: Dinner is ready. Wash your hands first.

M: All right.

7 ① M: 도와드릴까요?

　W: 예, 이 소포를 런던으로 보내고 싶어요.

② M: 뭐 먹고 싶어요?

　W: 도넛 2개와 아이스티 주세요.

③ M: 이 상자 옮기는 거 도와줄 수 있나요?

　W: 물론이죠.

④ M: 안녕하세요. 어떻게 도와드릴까요?

　W: 부산행 티켓 두 장 주세요.

8 G: 너는 장래에 무엇이 되고 싶어?

B: 나는 의사가 되고 싶어. 너는 어때?

G: 어렸을 때는 파이니스트가 되고 싶었어.
그런데 지금은 아빠처럼 요리사가 정말 되고 싶어.

B: 네 아빠의 음식은 정말 맛있어.

G: 고마워.

9 W: 도와드릴까요?

M: 예, 참치 샌드위치하고 소다를 주문하려고요. 얼마예요?

W: 참치 샌드위치는 4달러고, 소다는 2달러예요.

M: 여기 10달러요.

W: 여기 잔돈 있어요.

10 G: 엄마, 저 제시카 집에 가도 돼요?

W: 물론, 근데 몇 시에 돌아올 거야?

G: 저녁 먹을 때 집에 올게요.

W: 좋아, 거기에 데려다주기를 원하니?

G: 아니요, 걷기에 완벽한 날씨예요.

W: 알았어, 도착하면 전화주렴.

11 G: 안녕, 얘들아. 내 이름은 제시카 브라운이야. 나는 12살
이야. 나는 독일에서 왔어. 나는 인천에 살고 있어. 내가
좋아하는 음식은 프라이드치킨이야. 나는 음악 듣는 것을
좋아해. 나는 바이올린 연주를 잘 해.

12 ① W: 네가 좋아하는 과목이 뭐야?

M: 나는 야구 좋아해.

② W: 여기 근처에 은행이 있니?

M: 응, 모퉁이에 하나 있어.

③ W: 잘 지내니?

M: 꽤 좋아.

④ W: 저녁 준비됐어. 손 먼저 씻어.

M: 알았어.

13 ① W: How much is it?

M: It's 10 dollars.

② W: Can I help you?

M: Oh, yes. I'm looking for a wallet.

③ W: How much money do you have?

M: I have 20 dollars.

④ W: Excuse me. Is this your wallet?

M: Oh, yes. Thank you.

14 M: How much are these pears?

W: Two dollars each.

M: Okay, I'll just take one.

W: Do you need anything else?

M: Can I get a box of grapes?

W: Sure, it's 10 dollars.

15 G: Eric, what are you going to do tomorrow?

B: I don't have any special plans.

G: How about going on a picnic with me?

B: I would love to.

G: Could you bring a picnic blanket and a basket?

B: Okay!

16 B: Wow, Susan. What a nice bag!

G: Thanks, my mom made it for me.

B: Really? I like that style. What does your mother do?

G: She works at a clothing company as a designer.

B: That sounds great!

17 [Cellphone rings.]

G: Hello?

B: Hi, Sara. This is Mike.

G: What's up, Mike?

B: I'm afraid I can't meet you tonight.

G: What's wrong?

B: My sister is sick. So I have to take care of her.

G: ① How about meeting at 7 o'clock?

② Oh, that's too bad. I hope she will feel better soon.

③ I want to play with your sister.

④ I don't have any plans tonight.

13 ① W : 얼마예요?

M : 10달러요.

② W : 도와드릴까요?

M : 오, 예. 지갑을 찾고 있어요.

③ W : 돈이 얼마나 있나요?

M : 20달러 있어요.

④ W : 실례합니다. 이게 당신 지갑인가요?

M : 오, 예. 감사해요.

14 M : 이 배는 얼마예요?

W : 하나에 2달러요.

M : 좋아요, 그냥 하나 주세요.

W : 다른 것도 필요한가요?

M : 포도 한 상자를 주실 수 있나요?

W : 물론이죠, 10달러예요.

15 G. 에릭, 내일 뭐할 거야?

B : 특별한 계획 없어.

G : 나랑 피크닉 가는 거 어때?

B : 그러고 싶어.

G : 피크닉 담요랑 바구니 가져올래?

B : 좋아!

16 B : 와우, 수잔. 멋진 가방이구나!

G : 고마워, 엄마가 나를 위해 만들었어.

B : 정말? 나 그 스타일 좋아. 엄마는 뭐하시는데?

G : 엄마는 의류회사에서 디자이너로 일하셔.

B : 멋지다!

17 [휴대폰이 울린다.]

G : 여보세요?

B : 안녕, 사라. 나 마이크야.

G : 무슨 일이야, 마이크?

B : 오늘 저녁에 너를 못 만날 것 같아 유감이야.

G : 무슨 일이야?

B : 여동생이 아파. 그래서 내가 돌봐야 해.

G : ① 7시에 만나는 거 어때?

② 오, 그거 안됐다. 곧 나아지기를 바라.

③ 나는 네 여동생과 놀고 싶어.

④ 나는 오늘 저녁에 어떤 계획도 없어.

18 B: Mom, what are we having for lunch?

W: I'm thinking of making gimbap.

B: I love gimbap.

W: What kind of gimbap do you want?

B: ① I like all kinds of gimbap.

② I'm eating gimbap now.

③ Gimbap is my favorite food.

④ I have gimbap once a week.

19 W: What are you doing?

M: I'm watching TV.

W: What program are you watching?

M: It's a documentary about sharks.

W: Wow, awesome. Can I watch it with you?

M: ① I'd like to, but I have to watch TV.

② Yes, I like watching TV.

③ Sure. What time shall we meet?

④ Of course. It's very interesting. You will like it.

20 M: What are you going to do after school?

W: Nothing special. Why?

M: Would you take care of my dog?

W: ① Sure, what's your dog's name?

② Everything will be okay.

③ Sorry, I'm allergic to dogs.

④ No problem.

18 B: 엄마, 점심으로 뭐 먹어요?

W: 김밥을 만들까 생각 중이야.

B: 나 김밥 좋아해요.

W: 어떤 종류의 김밥을 원해?

B: ① 저는 모든 종류의 김밥이 좋아요.

② 저는 지금 김밥을 먹고 있어요.

③ 김밥은 내가 좋아하는 음식이에요.

④ 나는 일주일에 한 번 김밥을 먹어요.

19 W: 뭐하고 있어?

M: TV 보고 있어.

W: 무슨 프로그램을 보고 있어?

M: 이것은 상어에 대한 다큐멘터리야.

W: 와우, 멋지다. 너랑 같이 볼 수 있니?

M: ① 그러고 싶은데 나 TV를 봐야 해.

② 응, 나 TV 보는 거 좋아해.

③ 물론. 우리 몇 시에 만날까?

④ 물론. 이거 아주 재미있어. 너도 좋아할 거야.

20 M: 너는 방과 후에 뭐할 거야?

W: 특별한 거 없어. 왜?

M: 내 개를 돌봐줄 수 있니?

W: ① 물론, 네 개 이름이 뭐야?

② 모든 것이 괜찮아질 거야.

③ 미안해, 나 개에 알러지가 있어.

④ 문제없어.

Word Check 본책 p. 40

01 daughter 딸

02 choice 선택

03 enough 충분한

04 scared 무서워하는

05 stand 서 있다

06 designer 디자이너

07 package 소포

08 change 잔돈

09 perfect 완벽한

10 pretty 꽤

11 wallet (남성용) 지갑

12 special 특별한

13 blanket 담요

14 documentary 다큐멘터리

15 awesome 멋진

Sentence Check 본책 p. 41

01 I'm going out to play soccer now.

02 You will need an adult to ride with you.

03 I'm scared to ride a bike.

04 I'll give it a try.

05 She works at a hospital in town.

06 Do you have any special plans?

07 I'd like to send this package to London.

08 I really want to be a chef like my dad.

09 Here's your change.

10 It's perfect weather to walk.

11 I'm good at playing the violin.

12 There is at the corner.

13 How about going on a picnic with me?

14 She works at a clothing company as a designer.

15 I'm afraid I can't meet you tonight.

1 ②	2 ③	3 ④	4 ②	5 ①	6 ④	7 ②	8 ②	9 ②	10 ②
11 ④	12 ④	13 ②	14 ②	15 ②	16 ②	17 ①	18 ③	19 ④	20 ②

듣기 대본 본책 p. 46

1 W: Can I help you?
M: Yes, I'm looking for a sweater.
W: How about this red one?
M: I don't like its color.
Can you show me the blue sweater?
W: Do you mean the one with the deer on it?
M: Yes, I'll take that. How much is it?

2 G: Hi, Jack. Can you come to the music festival?
B: When is the festival?
G: It's next Tuesday.
B: Next Tuesday? Do you mean October 10?
G: Yes, it is.
B: I'm not sure. I have a swimming lesson on that day.

3 B: Mom, can I go out and play basketball with Steve?
W: Yes, but did you finish your homework?
B: Yes, I did.
W: What about cleaning your room?
B: Oh, I forgot. Can I do it when I come back?
W: No, clean your room, and then you can go out.
B: Okay.

4 B: Susan, what did you do yesterday?
G: I went to the park.
B: What did you do there?
G: I took pictures of flowers.
B: Can you show me the pictures?
G: Sure.

5 W: Good afternoon, how may I help you?
M: I need two tickets to Boston.
W: Okay, we have tickets left for the 3 o'clock train and the 4 o'clock train.
M: I'd like the 4 o'clock train.
W: It will be 80 dollars.

해석

1 W: 도와드릴까요?
M: 예, 스웨터를 찾고 있어요.
W: 이 빨간 거는 어때요?
M: 그 색을 좋아하지 않아요.
파란색 스웨터 보여줄 수 있나요?
W: 사슴이 있는 이거 말하는 거예요?
M: 예, 그걸로 살게요. 얼마예요?

2 G: 안녕, 잭. 음악 축제에 올 수 있니?
B: 축제가 언제야?
G: 다음 주 화요일.
B: 다음 주 화요일? 10월 10일 말하는 거야?
G: 응, 그래.
B: 잘 모르겠어. 그날 수영 수업이 있어.

3 B: 엄마, 저 나가서 스티브랑 농구해도 되나요?
W: 응, 그런데 숙제는 다했니?
B: 예, 했어요.
W: 네 방 청소는 어때?
B: 오, 잊어버렸어요. 돌아와서 해도 되나요?
W: 아니, 네 방 청소하고 나갈 수 있어.
B: 알겠어요.

4 B: 수잔, 어제 뭐했어?
G: 나는 공원에 갔어.
B: 거기서 뭐했는데?
G: 꽃들 사진을 찍었어.
B: 사진 보여줄 수 있니?
G: 물론이지.

5 W: 안녕하세요. 어떻게 도와드릴까요?
M: 보스턴행 티켓 2장 주세요.
W: 알겠어요. 3시에 떠나는 기차와 4시에 떠나는 기차가 있어요.
M: 4시 기차로 주세요.
W: 80달러예요.

6 G: Did you see the new English teacher?

B: No, I didn't. Where is he from?

G: He's from England.

B: Did you meet him?

G: Yes, he can also speak Korean very well. He said he studied Korean in England.

B: Really? That's awesome.

6 G: 새로운 영어 선생님 봤니?

B: 아니. 어디에서 오셨니?

G: 영국에서 오셨어.

B: 너는 만났어?

G: 응, 한국말도 아주 잘하셔. 영국에서 한국어를 공부하셨다고 말했어.

B: 정말? 멋지다.

7 ① M: May I help you?

W: Yes. How much is this book?

② M: What can I do for you?

W: I would like to return this shirt.

③ M: Are you busy this afternoon?

W: No, I'm free.

④ M: Where did you get that shirt?

W: My dad bought it for me.

7 ① M: 도와드릴까요?

W: 예. 이 책 얼마에요?

② M: 무엇을 해드릴까요?

W: 이 셔츠를 환불하고 싶어요.

③ M: 오늘 오후에 바쁘니?

W: 아니, 한가해.

④ M: 그 셔츠 어디에서 났어?

W: 아빠가 사주셨어.

8 W: What do you want for lunch?

M: I want a cheese sandwich.

W: We don't have any cheese now.

M: Then, how about we eat creamy shrimp pasta?

W: Sounds good. We should add bacon, too.

M: Great. I will help you cook.

8 W: 점심으로 뭐 먹고 싶어?

M: 치즈 샌드위치 먹고 싶어.

W: 우리 지금 치즈가 없어.

M: 그러면, 새우 크림 파스타 만드는 거 어때?

W: 좋은 생각이야. 베이컨도 추가해야지.

M: 좋아. 내가 너 요리하는 거 도와줄게.

9 M: Can I help you?

W: Yes, I'm looking for a cake.

M: We have two kinds: cheesecake and chocolate cake.

W: They look delicious. How much are they?

M: The cheesecake is 20 dollars, and the chocolate cake is 25 dollars.

W: Okay. I'll take the cheesecake.

9 M: 도와드릴까요?

W: 예, 케이크를 찾고 있어요.

M: 우리는 치즈케이크와 초콜릿 케이크 두 종류가 있어요.

W: 맛있어 보이네요. 얼마예요?

M: 치즈케이크는 20달러고 초콜릿 케이크는 25달러예요.

W: 알겠어요. 치즈케이크로 살게요.

10 ① W: What kind of movie do you like?

M: I like action movies.

② W: How can I get to the bookstore?

M: It takes 30 minutes.

③ W: What do you have for breakfast?

M: I have some bread and milk.

④ W: How was your weekend, Tom?

M: It was pretty good.

10 ① W: 너는 무슨 종류의 영화를 좋아해?

M: 나는 액션영화를 좋아해.

② W: 서점에 어떻게 가니?

M: 30분 걸려.

③ W: 아침식사로 뭐 먹니?

M: 빵과 우유를 좀 먹어.

④ W: 주말 어땠어, 톰?

M: 꽤 좋았어.

11 M: What time is it now?

W: It's already 1:30.

M: We are late. Let's take the subway.

W: The subway station is far from here. Let's take a taxi.

M: Sounds great.

11 M: 지금 몇 시야?

W: 벌써 1시 30분이야.

M: 우리 늦었어. 지하철을 타자.

W: 하지만 지하철역까지는 여기서 너무 멀어. 택시를 타자.

M: 좋은 생각이야.

12 G: Do you have any hobbies, Mike?

B: Yes, I love listening to classical music.

G: How often do you listen to classical music?

B: I listen to it every day.

G: Wow, you really like listening to music.

13 [Cellphone rings.]

G: Hello?

B: Hi, Cathy! This is Tony. I think I left my notebook at your house.

G: Your notebook?

B: Yes, can you check the table by the bookshelf?

G: Is it the one with a cartoon character on it?

B: Yes, that's the one! Can you bring it to school tomorrow?

14 G: Jack, how about going to the zoo tomorrow?

B: Sounds good. Let's go there by bike.

G: I don't have a bike. Let's take the subway.

B: Okay. When and where shall we meet tomorrow?

G: Let's meet at 11 at the subway station.

B: Okay. See you tomorrow.

15 W: Jim, make sure you wear warm clothes today. It's going to snow all day today.

B: Did you see my gloves?

W: I saw them on your desk.

B: They're not there.

W: Then, why don't you look under the desk.

B: Here they are. Thank you, Mom.

16 G: What do you do when you are free?

B: I go fishing once a month.

G: Sounds interesting!

B: Do you have any hobbies?

G: I like drawing. I want to be an artist when I grow up.

17 B: What are you doing?

G: I am practicing for the speech contest.

B: When is the contest?

G: It's next Monday.

B: ① Good luck, I'm sure you will do fine.

② Wow, it's wonderful.

③ Really? That sounds interesting.

④ Thank you very much.

---

12 G : 너 무슨 취미 있니, 마이크?

B : 응, 나 고전음악 듣는 거 좋아해.

G : 얼마나 자주 고전음악을 들어?

B : 매일 들어.

G : 와우, 너 정말 음악 듣는 거 좋아하는구나.

13 [휴대폰이 울린다.]

G : 여보세요?

B : 안녕, 캐시! 나 토니야.
내가 네 집에 내 공책을 놓고 온 거 같아.

G : 네 공책?

B : 응, 책장 옆에 있는 탁자 확인해 줄 수 있니?

G : 그거 만화 캐릭터가 있는 거니?

B : 맞아, 그거야! 내일 학교에 가져올 수 있니?

14 G : 잭, 내일 동물원 가는 거 어때?

B : 좋아. 자전거 타고 가자.

G : 나 자전거 없어. 지하철 타고 가자.

B : 좋아. 언제 어디서 내일 만날까?

G : 11시에 지하철역 앞에서 만나자.

B : 좋아. 내일 보자.

15 W : 짐, 오늘 반드시 따뜻한 옷을 입어라.
오늘 하루 종일 눈이 올 거야.

B : 제 장갑 보셨어요?

W : 네 책상 위에서 봤어.

B : 거기 없어요.

W : 그럼, 책상 아래 살펴보는 게 어때?

B : 여기 있어요. 감사해요, 엄마.

16 G : 너는 한가할 때 뭐해?

B : 나는 한 달에 한 번 낚시를 해.

G : 재미있겠다!

B : 너는 취미가 있니?

G : 나는 그림 그리는 거를 즐겨. 나는 커서 화가가 되고 싶어.

17 B : 너 뭐하고 있어?

G : 말하기 대회 연습을 하고 있어.

B : 대회가 언제야?

G : 다음 주 월요일.

B : ① 행운을 빌어. 너 잘 할 게 확실해.

② 와우, 그거 멋지다.

③ 정말? 재미있을 거 같다.

④ 정말 감사합니다.

18 M: Happy birthday, Susie.

W: Thank you for coming, Jack. By the way, have you seen Tom today? I called him, but he didn't answer his phone.

M: No. I think he is in the hospital. Yesterday, he had a car accident.

W: ① Here you are.

② I'm sorry, but I can't.

③ I'm sorry to hear that.

④ Where is his house?

18 M: 생일 축하해, 수지.

W: 와줘서 고마워, 잭. 그런데 오늘 톰 봤니? 그에게 전화했는데 전화를 받지 않아.

M: 아니. 병원에 입원해 있을 거야. 어제 자동차 사고를 당했거든.

W: ① 여기 있어.

② 미안한데 할 수 없어.

③ 그거 들으니 안됐다.

④ 그의 집이 어디야?

19 B: What happened to your foot?

G: I went ice skating with my family, and I fell.

B: Oh no, did you break it?

G: Unfortunately, yes.

B: ① I don't like ice skating.

② I was in the hospital.

③ So, I stayed in bed.

④ I hope you get better soon.

19 B: 너 발은 무슨 일이야?

G: 가족이랑 빙상 스케이트 타러 갔다가 넘어졌어.

B: 오, 안 돼, 부러졌니?

G: 불행하게도, 그래.

B: ① 난 빙상 스케이트를 좋아하지 않아.

② 나 입원했어.

③ 그래서 침대에 누워 있어.

④ 네가 곧 낫기를 바라.

20 W: Hi, how can I help you?

M: I am looking for a bag.

W: How about this blue one? It's on sale.

M: ① Okay. I'll take it.

② It's not my bag.

③ How much is it?

④ It's not my style. Do you have another one?

20 W: 안녕하세요, 어떻게 도와드릴까요?

M: 가방을 찾고 있어요.

W: 이 파란색은 어때요? 세일 중이에요.

M: ① 좋아요. 그걸로 살게요.

② 그것은 내 가방이 아니에요.

③ 얼마예요?

④ 그건 내 스타일이 아니에요. 다른 거 있나요?

Word Check
본책 p. 52

01 sweater 스웨터

02 festival 축제

03 forget 잊다

04 return 환불하다

05 add 첨가하다

06 bacon 베이컨

07 already 이미, 벌써

08 cartoon 만화

09 character 캐릭터

10 call 전화하다

11 unfortunately 불행하게도

12 wonderful 멋진

13 car accident 자동차 사고

14 classical music 고전음악

15 speech contest 말하기 대회

Sentence Check
본책 p. 53

01 Can you show me the blue sweater?

02 I have a swimming lesson on that day.

03 Clean your room, and then you can go out.

04 I took pictures of flowers.

05 He can also speak Korean very well.

06 I would like to return this shirt.

07 How can I get to the bookstore?

08 The subway station is far from here.

09 Do you have any hobbies?

10 I think I left my notebook at your house.

11 Let's take the subway.

12 It's going to snow all day today.

13 I want to be an artist when I grow up.

14 I am practicing for the speech contest.

15 Yesterday, he had a car accident.

1 ②	2 ③	3 ①	4 ②	5 ②	6 ④	7 ④	8 ②	9 ③	10 ①
11 ②	12 ④	13 ②	14 ④	15 ④	16 ②	17 ①	18 ③	19 ④	20 ④

듣기 대본
본책 p. 58

해석

1
B: Mom, what are we having for lunch?
W: How about bibimbap?
B: We had bibimbap yesterday.
W: Then, how about we order pizza?
B: Sounds great, Mom! Let me order pizza online.

1
B: 엄마, 우리 점심으로 뭐 먹어요?
W: 비빔밥은 어떠니?
B: 우리 어제도 비빔밥 먹었어요.
W: 그러면, 피자 주문할까?
B: 좋아요, 엄마! 제가 온라인으로 주문할게요.

2
W: Can you tell me how I can get to the post office?
M: You have to go straight and turn left when you see the church. It's across from the hospital.
W: Is it far from here?
M: It will take about ten minutes.
W: Okay, thank you

2
W: 우체국에 어떻게 가는지 알려주실 수 있나요?
M: 곧장 가서 교회가 보이면 왼쪽으로 도세요. 병원 맞은편에 있어요.
W: 여기서 멀어요?
M: 10분 정도 걸릴 거예요.
W: 알겠어요. 감사합니다.

3
G: My sister wrote this poem.
B: Wow. She writes poems very well.
G: Yes. She loves writing. When she is free, she always writes poems.
B: I think she will become a great writer.
G: It is her dream to become a writer.

3
G: 내 언니가 이 시를 썼어.
B: 와우. 네 언니는 시를 무척 잘 쓰네.
G: 응. 시 쓰는 것을 좋아해. 한가할 때면 항상 시를 써.
B: 내 생각에 훌륭한 작가가 될 거 같아.
G: 작가가 되는 게 그녀의 꿈이야.

4
B: Mom, I am hungry.
Can I have something to eat?
W: Sure, I baked some cookies.
Do you want some?
B: No, I want chocolate cake.
W: You ate that last night. How about some sweet potatoes?
B: Okay, Mom. I will have some.

4
B: 엄마, 나 배고파요.
먹을 게 좀 있어요?
W: 물론, 쿠키를 좀 구웠어.
좀 줄까?
B: 아뇨, 초콜릿 케이크를 먹고 싶어요.
W: 지난밤에도 먹었잖아. 고구마는 어때?
B: 알겠어요, 엄마. 좀 먹을게요.

5
G: Paul, do you know that my birthday is coming up soon?
B: When is it?
G: It's next Tuesday.
B: September 10?
G: Yes, my birthday is September 10.
Can you come to my birthday party?
B: Of course.

5
G: 폴, 내 생일이 곧 다가오는 거 아니?
B: 언제야?
G: 다음 주 화요일.
B: 9월 10일?
G: 응, 내 생일이 9월 10일이야.
내 생일 파티에 올 수 있니?
B: 물론이지.

6 ① W: How often do you take a shower?

M: I take a shower every day.

② W: What do you want for dinner?

M: What about noodles?

③ W: How are you doing today?

M: Not bad.

④ W: Can you help me wash the dishes?

M: Sure. No problem.

6 ① W: 너는 얼마나 자주 샤워해?

M: 난 매일 샤워해.

② W: 저녁에 뭐 먹을래?

M: 국수는 어때?

③ W: 오늘 어땠어?

M: 나쁘지 않았어.

④ W: 나 설거지하는 거 도와줄 수 있니?

M: 물론이지. 문제없어.

7 W: Sam, did you see my swimming goggles?

B: No, Mom. Where did you leave them?

W: I thought I put them in the drawer.

B: Nothing's there, Mom. Did you check the table?

W: Yes, I did.

B: Oh, I found them, Mom. They are on your bed.

7 W: 샘, 내 물안경 봤니?

B: 아뇨, 엄마. 어디에 두셨는데요?

W: 서랍 안에 둔 거 같아.

B: 거기에 아무것도 없어요, 엄마. 탁자 보셨어요?

W: 응, 봤어.

B: 오, 찾았어요, 엄마. 침대 위에 있어요.

8 B: Can you believe today is the last day of March?

G: Time goes by fast, doesn't it? But I like the month of April.

B: Why?

G: My birthday is in April.

B: Oh, that's why you like April.

G: Yes, I will have a birthday party. Can you come?

B: Sure.

8 B: 오늘이 3월의 마지막 날인 걸 믿을 수 있니?

G: 시간이 빨리 간다, 그렇지 않니? 하지만 나는 4월을 좋아해.

B: 왜?

G: 내 생일이 4월이거든.

B: 오, 그게 네가 4월을 좋아하는 이유구나.

G: 응. 생일 파티를 할 거야. 올 수 있니?

B: 물론이지.

9 G: Tim, is your friend Mike in this picture?

B: Yes, he is in the picture.

G: Is he wearing blue jeans?

B: No, he's wearing shorts.

G: Is he reading a book?

B: No, he's holding a ball in his hand.

9 G: 팀, 네 친구 마이크가 이 사진에 있니?

B: 응, 사진에 있어.

G: 청바지를 입고 있니?

B: 아니, 반바지를 입고 있어.

G: 책을 읽고 있니?

B: 아니, 손에 공을 들고 있어.

10 B: Did you buy a Christmas present for your younger sister?

G: No, not yet, but I will buy a backpack for her.

B: That's good. I don't know what to get for my brother.

G: How about a toy robot?

B: He has many toy robots.

G: Then, how about a toy train?

B: That's a good idea. He doesn't have a toy train.

10 B: 네 여동생에게 줄 크리스마스 선물 샀니?

G: 아니, 아직. 하지만 배낭을 살 거야.

B: 좋네. 난 남동생한테 뭘 사줄지 아직 모르겠어.

G: 장난감 로봇은 어때?

B: 장난감 로봇이 많아.

G: 그러면, 장난감 기차는 어때?

B: 좋은 생각이야. 장난감 기차는 없어.

11 B: How was your weekend?

G: It was great.

B: Did you go to the movies?

G: No, I didn't.

B: What did you do?

G: I went to a K-pop concert with my cousins.

B: Really? Sounds interesting.

G: Yeah, the concert was perfect.

11 B: 주말 어땠어?

G: 좋았어.

B: 영화 보러 갔니?

G: 아니.

B: 뭐했어?

G: 사촌들이랑 K팝 콘서트에 갔어.

B: 정말? 재미있었겠다.

G: 응, 콘서트는 완벽했어.

12 ① W: Hi, John. How's it going?

M: Pretty good.

② W: What time does your school begin?

M: It's next to the hospital.

③ M: Hi. My name is Scott Brown.

W: I'm Jane Smith. Nice to meet you.

④ W: What would you like to have?

M: I'll have French fries and a Coke.

13 M:① The woman is cooking in the kitchen.

② The woman is ordering food at a restaurant.

③ The woman is eating food at a restaurant.

④ The woman is wearing a baseball cap.

14 W: How may I help you?

B: I want to buy these donuts.

W: How many donuts do you want?

B: Four please.

W: Okay, that will be 6 dollars.

B: Here you are.

15 [Cellphone rings.]

W: Hello.

M: Hello, Alice. Where are you?

W: I'm at home. I'm making a cake for the party.

M: Alice, I will be late for the party.

W: Why?

M: It's raining, and the traffic is very heavy.

W: Oh, I see.

16 B: I have an older sister. Her name is Nancy. She is five years older than me. She is very tall and has short curly hair. She loves to play the violin. When she grows up, she wants to become a teacher.

17 W: How may I help you?

B: I want to buy some flowers for my mom's birthday.

W: Okay, which ones would you like?

B: Can I get these roses and tulips?

W: Sure. Anything else?

B: ① No, that's all. Thank you.

② No, I like tulips.

③ How many roses do you want?

④ Sorry, we don't have tulips.

12 ① W: 안녕, 존. 어떻게 지내?

M: 꽤 좋아.

② W: 네 학교는 몇 시에 시작해?

M: 병원 옆에 있어.

③ M: 안녕하세요. 제 이름은 스콧 브라운이에요.

W: 저는 제인 스미스예요. 만나서 반가워요.

④ W: 무엇으로 하실래요?

M: 감자튀김과 콜라 주세요.

13 M: ① 여자가 부엌에서 요리하고 있다.

② 여자가 식당에서 음식을 주문하고 있다.

③ 여자가 식당에서 음식을 먹고 있다.

④ 여자가 야구모자를 쓰고 있다.

14 W: 어떻게 도와드릴까요?

B: 이 도넛을 사고 싶어요.

W: 도넛을 몇 개 드릴까요?

B: 네 개요.

W: 좋아요, 6달러예요.

B: 여기 있어요.

15 [휴대폰이 울린다.]

W: 여보세요.

M: 안녕, 앨리스. 어디야?

W: 나는 집이야. 파티를 위해서 케이크를 만들고 있어.

M: 앨리스, 나 파티에 늦을 거 같아.

W: 왜?

M: 비가 내리고 있고 교통이 무척 정체돼.

W: 오, 알았어.

16 B: 나는 누나가 있다. 그녀의 이름은 낸시다. 그녀는 나보다 다섯 살 더 많다. 그녀는 매우 키가 크고 짧은 곱슬머리다. 그녀는 바이올린 연주를 좋아한다. 그녀는 커서 선생님이 되고 싶어한다.

17 W: 어떻게 도와드릴까요?

B: 엄마 생신에 꽃을 사고 싶어요.

W: 좋아요, 어떤 것이 좋아요?

B: 이 장미랑 튤립을 주시겠어요?

W: 예. 다른 것은요?

B: ① 아니요, 됐어요. 감사해요.

② 아니요, 저는 튤립을 좋아해요.

③ 얼마나 많은 장미를 원해요?

④ 죄송해요, 우리는 튤립이 없어요.

18 W: Charlie, did you finish your homework?

B: Yes, I did.

W: Then, can you do me a favor?

B: ① Here you are.

② I'm free today.

③ Sure. What is it?

④ It's my pleasure.

19 M: Where are you going, Julie?

W: I'm going to the convenience store.

M: Why are you going there?

W: I will buy some water and ice cream. Do you want me to buy you some chocolate?

M: ① I think it will be lots of fun.

② Where is the store?

③ What kind of chocolate do you like?

④ No, thank you. I'm on a diet.

20 M: May I help you?

G: There is something wrong with my computer.

M: Okay. Let me take a look at it.

G: Did you find any problems?

M: ① How much is it?

② I think it's expensive.

③ Let's find it together.

④ I think your computer has a virus.

18 W: 찰리, 숙제는 다 했니?

B: 예, 다 했어요.

W: 그럼, 부탁 하나 들어줄래?

B: ① 여기 있어요.

② 오늘 한가해요.

③ 물론이죠. 뭐예요?

④ 제가 즐겁죠.

19 M: 어디 가니, 줄리?

W: 편의점에 가고 있어.

M: 거기는 왜 가?

W: 물이랑 아이스크림을 좀 사려고. 초콜릿을 좀 사다줄까?

M: ① 내 생각에 무척 재미있을 거야.

② 가게가 어디에 있어?

③ 무슨 종류의 초콜릿을 좋아하니?

④ 아니, 고마워. 나 다이어트 중이야.

20 M: 도와드릴까요?

G: 제 컴퓨터가 잘못됐어요.

M: 알겠어요. 확인해 볼게요.

G: 문제가 있나요?

M: ① 얼마예요?

② 비쌀 것 같아요.

③ 함께 찾아봐요.

④ 컴퓨터가 바이러스에 걸린 거 같아요.

Word Check 본책 p. 64

01 online 온라인으로

02 poem 시

03 dream 꿈

04 something 무언가

05 drawer 서랍

06 believe 믿다

07 hold 들다, 잡다

08 concert 콘서트

09 donut 도넛

10 traffic 교통

11 heavy 많은, 심한

12 favor 부탁, 요청

13 wrong 잘못된

14 sweet potato 고구마

15 convenience store 편의점

Sentence Check 본책 p. 65

01 Sounds great.

02 It will take about ten minutes.

03 It is her dream to become a writer.

04 Can I have something to eat?

05 My birthday is coming up soon.

06 I take a shower every day.

07 I thought I put them in the drawer.

08 Time goes by fast, doesn't it?

09 He is holding a ball in his hand.

10 The woman is ordering food at a restaurant.

11 It's raining, and the traffic is very heavy.

12 She is very tall and has short curly hair.

13 Can you do me a favor?

14 I'm going to the convenience store.

15 There is something wrong with my computer.

6회 영어 듣기 모의고사

| 1 ② | 2 ③ | 3 ② | 4 ② | 5 ④ | 6 ④ | 7 ③ | 8 ④ | 9 ③ | 10 ② |
| 11 ③ | 12 ④ | 13 ① | 14 ④ | 15 ③ | 16 ② | 17 ④ | 18 ③ | 19 ② | 20 ① |

듣기 대본
본책 p. 70

1 M: Lisa, which one is your sister?
W: There she is. She's wearing a dress and glasses.
M: Does she have long hair?
W: Yes, she has long curly hair.

2 [Cellphone rings.]
W: Hello?
M: Jane, it's me Kevin.
W: Oh, Hi Kevin! What's up?
M: It's Mike's birthday tomorrow. Can you come to his birthday party with me?
W: Sure. Where is the party?
M: He's going to have a party at his home at 1 o'clock.
W: Okay, let's meet at the bus stop at noon.

3 G: Check this out.
B: Awesome! Did you get a new bike?
G: Yes, it was a birthday present from my aunt.
B: I love the color.
G: Me too. Let's go for a ride.
B: Okay, let's go!

4 W: Hello. Can I speak to Mr. Wilson, please?
M: Sorry. He's not in. Can I take a message?
W: Yes, my name is Cindy.
Please ask him to call me.
M: Okay. What's your phone number?
W: It's 012-733-4528.
M: Excuse me? Can you repeat that, please?
W: 012-733-4528.

5 G: Jack, what did you do yesterday?
B: I went to the beach with my friends.
G: Oh, did you? What did you do there?
B: I swam in the sea.
G: It must have been fun.
Can I join you next time?
B: Sure. I will call you later.

해석

1 M: 리사, 누가 네 여동생이야?
W: 저기 있어. 원피스를 입고 안경을 썼어.
M: 긴 머리니?
W: 응, 긴 곱슬머리야.

2 [휴대폰이 울린다.]
W: 여보세요?
M: 제인, 나 케빈이야.
W: 오, 안녕, 케빈. 무슨 일이야?
M: 내일 마이크 생일이잖아. 나랑 같이 생일 파티 갈래?
W: 물론. 파티 어디서 해?
M: 그의 집에서 1시에 할 거야.
W: 좋아, 버스정류장에서 정오에 만나자.

3 G: 이것 봐.
B: 멋지다! 새 자전거 받았어?
G: 응, 고모가 주신 생일 선물이야.
B: 색깔 마음에 들어.
G: 나도. 자전거 타러 가자.
B: 좋아, 가자!

4 W: 여보세요. 윌슨 씨랑 통화할 수 있나요?
M: 죄송해요. 그는 여기 없어요. 메시지 남기시겠어요?
W: 예, 제 이름은 신디에요.
나에게 전화해 달라고 전해주세요.
M: 알겠어요. 전화번호가 어떻게 되죠?
W: 012-733-4528이에요.
M: 뭐라고요? 다시 말해 주시겠어요?
W: 012-733-4528이에요.

5 G: 잭, 어제 뭐했어?
B: 친구들이랑 해변에 갔어.
G: 오, 그랬어? 거기서 뭐했는데?
B: 바다에서 수영했어.
G: 재미있었겠다.
다음번에 나도 함께 갈 수 있니?
B: 물론. 나중에 내가 전화할게.

6 ① W: What are you doing?

M: I'm talking on the phone.

② W: Do you have a cellphone?

M: No, I don't.

③ W: What do you want for your birthday?

M: I want a cellphone.

④ W: What's wrong with your cellphone?

M: I dropped it, and the screen cracked.

6 ① W: 뭐하고 있어?

M: 통화하고 있어.

② W: 너는 휴대전화 있니?

M: 아니, 없어.

③ W: 생일에 뭐 받고 싶어?

M: 나는 휴대전화를 원해.

④ W: 휴대전화에 무슨 일이야?

M: 떨어뜨려서 화면이 금이 갔어.

7 G: Hello, everyone. I'll introduce myself to you. My name is Cindy. I'm from Canada. I live in Seoul. We moved to Seoul three years ago. I like to listen to K-pop and watch K-dramas. I want to be a singer when I grow. I hope my dream will come true.

7 G: 안녕, 얘들아. 너희에게 내 소개를 할게. 내 이름은 신디야. 나는 캐나다에서 왔어. 나는 서울에 살고 있어. 나는 3년 전에 서울로 이사 왔어. 나는 K팝 듣는 거랑 K드라마 보는 거를 좋아해. 나는 커서 가수가 되고 싶어. 나는 내 꿈이 이루어지길 바라.

8 B: Amy, look at those flowers! They are so beautiful.

G: Do you like flowers?

B: Yes, I do. I like tulips most. How about you?

G: The rose is my favorite flower.

B: Why do you like it?

G: I love its red color.

8 B: 에이미, 저 꽃들 좀 봐! 너무 아름다워.

G: 너 꽃 좋아하니?

B: 응, 그래. 나는 튤립을 가장 좋아해. 너는 어때?

G: 장미가 내가 좋아하는 꽃이야.

B: 왜 그것을 좋아해?

G: 나는 빨간색이 너무 좋아.

9 W: Good morning, Here's the weather for today. It will be cloudy in Seoul and Suwon. In Incheon, it will be rainy, but it will be sunny in Busan.

9 W: 안녕하세요. 오늘의 날씨입니다. 서울과 수원은 흐리겠습니다. 인천은 비가 오겠지만, 부산은 맑겠습니다.

10 M: Can I make a campfire here?

W: ① Sure, no problem.

② Sorry, you can't.

③ No, you can't smoke here.

④ Of course, you can.

10 M: 여기에 캠프파이어해도 되나요?

W: ① 물론이죠, 문제없어요.

② 죄송한데, 할 수 없어요.

③ 아니요, 여기서 담배 피우면 안 돼요.

④ 물론, 할 수 있어요.

11 B: Hi, Susan, where are you going?

G: I'm going to the park. Will you come with me?

B: Sure. But can we go to the library first? I have to return these books.

G: Okay. Let's go there first.

11 B: 안녕, 수잔, 어디 가고 있어?

G: 공원에 가고 있어. 나랑 같이 갈래?

B: 물론. 그런데 우리 도서관 먼저 갈 수 있니? 나 이 책들을 반납해야 해.

G: 좋아. 거기 먼저 가자.

12 ① B: How was the musical?

G: It was great.

② B: Can I borrow a pencil?

G: I'm sorry. I don't have an extra pencil.

③ B: What are you going to do today?

G: I'm eating dinner now.

④ B: What's your favorite subject?

G: I like history.

12 ① B: 뮤지컬 어땠어?

G: 멋졌어.

② B: 연필 빌릴 수 있니?

G: 미안해. 여분의 연필이 없어.

③ B: 너 오늘 뭐할 거야?

G: 나는 지금 저녁을 먹고 있어.

④ B: 네가 좋아하는 과목이 뭐야?

G: 난 역사를 좋아해.

13 G: Do you want to come to my house and play computer games?

B: Today?

G: Yes.

B: I'd like to, but I can't today.

G: Why not?

B: I have an English test tomorrow, and I have to study for it. How about tomorrow after school?

G: Okay, tomorrow is fine with me.

13 G: 우리 집에 와서 컴퓨터 게임을 할래?

B: 오늘?

G: 응.

B: 그러고 싶은데, 오늘은 안 돼.

G: 왜?

B: 내일 영어 시험이 있어서 오늘 공부해야 해. 내일 방과 후에 어때?

G: 좋아, 난 내일 괜찮아.

---

14 W: Excuse me. How much are these carrots?

M: It's 5 dollars for a bag.

W: Can I get three bags of carrots?

M: Okay. That will be 15 dollars. Do you need anything else?

W: No, it's okay. I came to the market just for carrots.

14 W: 실례합니다. 이 당근들은 얼마예요?

M: 한 봉지에 5달러예요.

W: 당근 세 봉지 주시겠어요?

M: 좋아요. 15달러예요. 다른 거 더 필요하세요?

W: 아니요, 됐어요. 시장에 당근만 사러 왔어요.

---

15 B: Wow, great! Where did you draw these pictures?

G: I drew them at the park last week.

B: I think you're really good at drawing.

G: Thank you.

B: Do you want to become an artist?

G: Yes, I do.

B: I think you will be a great artist.

15 B: 와우, 멋지다! 이 그림들 어디에서 그렸어?

G: 지난주에 공원에서 그렸어.

B: 너 정말 그림을 잘 그린다고 생각해.

G: 고마워.

B: 니는 화가가 되고 싶니?

G: 응, 그래.

B: 너는 훌륭한 화가가 될 거라고 생각해.

---

16 M: Cathy, how about going to the museum tomorrow?

W: Great! What time shall we meet?

M: Let's meet at 2:30. Do you want to meet me at the bus stop?

W: Sure. Let's meet at the bus stop at 2:30.

M: Okay. See you tomorrow.

16 M: 캐시, 내일 박물관 가는 거 어때?

W: 좋아! 몇 시에 만날까?

M: 2시 30분에 만나자. 버스정류장에서 만나고 싶어?

W: 물론. 2시 30분에 버스정류장에서 만나자.

M: 좋아. 내일 보자.

---

17 G: Jim, what did you eat for lunch today?

B: I had a slice of pizza.

G: That's it?

B: Yes. I wasn't that hungry. What did you eat, Kelly?

G: I had pasta with my mom.

B: Sounds yummy. What kind of pasta did you have?

G: ① I like Italian food.

② I don't like pasta.

③ I like potato pizza.

④ We had tomato shrimp pasta.

17 G: 짐, 오늘 점심으로 뭐 먹었어?

B: 피자 한 조각 먹었어.

G: 그게 다야?

B: 응. 그렇게 배고프지 않았어. 너는 뭐 먹었어, 켈리?

G: 나는 엄마랑 파스타 먹었어.

B: 맛있었겠다. 무슨 종류의 파스타 먹었어?

G: ① 나는 이탈리아 음식을 좋아해.

② 나는 파스타를 좋아하지 않아.

③ 나는 포테이토 피자 좋아해.

④ 우리 토마토 새우 파스타 먹었어.

18 W: May I help you?

　　M: Yes, I'm looking for a T-shirt.

　　W: What color would you like?

　　M: ① I want a large size.

　　　② No thanks. I'm full.

　　　③ I want a blue one.

　　　④ It's 20 dollars.

18 W: 도와드릴까요?

　　M: 예, 티셔츠를 찾고 있어요.

　　W: 무슨 색을 좋아하세요?

　　M: ① 저는 큰 사이즈를 원해요.

　　　② 아니, 감사해요. 배불러요.

　　　③ 파란 티셔츠를 원해요.

　　　④ 20달러예요.

19 M: May I help you?

　　W: Yes, please. I'm looking for a skirt.

　　M: What color do you want?

　　W: I want a red one.

　　M: How about this one?

　　W: ① Size six.

　　　② Good. May I try it on?

　　　③ Yes, that's all.

　　　④ How was it?

19 M: 도와드릴까요?

　　W: 예. 치마를 찾고 있어요.

　　M: 무슨 색을 원하세요?

　　W: 빨간 치마를 원해요.

　　M: 이거 어때요?

　　W: ① 사이즈 6이요.

　　　② 좋아요. 입어봐도 되나요?

　　　③ 예, 그게 다예요.

　　　④ 그거 어땠어요?

20 W: Excuse me.

　　M: Yes? How may I help you?

　　W: You dropped your wallet.

　　M: Oh, thank you very much.

　　W: ① It's not mine.

　　　② No problem. You should be careful.

　　　③ You're welcome,

　　　④ It's my pleasure.

20 W: 실례합니다.

　　M: 예? 무슨 일이죠?

　　W: 지갑을 떨어뜨렸어요.

　　M: 오, 정말 감사합니다.

　　W: ① 그것은 제 것이 아니에요.

　　　② 별말씀을요. 조심하세요.

　　　③ 천만에요,

　　　④ 도움 되서 기뻐요.

Word Check
본책 p. 76

01 noon 정오

02 awesome 멋진

03 repeat 반복하다

04 slice (음식을 얇게 썬) 조각

05 drop 떨어뜨리다

06 screen 화면

07 crack 금이 가다

08 dream 꿈

09 campfire 캠프파이어

10 musical 뮤지컬

11 extra 여분의

12 artist 예술가, 화가

13 wallet (남성용) 지갑

14 curly hair 곱슬머리

15 phone number 전화번호

Sentence Check
본책 p. 77

01 Which one is your sister?

02 Let's meet at the bus stop at noon.

03 Let's go for a ride.

04 Please ask him to call me.

05 Can I take a message?

06 I dropped it and the screen cracked.

07 I'll introduce myself to you.

08 Here's the weather for today.

09 I have to return these books.

10 I'd like to, but I can't today.

11 Tomorrow is fine with me.

12 I came to the market just for carrots.

13 I think you will be a great artist.

14 What kind of pasta did you have?

15 You dropped your wallet.

7 영어 듣기 모의고사

1 ③	2 ②	3 ③	4 ④	5 ①	6 ③	7 ④	8 ③	9 ③	10 ④
11 ④	12 ④	13 ④	14 ③	15 ③	16 ③	17 ④	18 ②	19 ①	20 ③

듣기 대본
본책 p. 82

해석

1 W: ① A man is taking a shower.
   ② A man is using a computer.
   ③ A man is talking on the phone.
   ④ A man is taking a picture with his cellphone.

1 W: ① 한 남자가 샤워를 하고 있다.
   ② 한 남자가 컴퓨터를 사용하고 있다.
   ③ 한 남자가 통화를 하고 있다.
   ④ 한 남자가 휴대전화로 사진을 찍고 있다.

2 W: Jim! You're always late.
   Why don't you get up early?
   B: I'm really sorry. I'll try.
   W: Good! You have to be in class by 8:30. Don't be late tomorrow.

2 W: 짐! 너는 항상 늦는구나.
   일찍 일어나는 게 어떠니?
   B: 정말 죄송해요. 노력할게요.
   W: 좋아! 8시 30분까지는 교실에 와야 해.
   내일은 늦지 마라.

3 G: Jack, which one is your bicycle?
   B: Do you see the bicycle over there?
   G: Oh, the green one?
   B: No, the blue one.
   G: There are two blue bicycles.
   B: My bicycle has a basket in the front.

3 G: 잭, 어느 것이 네 자전거야?
   B: 저쪽에 자전거 보여?
   G: 오, 초록색 자전거?
   B: 아니, 파란색 자전거.
   G: 파란 자전거가 두 개 있어.
   B: 내 자전거는 앞에 바구니가 있어.

4 B: Mom, I'm home.
   W: David, you look happy.
   Did you have fun at school?
   B: I had a math test.
   W: So how did it go?
   B: I got 100 percent.
   W: Good for you.

4 B: 엄마, 저 왔어요.
   W: 데이비드, 행복해 보이네. 학교에서 즐거웠니?
   B: 수학 시험을 봤어요.
   W: 그래서 어땠어?
   B: 100점 맞았어요.
   W: 잘했구나.

5 G: Jack, where are you going?
   B: I'm going to my piano lesson.
   I have a piano competition this Saturday.
   G: Oh, I see. Are you nervous?
   B: Yes, I am. Can you come to the competition?
   G: Sorry, I can't. I have to visit my grandmother.
   She's in the hospital now.

5 G: 잭, 어디 가고 있어?
   B: 피아노 수업 가고 있어.
   이번 토요일에 피아노 대회가 있어.
   G: 오, 알겠어. 긴장되니?
   B: 응, 그래. 대회에 올 수 있니?
   G: 미안해, 갈 수 없어. 나 할머니를 방문해야 해.
   지금 입원해 계셔.

6 ① G: What time do you get up?
   B: I get up at 7.
   ② G: Where are you going?
   B: I'm going to the dentist.
   ③ G: I have a cold.
   B: That's too bad. Go and see a doctor.
   ④ G: I'm hungry.
   B: Dinner will be ready soon.

6 ① G: 몇 시에 일어나니?
   B: 7시에 일어나.
   ② G: 어디 가고 있니?
   B: 치과에 가고 있어.
   ③ G: 나 감기 걸렸어.
   B: 안됐다. 병원에 가.
   ④ G: 나 배고파.
   B: 저녁이 곧 준비될 거야.

7 W: Tony, can you come here?

B: Mom, I'm playing a computer game.

W: Come here right now.

B: What's wrong?

W: I told you to wash the dishes, and you still didn't.

B: I'm sorry. Can I do it after the game?

W: No. Do it right now.

7 W: 토니, 여기 와줄래?

B: 엄마, 나 컴퓨터 게임하고 있어요.

W: 지금 당장 여기 와.

B: 무슨 일이에요?

W: 내가 설거지하라고 했는데 여전히 안 했어.

B: 죄송해요. 게임하고 나서 해도 되나요?

W: 안 돼. 지금 당장 해.

8 G: Dad, have you seen my watch?

M: It's on your desk.

G: My desk? It isn't there. I have already checked.

M: Did you check in the drawer?

G: Oh, here it is. Thank you, Dad.

8 G: 아빠, 제 손목시계 보셨어요?

M: 책상 위에 있어.

G: 내 책상이요? 거기 없어요. 이미 확인했어요.

M: 서랍을 봤니?

G: 오, 여기 있어요. 감사해요, 아빠.

9 B: My birthday is coming soon.

G: When is it?

B: It's November 11.

G: What do you want for your birthday?

B: Well. I'd like to have a new bike.

G: Did you tell your parents what you want?

B: Yes, I did.

9 B: 내 생일이 다가오고 있어.

G: 언제야?

B: 11월 11일.

G: 생일에 뭐 받고 싶어?

B: 음. 난 새 자전거를 원해.

G: 네가 뭘 원하는지 부모님께 말했어?

B: 응, 그래.

10 B: Today, I played with my best friend Kevin. Kevin and I go to the same school. He is taller than me, and he has two older brothers. We like to play baseball and computer games.

10 B: 오늘 나는 가장 친한 친구 케빈과 놀았다. 케빈과 나는 같은 학교에 다닌다. 그는 나보다 키가 크고 형이 두 명 있다. 우리는 야구하고 컴퓨터 게임하는 것을 좋아한다.

11 W: Thomas, can I ask you a favor?

M: Sure. What is it?

W: Could you turn the music down a little?

M: Sorry. I didn't know it was so loud. I'll turn it down now.

W: Thanks.

11 W: 토마스, 부탁 하나 해도 될까?

M: 물론. 뭐야?

W: 음악 소리를 조금 줄여줄래?

M: 미안해. 그렇게 시끄러운지 몰랐어. 지금 줄일게.

W: 고마워.

12 G: Are you hungry?

B: Yeah, I'm hungry.

G: Do you want to go get some pizza?

B: I would love to, but I have to go to the department store before it closes.

G: Why?

B: It's my dad's birthday tomorrow, and I didn't buy a present for him yet.

12 G: 배고프니?

B: 응, 배고파.

G: 피자 먹으러 갈까?

B: 그러고 싶은데 백화점이 닫기 전에 가야 해.

G: 왜?

B: 내일이 아빠 생신인데 아직 선물을 사지 못 했어.

13 ① G: Eric, what are you going to do tomorrow?
B: I don't have any plans. Why?
② G: What do you do in your free time?
B: I play with my pet.
③ G: How about playing tennis after school?
B: Sounds great!
④ G: Hi, Tom. How are you doing?
B: I'm doing my homework.

13 ① G: 에릭, 내일 뭐할 거야?
B: 어떤 계획도 없어. 왜?
② G: 여가시간에 뭐해?
B: 내 반려동물이랑 놀아.
③ G: 방과 후에 테니스 치는 거 어때?
B: 좋아!
④ G: 안녕, 톰. 어떻게 지내?
B: 나는 숙제하고 있어.

14 G: Sam, is this you in this picture?
B: Yes, my family went to the beach last summer.
G: Who is the girl?
B: She's my younger sister, Jessie.
G: You were making a sandcastle.
B: Yes, Jessie and I like making sandcastles at the beach.

14 G: 샘, 이 사진에 네가 있니?
B: 응, 지난여름에 나의 가족이 해변에 갔어.
G: 이 소녀는 누구야?
B: 내 여동생 제시야.
G: 너희들 모래성을 만들고 있구나.
B: 응, 제시와 나는 해변에서 모래성 만드는 것을 좋아해.

15 W: Good morning! It's Monday! This is Susan with the weather report. It is cloudy at the moment, but this afternoon, it's going to rain. If you're going out in the afternoon, don't forget your umbrella.

15 W: 안녕하세요! 월요일입니다! 일기예보를 맡은 수잔입니다. 지금은 흐리지만 오후에는 비가 내리겠습니다. 오후에 외출하신다면 우산을 잊지 마세요.

16 W: May I help you?
M: Yes, I'm looking for some pencils. Where can I find them?
W: They're over there.
M: How much is this red pencil?
W: It's 2 dollars.
M: Okay. I'll take three.

16 W: 도와드릴까요?
M: 예, 연필을 좀 찾고 있어요. 어디에서 찾을 수 있죠?
W: 저쪽에 있어요.
M: 이 빨간 연필은 얼마예요?
W: 2달러예요.
M: 알겠어요. 세 개 살게요.

17 W: Mike, your party is great! I'm having a lot of fun.
M: Thank you, Helen. I'm really happy you are here. Do you want something to drink?
W: Sure. What kind of drink do you have?
M: ① Milk is good for your health.
② I like Korean food.
③ No, thanks. I'm full.
④ We have soda and orange juice.

17 W: 마이크, 네 파티 멋졌어! 나 무척 즐거워.
M: 고마워, 헬렌. 네가 여기 와줘서 정말 행복해. 뭐 마실 거 줄까?
W: 좋아. 무슨 종류의 음료수가 있어?
M: ① 우유는 건강에 좋아.
② 나는 한국 음식을 좋아해.
③ 아니, 고마워. 배불러.
④ 탄산음료랑 오렌지주스가 있어.

18 G: Hi, Robin! How was your vacation?
B: Hello, Lisa. My vacation was great. I had a lot of fun.
G: Did you go somewhere?
B: ① I want to visit Korea.
② Yes, I went to Busan with my family.
③ I stayed at the hotel.
④ I lived in Seoul.

18 G: 안녕, 로빈! 네 방학 어땠어?
B: 안녕, 리사. 내 방학 멋졌어. 무척 즐거웠어.
G: 어디 갔니?
B: ① 나는 한국을 방문하기를 원해.
② 응. 가족과 부산에 갔어.
③ 나는 호텔에 머물렀어.
④ 나는 서울에 살았어.

19 W: You look tired today.

M: Yes, I am. I'm very sleepy right now.

W: Did you play computer games late last night?

M: No, I didn't.

W: Then, what did you do?

M: ① I watched a movie until midnight.

② I was very tired.

③ I will do my homework.

④ I was very hungry last night.

20 G: Ted, I'm going to the concert tomorrow. Can you come with me?

B: Sure. What time shall we meet?

G: Let's meet at 3 o'clock.

B: Well, how about 1 o'clock at the bus stop? Let's have lunch before the concert.

G: ① We have lunch at noon.

② Yes, I like pizza very much.

③ Okay. See you tomorrow.

④ I don't drink coffee.

19 W: 너 오늘 피곤해 보여.

M: 응, 그래. 지금 당장 매우 피곤해.

W: 지난밤에 늦게까지 컴퓨터 게임했니?

M: 아니, 그렇지 않아.

W: 그러면, 뭐했는데?

M: ① 자정까지 영화를 봤어.

② 나 무척 피곤해.

③ 나 숙제 할 거야.

④ 지난밤에 매우 배고팠어.

20 G: 테드, 나 내일 콘서트 갈 거야. 나랑 같이 갈래?

B: 물론. 몇 시에 만날까?

G: 3시에 만나자.

B: 음, 1시에 버스 정류장에서 만나는 거 어때? 콘서트 전에 점심 먹자.

G: ① 우리는 정오에 점심을 먹어.

② 응, 나는 피자를 무척 좋아해.

③ 좋아. 내일 보자.

④ 나는 커피 마시는 것을 좋아하지 않아.

Word Check

본책 p. 88

01 always 언제나

02 basket 바구니

03 front 앞

04 competition 대회

05 nervous 긴장한

06 soon 곧

07 drawer 서랍

08 loud 시끄러운

09 sandcastle 모래성

10 forget 잊다

11 somewhere 어딘가

12 right now 지금 당장

13 best friend 가장 친한 친구

14 department store 백화점

15 weather report 일기예보

Sentence Check

본책 p. 89

01 A man is taking on the phone.

02 You have to be in class by 8:30.

03 My bicycle has a basket in the front.

04 I had a math test.

05 I have a piano competition this Saturday.

06 Dinner will be ready soon.

07 Did you check in the drawer?

08 Kevin and I go to the same school.

09 Could you turn the music down a little?

10 Jessie and I like making sandcastles at the beach.

11 This is Susan with the weather report.

12 I'm really happy you are here.

13 How was your vacation?

14 I'm very sleepy right now.

15 Let's have lunch before the concert.

1 ④	2 ②	3 ④	4 ①	5 ②	6 ③	7 ②	8 ③	9 ③	10 ②
11 ①	12 ④	13 ③	14 ①	15 ④	16 ④	17 ③	18 ②	19 ④	20 ②

듣기 대본 본책 p. 94

1
B: Mom, can you give me a ride to school today? It's raining.
W: Sure. What time do we need to leave the house?
B: We need to leave in about 20 minutes. Can we also pick up James?
W: Not a problem.

2
W: ① People are waiting for the traffic light to change.
② People are crossing the street.
③ There is a blue bus on the road.
④ Some children are running along the beach.

3
G: James, what are you going to do this weekend?
B: I don't have any special plans. What about you?
G: I will go skiing with my cousins.
B: Wow. That sounds very exciting!
G: Would you like to join us?
B: Sure, I'd love to.

4
① G: Jack, I got a new cellphone.
B: What a nice phone! Where did you get it?
② G: Can I use your cellphone?
B: Sorry, it's not my cellphone.
③ G: Jack, what are you doing?
B: I'm playing a game on my phone.
④ G: What do you want for your birthday?
B: I want a new bicycle.

5
M: May I help you?
W: Yes, I'm looking for running shoes for my husband.
M: What size do you want?
W: Size 10, please.
M: How about these blue ones? They just came in.
W: Oh, I like them. How much are they?

해석

1
B: 엄마, 오늘 학교까지 태워주실 수 있어요? 비가 오고 있어요.
W: 물론. 몇 시에 집에서 출발해야 하니?
B: 대략 20분 안에 나가야 해요. 제임스도 태워줄 수 있어요?
W: 문제없어.

2
W: ① 사람들이 교통신호가 바뀌기를 기다리고 있다.
② 사람들이 길을 건너고 있다.
③ 도로에 파란 버스가 있다.
④ 몇몇 아이들이 해변을 따라 달리고 있다.

3
G: 제임스, 이번 주말에 뭐할 거야?
B: 특별한 계획이 없어. 너는 어때?
G: 나는 사촌들하고 스키 타러 갈 거야.
B: 와우. 무척 재미있겠다!
G: 우리랑 함께 갈래?
B: 물론, 그러고 싶어.

4
① G: 잭, 나 새 휴대전화 받았어.
B: 정말 멋진 전화기다! 어디서 받았어?
② G: 네 휴대전화를 써도 되니?
B: 미안, 이것은 내 휴대전화가 아니야.
③ G: 잭, 뭐하고 있어?
B: 나 전화기로 게임하고 있어.
④ G: 네 생일에 뭘 받고 싶어?
B: 나는 새 자전거를 원해.

5
M: 도와드릴까요?
W: 예, 남편을 위한 운동화를 찾고 있어요.
M: 무슨 사이즈를 찾으시죠?
W: 10 사이즈로 주세요.
M: 이 파란색은 어떠세요? 막 나왔어요.
W: 오, 좋아요. 얼마예요?

6 *[Telephone rings.]*

M: Rainbow Restaurant. How may I help you?

W: I left my purse at your restaurant yesterday.

M: What does it look like?

W: It's small and red. It has a star on it.

M: Yes, we have it here.

W: Oh, thank you. I'll pick it up this afternoon.

7 G: Mom, can I play computer games?

W: Sure. Did you clean your room?

G: Yes, I cleaned up my room and vacuumed the living room.

W: Did you finish your homework?

G: No, I didn't.

W: You know the rules. You have to finish your homework before you play computer games.

G: Okay, Mom. I'll do it right now.

8 G: What do you do in your free time?

B: I play tennis.

G: Sounds interesting! How often do you play tennis?

B: I play four times a week.

G: Wow, that's a lot.

9 B: Hello, my name is Ben. I am 13 years old. I have an older brother. His name is Jim. He is three years older than me. He has big brown eyes, and he is very tall. He loves to play basketball and tennis. He often helps me do my homework. We have small fights, but I love him very much.

10 B: Jina, how about going to the park tomorrow?

G: It is going to rain tomorrow.

B: How about next Saturday?

G: You mean April 6?

B: Yes, April 6.

G: I'm free on that day.

B: Okay. Let's go to the park next Saturday.

11 B: Susan, do you like sports?

G: No, I don't. But I'd like to play table tennis.

B: Table tennis?

G: Yes, it is a sport for everyone. How about you? What is your favorite sport?

B: I like soccer because it's a very active and exciting sport.

6 *[전화벨이 울린다.]*

M: 레인보우 식당입니다. 어떻게 도와드릴까요?

W: 제가 어제 식당에 지갑을 두고 왔어요.

M: 무슨 모양이죠?

W: 작고 빨간색이에요. 별이 있어요.

M: 예, 여기에 있어요.

W: 오, 감사해요. 오후에 가지러 갈게요.

7 B: 엄마, 컴퓨터 게임 해도 되나요?

W: 물론. 네 방 청소는 했니?

B: 예, 방 청소했고 거실은 진공청소기로 청소했어요.

W: 네 숙제는 다했니?

B: 아니요, 못 했어요.

W: 너도 규칙을 알거야.
컴퓨터 게임을 하기 전에 숙제를 다해야 해.

B: 알겠어요, 엄마. 지금 당장 할게요.

8 M: 넌 여가시간에 무엇을 해?

W: 난 테니스를 쳐.

M: 재미있겠다! 얼마나 자주 테니스를 쳐?

W: 일주일에 네 번 쳐.

M: 와우, 많다.

9 B: 안녕, 내 이름은 벤이야. 나는 13살이야. 나는 형이 하나 있어. 그의 이름은 짐이야. 그는 나보다 3살 더 많아. 그는 커다란 갈색 눈을 가졌고, 키가 무척 커. 그는 농구랑 테니스 하는 거를 좋아해. 그는 종종 내 숙제를 도와줘. 우리는 소소한 일로 다투지만 나는 그를 아주 많이 사랑해.

10 B: 지나, 내일 공원에 가는 거 어때?

G: 내일 비가 올 거야.

B: 다음 주 토요일은 어때?

G: 4월 6일 말하는 거야?

B: 응, 4월 6일.

G: 그날은 한가해.

B: 좋아. 다음 주 토요일에 공원에 가자

11 B: 수잔, 너 운동 좋아하니?

G: 아니, 안 좋아해. 하지만 탁구는 치고 싶어.

B: 탁구?

G: 응, 탁구는 모두를 위한 운동이야.
너는 어때? 네가 좋아하는 운동이 뭐야?

B: 나는 무척 활동적이고 흥미진진해서 축구를 좋아해.

12 W: May I help you?

M: Yes, I'm looking for a bed for my daughter.

W: What size are you looking for?

M: I want a single bed.

W: How about this one? It's on sale now.

M: How much is it?

13 ① B: This present is for you.

G: Thank you very much.

② B: Hello. May I speak to Sally?

G: Speaking.

③ B: How many sisters do you have?

G: I live with my sisters.

④ B: Where did you go last weekend?

G: I went to the zoo with my family.

14 B: Susie, how about playing tennis after school?

G: Sorry, I don't feel like playing tennis today.

B: What would you like to do then?

G: Why don't we go to the swimming pool?

B: Sounds great.

15 B: Mom doesn't look good today.

G: Let's do something for her.

B: Sure. What can we do?

G: Let's make dinner for her.

B: That's a great idea. She will really like that.

16 W: I work on a plane. My job is to make flights comfortable for passengers. I serve food and drinks to the passengers on the plane. I visit a lot of cities and countries every year.

17 [Cellphone rings.]

G: Hello.

B: Hi, Sara. This is Ted. What are you doing?

G: I'm watching TV.

B: I will go to the mall to buy John's birthday present. Will you join me?

G: Sure. What time?

B: Let's meet in front of the mall at 3 o'clock.

G: Okay.

12 W: 도와드릴까요?

M: 예, 딸아이를 위해 침대를 찾고 있어요.

W: 무슨 사이즈를 찾고 있어요?

M: 1인용 침대요.

W: 이거 어때요? 지금 할인 중이에요.

M: 얼마예요?

13 ① B: 널 위한 선물이야.

G: 정말 고마워.

② B: 여보세요. 샐리와 통화할 수 있나요?

G: 전데요.

③ B: 너는 자매가 몇이나 있어?

G: 나는 언니들하고 살아.

④ B: 지난 주말에 어디에 갔어?

G: 가족이랑 동물원에 갔어.

14 B: 수지, 방과 후에 테니스 치는 거 어때?

G: 미안, 오늘은 테니스를 치고 싶지 않아.

B: 그러면 뭐하고 싶어?

G: 수영장 가는 거 어때?

B: 좋아.

15 B: 엄마가 오늘 좋아 보이시지 않아.

G: 엄마를 위해 무언가 하자.

B: 좋아. 우리가 무얼 할 수 있니?

G: 엄마를 위해 저녁을 만들자.

B: 좋은 생각이야. 엄마가 정말 좋아하실 거야.

16 W: 나는 비행기에서 일한다. 나의 일은 승객들이 편안하게 비행하도록 만드는 것이다. 나는 비행기 승객들에게 음식과 음료를 제공한다. 나는 매년 많은 도시와 나라들을 방문한다.

17 [휴대폰이 울린다.]

G: 여보세요.

B: 안녕, 사라. 나 테드야. 뭐하고 있어?

G: TV 보고 있어.

B: 나 존의 생일 선물을 사러 쇼핑몰에 갈 거야. 같이 갈래?

G: 물론이지. 몇 시에?

B: 3시에 쇼핑몰 앞에서 만나자.

G: 좋아.

18 G: Steve, what do you do in your free time?

B: I <u>read</u> <u>books</u>. How about you?

G: I <u>watch</u> <u>movies</u>. I want to be an actor when I grow up.

B: Really? I didn't know that. <u>What</u> <u>kind</u> of movie do you like to watch?

G: ① I like all kinds of books.

② I like action movies.

③ I want to be a writer.

④ I read books every day.

19 B: Do you have a favorite sport?

G: I enjoy <u>playing</u> <u>basketball</u>. How about you?

B: I like playing basketball, too! Do you want to <u>go</u> and <u>play</u> basketball with me right now?

G: ① Yes, I want to go home.

② No, I don't like sports.

③ Thanks, but I'm full.

④ I'd love to, but I have to go home for dinner.

20 G: You look so sad. What's wrong?

B: I <u>lost</u> <u>my</u> <u>bag</u> on the bus.

G: Did you go to the Lost and Found?

B: Yes, I did. But I <u>couldn't</u> <u>find</u> my bag there.

G: ① I'm okay. Thank you.

② Oh, I'm sorry to hear that.

③ Don't worry. He will be all right.

④ When did you find it?

18 G: 스티브, 너는 여가시간에 뭐해?

B: 나는 책 읽어. 너는 어때?

G: 나는 영화를 봐. 나는 커서 배우가 되고 싶어.

B: 정말? 나 그거 몰랐어.

너는 무슨 종류의 영화 보는 거 좋아해?

G: ① 나는 모든 종류의 책을 좋아해.

② 나는 액션 영화를 좋아해.

③ 나는 작가가 되고 싶어.

④ 나는 매일 책을 읽어.

19 B: 너 좋아하는 운동 있니?

G: 나 농구하는 거 즐겨. 너는 어때?

B: 나도 농구하는 거 좋아해! 지금 당장 가서 나랑 농구할래?

G: ① 응, 나 집에 가고 싶어.

② 아니, 나 운동을 좋아하지 않아.

③ 고마워, 하지만 배불러.

④ 그러고 싶은데 저녁 먹으러 집에 가야 해.

20 G: 너 슬퍼 보여? 무슨 일이야?

B: 나 버스에서 가방을 잃어버렸어.

G: 분실물 보관소 가봤어?

B: 응, 그래. 하지만 거기서 내 가방을 찾을 수 없었어.

G: ① 난 좋아. 고마워.

② 오, 그말 들으니 유감이다.

③ 걱정하지 마. 그는 괜찮을 거야.

④ 언제 그것을 찾았어?

Word Check
본책 p. 100

01 leave 출발하다

02 about 대략

03 wrong 잘못된, (잘못된) 일이 있는

04 cross 건너다

05 rainbow 무지개

06 purse 지갑

07 vacuum 진공청소하다

08 country 나라

09 daughter 딸

10 flight 비행

11 comfortable 편안한

12 passenger 승객

13 table tennis 탁구

14 traffic light 교통신호

15 running shoes 운동화

Sentence Check
본책 p. 101

01 Can you give me a ride to school today?

02 People are crossing the street.

03 People are waiting for the traffic light to change.

04 I don't have any special plans.

05 I'm playing a game on my phone.

06 I'm looking for running shoes for my husband.

07 I left my purse at your restaurant yesterday.

08 I'll pick it up this afternoon.

09 I play four times a week.

10 He often helps me do my homework.

11 I like soccer because it's a very active and exciting sport.

12 May I speak to Sally?

13 Why don't we go to the swimming pool?

14 My job is to make flights comfortable for passengers.

15 I want to be an actor when I grow up.

1 ③	**2** ②	**3** ④	**4** ②	**5** ④	**6** ①	**7** ④	**8** ③	**9** ②	**10** ③
11 ④	**12** ②	**13** ④	**14** ③	**15** ②	**16** ③	**17** ①	**18** ③	**19** ③	**20** ②

듣기 대본 본책 p. 106

1 G: My friend Susan is over there.
B: Where is she?
G: Do you see the girl with short hair?
B: Is she wearing a skirt?
G: No, she's wearing a pink blouse and shorts.
B: Oh, I see her.

2 [Cellphone rings.]
G: Hello.
B: Hello, Susie. This is John.
G: What's up, John?
B: I emailed you last night. Did you read it?
G: No, I didn't.
B: Please check your email. I sent you a birthday card.
G: Okay. I will check it right away.

3 W: James, where are you going?
M: I'm going to the cafeteria to have lunch.
W: Can I join you?
M: Sure. What are you going to eat for lunch?
W: I'm having a chicken salad. How about you?
M: I'll have the same. I'm on a diet.

4 B: Jane, what are you going to do this weekend?
G: I will go to the amusement park with my cousins.
B: Sounds fun. How will you get there? Will your parents give you a ride?
G: No, we will take the subway.
B: Oh, I see. Have a nice weekend.

5 B: Lisa, what did you do yesterday?
G: I went fishing with my dad.
B: How was the fishing?
G: It was good. We caught a lot of fish. How about you?
B: It was my mom's birthday, so I made dinner for her.
G: Really? What did you cook for her?
B: I cooked pasta.

해석

1 G: 내 친구 수잔이 저쪽에 있어.
B: 어디 있어?
G: 단발머리 소녀 보여?
B: 치마 입고 있니?
G: 아니, 분홍 블라우스에 반바지를 입고 있어.
B: 오, 알겠어.

2 [휴대폰이 울린다.]
G: 여보세요.
B: 안녕, 수지. 나 존이야.
G: 무슨 일이야, 존?
B: 내가 지난밤에 이메일을 보냈어. 읽어봤니?
G: 아니, 안 봤어.
B: 네 이메일을 확인해 봐. 내가 생일 카드를 보냈어.
G: 알았어. 바로 확인할게.

3 W: 제임스, 어디 가고 있어?
M: 점심 먹으려고 구내식당에 가고 있어.
W: 같이 가도 되니?
M: 물론. 점심으로 뭐 먹을 거야?
W: 치킨 샐러드 먹을 거야. 너는 어때?
M: 나도 같은 걸로 먹을 거야. 나 다이어트 중이야.

4 B: 제인, 이번 주말에 뭐할 거야?
G: 사촌들이랑 놀이공원에 갈 거야.
B: 재미있겠다. 거기 어떻게 갈 거야? 네 부모님이 태워주시니?
G: 아니, 우리 지하철을 타고 갈 거야.
B: 오, 알겠어. 즐거운 주말 보내,

5 B: 리사, 어제 뭐했어?
G: 나 아빠랑 낚시 갔어.
B: 낚시 어땠어?
G: 좋았어. 우리 물고기를 많이 잡았어. 너는 어때?
B: 엄마 생신이어서 내가 엄마를 위해 저녁을 만들었어.
G: 정말? 엄마를 위해 뭘 요리했어?
B: 파스타를 요리했어.

6 ① W: What do you think of my picture?

　　M: Wow, you're very good at painting.

② W: What's wrong?

　　M: I have a fever and a runny nose.

③ W: I don't feel well. I have a headache.

　　M: Sorry to hear that. Why don't you take some medicine?

④ W: I'm very hungry. What's for dinner?

　　M: Fried rice. It's on the table.

7 G: Donovan, what are you going to do tomorrow?

B: I will go to the beach.

G: Are you going to swim there?

B: No, there is a drawing contest at the beach. I'm going to take part in the contest.

G: Really? Good luck.

8 W: What sports do you like?

M: I like basketball.

W: I like basketball, too. I especially like watching basketball games.

M: Really? Why don't we go to the gym tomorrow? There will be a basketball game the Tigers against the Bears.

W: Okay. That's so exciting!

9 [Cellphone rings.]

G: Hello.

M: Hello, Ellen. What's up?

G: Dad, where are you?

M: I'm at home. Why?

G: It's raining a lot now. Can you bring me an umbrella?

M: Where are you now?

G: I'm at the bus stop.

10 W: Tony, can you bring me my sunglasses? They are on the sofa.

B: Okay. [Pause] Mom, they are not here. Didn't you leave them on the table?

W: I don't think so. Please check around the table.

B: Oh, I found them. They are under the table.

6 ① W : 내 그림 어때?

　　M : 와우. 너 그림을 무척 잘 그리는구나.

② W : 무슨 일이야?

　　M : 나 열이 있고 콧물이 나.

③ W : 몸이 좋지 않아. 두통이 있어.

　　M : 안됐다. 약을 먹는 게 어때?

④ W : 무척 배고파. 저녁이 뭐야?

　　M : 볶음밥. 식탁 위에 있어.

7 G : 도노반, 내일 뭐할 거야?

B : 해변에 갈 거야.

G : 거기서 수영할 거야?

B : 아니, 사생대회가 해변에서 열려. 그 대회에 참가할 거야.

G : 정말? 행운을 빌어.

8 W : 너는 무슨 운동 좋아해?

M : 나는 농구 좋아해.

W : 나도 농구 좋아해. 나는 특히 농구 경기 보는 거 좋아해.

M : 정말? 내일 체육관에 가는 거 어때? 타이거와 베어스의 농구 경기가 있어.

W : 좋아. 무척 흥미진진하겠다!

9 [휴대폰이 울린다.]

G : 여보세요.

M : 안녕, 헬렌. 무슨 일이야?

G : 아빠, 어디 계세요?

M : 집에 있어. 왜?

G : 지금 비가 많이 와요. 저한테 우산 가져오실 수 있으세요?

M : 지금 어디에 있니?

G : 버스 정류장에 있어요.

10 W : 토니, 내 선글라스를 가져올래? 소파 위에 있어.

B : 알겠어요. [잠시 후]엄마, 여기 없어요. 탁자 위에 두셨어요?

W : 그렇지 않은 거 같아. 탁자 주변을 확인해줘.

B : 오, 찾았어요. 탁자 아래에 있어요.

11 [Cellphone rings.]

B: Hello?

G: Hi, Jack!

B: Hi, Sue. How is it going?

G: Good! I called because I lost Leo's phone number. Do you mind telling me his number?

B: Not at all. It's 1542-7855.

G: 1542-8855?

B: No, it's 1542-7855. It's not 88, it's 78.

G: Okay. Thank you so much.

12 G: When is our science homework due?

B: Next Monday.

G: Do you want to come over to my house and do the homework together?

B: Sure, but I'm hungry right now. Let's grab a sandwich at the food court.

G: Good idea. Let's go.

13 G: My name is Annie. I usually wake up at 7:30. After taking a shower, I eat breakfast. I usually eat some bread and eggs for breakfast. I go to school by 9 o'clock. I like going to school because I like learning new things.

14 ① B: Hi, Claire. Are you free tomorrow?

G: Yes, I'm free after school. Why?

② B: Can you do me a favor, Jennie?

G: Sure. What is it?

③ G: What's wrong, Sam?

B: Okay, I'll take it.

④ G: Let's go to the shopping mall.

B: Sounds good to me.

15 G: Jack's birthday is coming up.

B: Did you buy a gift for him?

G: No, not yet. I'm going to buy a baseball cap. How about you?

B: I'm going to buy a baseball glove. His glove is very old.

G: That's a good idea.

16 B: Your school's field trip is this Friday, right?

G: No, it was changed because it'll be windy and rainy this Friday.

B: Really? So when is the field trip?

G: It's next Monday.

11 [휴대폰이 울린다.]

B: 여보세요?

G: 안녕, 잭!

B: 안녕, 수. 어떻게 지내?

G: 좋아! 레어의 전화번호를 잃어버려서 전화했어. 그의 번호 좀 알려줄래?

B: 물론. 1542-7855번이야.

G: 1542-8855?

B: 아니, 1542-7855번. 88이 아니고 78이야.

G: 알았어. 정말 고마워.

12 G: 우리 과학 숙제 언제 내야 해?

B: 다음 주 월요일.

G: 우리 집에 와서 함께 숙제할까?

B: 좋아, 하지만 지금 당장은 배고파. 푸드코트에서 샌드위치 먹자.

G: 좋은 생각이야. 가자.

13 G: 내 이름은 앤이야. 나는 보통 7시 30분에 일어나. 샤워 후에는 아침을 먹어. 아침으로는 주로 빵과 달걀을 먹어. 나는 9시까지 학교에 가. 나는 새로운 것을 배우는 게 좋아서 학교 가는 게 좋아.

14 ① B: 안녕, 클레어. 내일 시간 있니?

G: 응, 방과 후에 한가해. 왜?

② B: 부탁 하나 들어줄래, 제니?

G: 물론. 뭔데?

③ G: 무슨 일이야, 샘?

B: 좋아. 그거 살게.

④ G: 쇼핑몰에 가자.

B: 난 좋아.

15 G: 잭의 생일이 다가오고 있어.

B: 그에게 줄 선물 샀니?

G: 아니, 아직. 난 야구모자를 살 거야.

B: 나는 야구 글러브 살 거야. 그의 글러브가 무척 낡았어.

G: 그거 좋은 생각이야.

16 B: 네 학교 현장학습이 이번 주 금요일이지, 맞지?

G: 아니, 이번 주 금요일에 바람 불고 비 온다고 해서 바뀌었어.

B: 정말? 그러면 현장학습이 언제야?

G: 다음 주 월요일.

17 W: Mike, can you help me?

B: Sure, Ms. Brown. What can I do for you?

W: Can you help me carry these boxes to the car?

B: ① I'd be glad to. Anything else?

② I don't think so.

③ I feel better today.

④ I'll take it.

17 W: 마이크, 나 좀 도와줄래?

B: 물론이죠, 브라운 선생님. 무엇을 도와드릴까요?

W: 이 상자를 자동차로 옮기는 것을 도와줄래?

B: ① 그럴게요. 다른 거는요?

② 전 그렇게 생각하지 않아요.

③ 오늘 더 나아졌어요.

④ 제가 가져갈게요.

18 B: What are you going to do after school?

G: I will go to the library.

B: With who?

G: ① It's on the second floor.

② I'll borrow the books.

③ Jane and Lisa

④ I'll take the subway.

18 B: 방과 후에 뭐할 거야?

G: 도서관에 갈 거야.

B: 누구랑?

G: ① 2층이야.

② 책을 빌릴 거야.

③ 제인이랑 리사.

④ 지하철을 탈 거야.

19 W: Hello, can I help you?

M: Yes, I want to return this sweater.

W: Okay. Is there something wrong with it?

M: ① I got up late.

② I have a cold.

③ Yes, it's too big for me.

④ Yes, I like that color.

19 W: 안녕하세요, 도와드릴까요?

M: 예, 이 스웨터를 환불하러 왔어요.

W: 알겠어요. 그것에 무슨 문제가 있나요?

M: ① 늦게 일어났어요.

② 감기에 걸렸어요.

③ 예, 저한테 너무 커요.

④ 예, 그 색을 좋아해요.

20 W: Hi, how can I help you?

M: Can I get a hamburger, please?

W: What kind of hamburger would you like?

M: I will have a cheeseburger.

W: Okay, and anything to drink?

M: ① No, that's all.

② I'm on a diet.

③ Do you have diet soda?

④ What do you have?

20 W: 안녕하세요, 어떻게 도와드릴까요?

M: 햄버거 주실 수 있나요?

W: 무슨 종류의 햄버거를 원하세요?

M: 치즈버거로 주세요.

W: 알겠어요, 그리고 음료는요?

M: ① 아니요, 그게 다예요.

② 다이어트 중이에요.

③ 다이어트 콜라 있나요?

④ 무엇이 있나요?

Word Check　　　　　　　　　　　　　　　　　　　　　　　본책 p. 112

01 blouse 블라우스

02 cafeteria 구내식당

03 ride 탈것

04 catch 잡다

05 luck 행운

06 especially 특히

07 gym 체육관

08 bring 가져오다

09 windy 바람이 부는

10 mind 꺼리다

11 carry 옮기다

12 wake up 일어나다

13 amusement park 놀이공원

14 drawing contest 사생대회

15 field trip 현장학습

Sentence Check

01 She's wearing a pink blouse and shorts.

02 I emailed you last night.

03 I'm on a diet.

04 Have a nice weekend.

05 It was my mom's birthday, so I made dinner for her.

06 Why don't you take some medicine?

07 I'm going to take part in the contest.

08 I especially like watching basketball games.

09 Can you bring me an umbrella?

10 I called because I lost Leo's phone number.

11 Let's grab a sandwich at the food court.

12 Can you help me carry these boxes to the car?

13 I want to return this sweater.

14 Is there something wrong with it?

15 Okay, and anything to drink?

10회 영어 듣기 모의고사

1 ③	2 ②	3 ②	4 ③	5 ④	6 ②	7 ③	8 ③	9 ①	10 ④
11 ③	12 ④	13 ③	14 ①	15 ④	16 ③	17 ③	18 ④	19 ④	20 ②

듣기 대본

1 G: James, do you still want to be a movie director?
B: Yes, I do. How about you, Amy?
G: I want to be a doctor like my uncle.
B: Really? I thought you wanted to be a teacher.
G: I did, but I changed my mind.

2 [Cellphone rings.]
B: Hello.
W: Hello, Ted? What's up?
B: Mom, where are you?
W: I'm at home. Why?
B: I forgot to turn off the light in my room. Could you turn it off?
W: Okay.

3 G: Winter vacation is coming soon.
B: What are you planning to do?
G: I will learn Chinese. What is your plan?
B: I will take cooking classes.
G: Cooking classes?
B: Yes, I want to be a chef when I grow up.

4 M: May I help you?
G: Yes, I'm looking for a cake for my younger sister.
M: What kind of cake do you want?
G: I want a cheesecake.
M: Sorry, we only have a chocolate cake today.
G: Okay. I will take it. How much is it?
M: It's 24 dollars.

해석

1 G: 제임스, 너는 여전히 영화감독이 되고 싶니?
B: 응, 너는 어때, 에이미?
G: 나는 삼촌처럼 의사가 되고 싶어.
B: 정말? 난 네가 선생님이 되고 싶어 한다고 생각했어.
G: 그랬는데 마음이 바뀌었어.

2 [휴대폰이 울린다.]
B: 여보세요.
W: 안녕, 테드? 무슨 일이야?
B: 엄마, 어디세요?
W: 나는 집에 있어. 왜?
B: 제가 방에 전등 끄는 걸 잊어버렸어요. 그거 꺼주실래요?
W: 알겠어.

3 G: 겨울방학이 다가오고 있어.
B: 뭐할 계획이야?
G: 난 중국어를 배울 거야. 네 계획은 뭐야?
B: 나는 요리 수업을 받을 거야.
G: 요리 수업?
B: 응, 나는 커서 주방장이 되고 싶어.

4 M: 도와드릴까요?
G: 예, 저는 여동생 케이크를 찾고 있어요.
M: 무슨 종류의 케이크를 원해요?
G: 치즈케이크를 사고 싶어요.
M 죄송해요, 우리는 오늘 초콜릿 케이크만 있어요.
G: 좋아요. 그걸로 살게요. 얼마예요?
M: 24달러예요.

5 W: Excuse me.

M: Yes?

W: You dropped your cellphone.

M: Oh, I didn't notice. Thank you.

W: No problem.

5 W: 실례합니다.

M: 예?

W: 휴대전화를 떨어뜨렸어요.

M: 오, 알아차리지 못했어요. 감사해요.

W: 천만에요.

6 B: I'm happy that final exams are over.

G: Me, too. How about going swimming?

B: Sure! The weather is very nice. But before we go, can we go to the shopping mall?

G: Why?

B: I lost my swimming cap, so I need a new one.

G: Okay. Let's go.

6 B: 기말고사가 끝나서 행복해.

G: 나도. 수영하러 가는 거 어때?

B: 좋아! 날씨가 무척 좋아. 그런데 가기 전에 쇼핑몰에 갈 수 있니?

G: 왜?

B: 나 수영 모자를 잃어버려서 새 것이 필요해.

G: 알겠어. 가자.

7 B: Mom, can I go for a bike ride?

W: Isn't it snowing outside?
I heard there will be heavy snow.

B: It's just cloudy now.

W: Alright, but come home when it starts to snow.

B: Okay, Mom.

7 B: 엄마, 자전거 타러 가도 되나요?

W: 밖에 눈 오지 않니? 폭설이 내릴 거라고 들었는데.

B: 지금 흐리기만 해요.

W: 알았어, 하지만 눈 내리기 시작하면 와라.

B: 알겠어요, 엄마.

8 W: Do you know where my car key is?

M: Did you look on the table?

W: Yes, I did.

M: What about on the sofa?

W: It's not there, either.

M: Oh, there it is.

W: Where?

M: It is on the shelf.

8 W: 내 자동차 열쇠가 어디 있는지 아니?

M: 식탁 위에 봤어?

W: 응, 봤어.

M: 소파 위는 어때?

W: 거기에도 없어.

M: 오, 저기 있어.

W: 어디?

M: 선반 위에 있어.

9 ① M: Can I try this on?

W: Sure. The fitting room is right over there.

② W: Have some more cake.

M: Thank you.

③ M: Can you help me with my report?

W: Sorry. I'm busy now.

④ M: Good afternoon. May I help you?

W: I'd like a sandwich, please.

9 ① M: 이거 입어 봐도 되나요?

W: 물론이죠. 탈의실은 바로 저쪽에 있어요.

② W: 케이크 더 먹어.

M: 고마워.

③ M: 내 보고서 도와줄 수 있니?

W: 미안. 난 지금 바빠.

④ M: 안녕하세요. 도와드릴까요?

W: 샌드위치 주세요.

10 M: Good afternoon. May I help you?

W: I'd like a hamburger, please.

M: Anything to drink?

W: Coke, please.

10 M: 안녕하세요. 도와드릴까요?

W: 햄버거 주세요.

M: 마실 것은요?

W: 콜라 주세요.

11 G: Yesterday was my twelfth birthday. I had a party at my house. I invited my friends to the party. My mom made a cake for me. My friends gave me presents. We played many games. The party was a lot of fun.

11 G: 어제 내 12번째 생일이었어. 나는 집에서 파티를 했어. 나는 친구들을 파티에 초대했어. 엄마가 날 위해 케이크를 만들어 주셨어. 내 친구들이 나한테 선물을 줬어. 우리는 많은 경기를 했어. 파티는 무척 재미있었어.

12 ① B: Alice, how was the movie last night?

G: It was great.

② B: Did you finish the math homework?

G: Not yet, but I did half of it.

③ B: Hi, Lina! Can I talk to you now?

G: Sure, Kevin. What's up?

④ B: What do you do in your free time?

G: I played tennis yesterday.

13 B: What are you going to do today?

G: I'm going to Jim's birthday party.

B: What? I thought Jim's birthday is on Friday.

G: Yes. Today is Friday.

B: Oh, my gosh! I thought today was Thursday. I didn't buy a gift for him yet. Let's go to the mall now.

G: Okay.

14 W: Where did you get this photo?

M: I took the photo in the garden last week.

W: Wow. The butterflies on the flowers are very beautiful. You are good at taking photos.

M: Thank you.

15 W: What do you need for the picnic?

M: I need some food and drinks.

W: What about a backpack?

M: Yes, I need a backpack to put food and drinks in.

W: Do you need a picnic basket?

M: No, I don't need it.

16 M: Susan, what did you do during the vacation?

W: I took a trip to Busan.

M: How was it?

W: It was not good.

M: Why?

W: It rained all throughout the vacation, so we stayed at a hotel.

M: Oh, I'm sorry to hear that.

17 W: How may I help you?

B: Can I get three red pens?

W: Sure. Is that all you need?

B: Do you have blue pens as well?

W: Of course. How many blue ones do you need?

B: Four, please.

W: ① How much is it?

② Sure. No problem.

③ Okay. Here you are.

④ No. Thank you.

12 ① B : 앨리스, 지난밤 영화 어땠어?

G : 훌륭했어.

② B : 수학 숙제 끝냈니?

G : 아니 아직, 하지만 반은 했어.

③ B : 안녕, 리나! 지금 말할 수 있어?

G : 물론, 케빈. 무슨 일이야?

④ B : 넌 여가시간에 뭐해?

G : 난 어제 테니스를 쳤어.

13 B : 오늘 뭐할 거야?

G : 짐의 생일 파티에 갈 거야.

B : 뭐? 짐의 생일이 금요일이라고 생각했어.

G : 응. 오늘이 금요일이야.

B : 오, 이런! 나는 오늘이 목요일이라고 생각했어. 아직 그를 위해 선물을 사지 못했어. 지금 쇼핑몰에 가자.

G : 알았어.

14 W : 이 사진 어디서 났어?

M : 내가 지난주에 정원에서 그 사진 찍었어.

W : 와우. 꽃 위에 나비들이 정말 아름답네. 너는 사진을 잘 찍는구나.

M : 고마워.

15 W : 소풍에 뭐가 필요해?

M : 음식이랑 마실 것들이 좀 필요해.

W : 배낭은?

M : 응, 음식이랑 마실 것 넣을 배낭이 필요해.

W : 소풍 바구니 필요해?

M : 아니, 필요 없어.

16 M : 수잔, 휴가 동안 뭐했어?

W : 부산으로 여행을 갔어.

M : 어땠어?

W : 좋지 않았어.

M : 왜?

W : 휴가 내내 비가 와서 우리는 호텔에 머물렀어.

M : 오, 그 말 들으니 유감이다.

17 W : 어떻게 도와드릴까요?

B : 빨간 펜 세 개 주실 수 있나요?

W : 물론이죠. 이게 필요한 거 다예요?

B : 파란 펜도 있나요?

W : 물론이죠. 얼마나 많이 파란 펜이 필요하세요?

B : 네 개 주세요.

W : ① 얼마예요?

② 물론이죠, 문제없어요.

③ 알겠어요, 여기 있어요.

④ 아니요, 감사해요.

18 G: Leo! What did you do yesterday?
　B: I stayed home all day.
　G: Why?
　B: I didn't feel good.
　G: Are you feeling better now?
　B: ① I'm reading a book.
　　② Yes, I feel like eating a sandwich.
　　③ No, I didn't take the medicine.
　　④ Yes, thank you for asking.

19 W: I went to Incheon with my family yesterday.
　M: Did you take the subway?
　W: No, I took an express bus.
　M: How long did it take?
　W: ① Thank you. Let's go.
　　② I can't drive a car.
　　③ It is 20 dollars.
　　④ It took about two hours.

20 W: What do you want for lunch?
　M: I'd like to have noodles.
　W: Well, I had noodles for lunch yesterday.
　M: Then, let's eat pizza.
　W: ① That's a good idea.
　　② What is your favorite food?
　　③ Okay. It's my favorite.
　　④ What kind of pizza do you want?

18 G: 레오! 어제 뭐했어?
　B: 하루 종일 집에 있었어.
　G: 왜?
　B: 몸이 좋지 않았어.
　G: 지금은 좀 나아졌어?
　B: ① 나 책 읽고 있어.
　　② 응, 나 샌드위치 먹고 싶어.
　　③ 아니, 약을 먹지 않았어.
　　④ 응, 물어봐 줘서 고마워.

19 W: 나 어제 가족이랑 인천에 갔어.
　M: 지하철을 탔니?
　W: 아니, 고속버스를 탔어.
　M: 얼마나 오래 걸렸어?
　W: ① 고마워. 가자.
　　② 나는 자동차를 운전하지 못해.
　　③ 20달러야.
　　④ 대략 2시간 걸렸어.

20 W: 점심으로 뭐 먹고 싶어?
　M: 난 국수 먹고 싶어.
　W: 응, 나 어제 점심에 국수 먹었어.
　M: 그러면, 피자를 먹자.
　W: ① 좋은 생각이야.
　　② 네가 좋아하는 음식이 뭐야?
　　③ 좋아. 그게 내가 좋아하는 거야.
　　④ 너는 어떤 종류 피자 먹고 싶어?

Word Check
본책 p. 124

01 mind 마음
02 forget 잊어버리다
03 notice 알아차리다
04 either 또한
05 shelf 선반
06 anything 무언가
07 invite 초대하다
08 half 절반
09 butterfly 나비
10 garden 정원
11 throughout 내내
12 problem 문제
13 final exam 기말고사
14 heavy snow 폭설
15 fitting room 탈의실

Sentence Check
본책 p. 125

01 I thought you wanted to be a teacher.
02 I forgot to turn off the light in my room.
03 Winter vacation is coming soon.
04 I'm happy that final exams are over.
05 I heard there will be heavy snow.
06 Come home when it starts to snow.
07 Do you know where my car key is?
08 The fitting room is right over there.
09 I invited my friends to the party.
10 What do you do in your free time?
11 The butterflies on the flowers are very beautiful.
12 I need a backpack to put food and drinks in.
13 It rained all throughout the vacation.
14 I stayed home all day.
15 I had noodles for lunch yesterday.

1 ②	2 ④	3 ②	4 ④	5 ②	6 ①	7 ③	8 ④	9 ③	10 ③
11 ③	12 ④	13 ②	14 ①	15 ①	16 ④	17 ②	18 ③	19 ①	20 ③

듣기 대본

본책 p. 130

1 W: John, did you see my necklace?
B: No, Mom. Where did you leave it?
W: I don't know, but maybe I put it on the bed.
B: Nothing's there, Mom. Didn't you put it in the drawer?
W: Maybe? Please look for it in the drawer or near the lamp.
B: Oh, here it is. It's in the drawer.

2 G: What's up? You look excited.
B: Guess what! My mom said I can go to the K-pop concert.
G: Wow, good for you.
B: Will you join us?
G: I wish I could, but I have to ask my dad first.
B: Okay, let's go to your house. I will help you.

3 M: I would like to check out these books.
W: Okay. Do you have your library card?
M: Yes. Here you are. Can I borrow these books for a month?
W: Sorry. You can only borrow the books for two weeks.

4 B: Alice, did you take this photo?
G: Yes, I took it at the park last month.
B: Wow, the tree is very big. By the way, who is the boy next to the tree?
G: The boy holding a balloon?
B: Yes, he is.
G: He's my cousin, Minsu.

5 G: You are a great football player, Chris.
B: Thanks. Do you enjoy football, Jen?
G: I do, but my favorite sport is ice hockey.
B: Really? Why?
G: I like skating on ice.
B: Will you teach me how to skate one day?
G: Of course, I can!

해석

1 W: 존, 내 목걸이 봤니?
B: 아뇨, 엄마. 어디에 두셨는데요?
W: 잘 모르겠지만 아마도 침대 위에 뒀을 거야.
B: 거기 아무것도 없어요, 엄마. 서랍 안에 두지 않으셨어요?
W: 어쩌면? 서랍 안이나 전등 근처를 봐줘.
B: 오, 여기 있어요. 서랍 안에 있어요.

2 G: 무슨 일이야? 신이 나 보여.
B: 있잖아! 엄마가 K팝 콘서트에 갈 수 있다고 하셨어.
G: 와우, 잘됐다.
B: 우리랑 같이 갈래?
G: 그러고 싶은데, 아빠한테 먼저 여쭤봐야 해.
B: 좋아, 네 집에 가자. 내가 도와줄게.

3 M: 이 책들을 대출하고 싶어요.
W: 예. 도서관 카드 있나요?
M: 예. 여기 있어요. 한 달 동안 이 책들을 대출할 수 있나요?
W: 죄송해요. 2주 동안만 책을 빌릴 수 있어요.

4 B: 앨리스, 네가 이 사진을 찍었니?
G: 응, 지난달에 공원에서 찍었어.
B: 와우, 나무가 무척 크다.
그런데 나무 옆에 소년은 누구야?
G: 풍선을 들고 있는 소년?
B: 응, 그래.
G: 내 사촌 민수야.

5 G: 너는 훌륭한 미식축구 선수야, 크리스.
B: 고마워. 너도 미식축구 좋아하니, 젠?
G: 그래, 그런데 내가 가장 좋아하는 운동은 아이스하키야.
B: 정말? 왜?
G: 얼음 위에서 스케이트를 타잖아.
B: 언제 어떻게 스케이트 타는지 가르쳐 줄래?
G: 물론, 할 수 있어!

6 G: Hey, Albert! How is it going?

B: I'm good, thanks for asking. How about you?

G: I'm doing well. Do you have John's phone number by any chance?

B: Yes. Hold on.

G: Okay.

B: His phone number is 983-1149.

G: 973-1149?

B: No, it's 983.

6 G : 안녕, 알버트! 어떻게 지내?

B : 잘 지내, 물어봐 줘서 고마워. 너는 어때?

G : 잘 지내. 너 혹시 존의 전화번호 알고 있니?

B : 응. 잠깐만.

G : 알았어.

B : 그의 전화번호는 983-1149야.

G : 973-1149?

B : 아니, 983번.

7 B: Hi, Stephanie. Do you want to go see a musical with me?

G: I would love to, but when?

B: Friday night.

G: I'm free that day. What time shall we meet?

B: The musical starts at 8 o'clock. Let's meet in front of the theater at 7:30.

G: Okay. See you then.

7 B : 안녕, 스테파니. 나랑 뮤지컬 보러 갈래?

G : 그러고 싶어, 그런데 언제?

B : 금요일 저녁.

G : 그날 한가해. 몇 시에 만날까?

B : 뮤지컬은 8시에 시작해.
극장 앞에서 7시 30분에 만나자.

G : 좋아. 그때 봐.

8 G: Look at the man over there. He's smoking on the street.

B: I don't really understand people smoking in public places.

G: Me, either.

B: Smoking is bad for both smokers and nonsmokers.

8 G : 저쪽에 남자를 봐. 거리에서 담배를 피우고 있어.

B : 나는 공공장소에서 담배 피우는 사람들을 이해할 수가 없어.

G : 나도, 그래.

B : 흡연은 흡연가나 담배 안 피우는 사람 모두에게 안 좋아.

9 B: Alice, what's your favorite subject?

G: My favorite subject is music. I like playing musical instruments.

B: What instruments can you play?

G: I can play the guitar, the harmonica, and the violin.

B: That's cool. What about the trumpet? Can you play it?

G: No, I can't, but I want to learn how to play it.

9 B : 앨리스, 네가 좋아하는 과목이 뭐야?

G : 내가 좋아하는 과목은 음악이야.
나는 악기 연주하는 것을 좋아해.

B : 무슨 악기를 연주할 수 있어?

G : 기타, 하모니카와 바이올린을 연주할 수 있어.

B : 멋지다. 트럼펫은? 그거 연주할 수 있니?

G : 아니, 못 하지만 어떻게 연주하는지 배우고 싶어.

10 ① W: Can you come to my birthday party?

M: Sure, I can.

② W: How often do you go swimming?

M: I go almost every day.

③ W: When does the movie start?

M: It starts at my house.

④ W: Who's that girl over there?

M: She's my sister.

10 ① W : 내 생일 파티에 올 수 있니?

M : 물론, 갈 수 있어.

② W : 얼마나 자주 수영하러 가니?

M : 나는 거의 매일 가.

③ W : 영화는 몇 시에 시작해?

M : 우리 집에서 시작해.

④ W : 저쪽에 있는 소녀는 누구야?

M : 내 누나야.

11 B: My family like sports. My parents like playing tennis. They play tennis twice a week. My older brother likes playing basketball. He often plays basketball after school. My younger sister likes playing table tennis. She wants to be a table tennis player.

11 B : 나의 가족은 운동을 좋아한다. 부모님은 테니스 치는 것을 좋아하신다. 그들은 일주일에 두 번 테니스를 친다. 내 형은 농구하는 것을 좋아한다. 그는 종종 방과 후에 농구를 한다. 내 여동생은 탁구 치는 것을 좋아한다. 그녀는 탁구 선수가 되고 싶어 한다.

12 M: Would you do me a favor?

W: Sure. What can I do for you?

M: Can I borrow some money?
I left my wallet at home.

W: Okay. How much do you want?

M: Thanks. Five dollars is good enough.

12 M: 부탁 하나 들어줄래?

W: 물론. 무엇을 해줄까?

M: 돈을 좀 빌릴 수 있니?
집에 지갑을 두고 왔어.

W: 좋아. 얼마나 원해?

M: 고마워. 5달러면 충분해.

13 M: ① A woman is drinking milk at a café.

② A woman is putting groceries into a cart.

③ A woman is selling vegetables at a market.

④ A woman is holding a book in her hand.

13 M: ① 한 여자가 카페에서 우유를 마시고 있다.

② 한 여자가 카트 안으로 식료품을 넣고 있다.

③ 한 여자가 시장에서 야채를 팔고 있다.

④ 한 여자가 손에 책을 들고 있다.

14 M: Alice, what are you doing here?

W: I'm riding my bike.

M: Did you see the sign over there?

W: Oh, I didn't see that.

M: The flea market opens here every Saturday, so you can't ride your bike around this area today.

14 M: 앨리스, 여기서 뭐해?

W: 나 자전거 타고 있어.

M: 저쪽에 표지판 못 봤어?

W: 오, 저거 못 봤어.

M: 벼룩시장이 토요일마다 여기서 열려서
오늘 이 지역에서는 자전거를 탈 수 없어.

15 G: Ted, what are you reading?

B: I am reading a science magazine about dinosaurs.

G: Dinosaurs?

B: Yes, I'm interested in dinosaurs.

G: Can I borrow the magazine when you finish reading it?

B: Sure. You should read this book, too.

15 G: 테드, 뭐 읽고 있어?

B: 공룡에 관한 과학 잡지를 읽고 있어.

G: 공룡?

B: 응, 난 공룡에 관심이 있어.

G: 너 다 읽으면 그거 내가 빌릴 수 있니?

B: 물론. 너도 읽어봐야 해.

16 B: Amy, which club are you in?

G: I'm in the reading club. How about you?

B: I'm still thinking.

G: You like basketball. What about joining the basketball club?

B: I'd like to. But first, I have to pass the test.

G: Don't worry about that. Just try out for it.

16 B: 에이미, 무슨 동아리 들었니?

G: 나는 독서 동아리에 있어. 너는 어때?

B: 난 여전히 생각 중이야.

G: 너 농구 좋아하잖아. 농구 동아리 가입하는 거 어때?

B: 그러고 싶어. 그런데 먼저 테스트에 통과해야 해.

G: 그거 걱정하지 마. 그냥 해 봐.

17 W: Good morning. How can I help you?

M: How much are these oranges?

W: It's 12 dollars for one box.

M: Oh, it's too expensive. How much are theses mangos?

W: It's one dollar each.

M: ① Here you are.

② Okay, I will take three mangos, please.

③ Where did you get them?

④ How many mangos do you want?

17 W: 안녕하세요. 어떻게 도와드릴까요?

M: 이 오렌지 얼마예요?

W: 한 박스에 12달러예요.

M: 오, 무척 비싸네요. 이 망고는 얼마예요?

W: 하나에 1달러예요.

M: ① 여기 있어요.

② 좋아요. 망고 세 개 주세요.

③ 그것들은 어디서 가져왔나요?

④ 망고를 얼마나 원하세요?

18 G: What time do you have lunch?

B: I have lunch at 12:30. After lunch, I usually play soccer.

G: Soccer is a lot of fun.

B: What do you do after lunch?

G: ① It will rain soon.

② I was busy yesterday.

③ I have swimming lessons.

④ Sure, I'll do it after school.

19 W: Kevin, how was your vacation?

M: It was great. I took a trip to Hawaii with my family.

W: Wow, that's cool. How long did you stay there?

M: ① Two weeks!

② Twenty dollars.

③ We went there by plane.

④ We stayed at a hotel.

20 W: What's the date today?

M: It's September 18.

W: My birthday is coming up.

M: Oh, when is it?

W: ① It's October 5th.

② Next Tuesday.

③ It want a new bike.

④ My birthday is the same as yours.

18 G: 너는 몇 시에 점심을 먹어?

B: 나는 12시 30분에 점심을 먹어. 점심 먹고 나서는 보통 축구를 해.

G: 축구는 무척 재미있지.

B: 너는 점심 먹고 뭐해?

G: ① 비가 곧 올 거야.

② 어제는 바빴어.

③ 나는 수영 수업이 있어.

④ 물론. 방과 후에 그것을 할 거야.

19 W: 케빈, 네 휴가가 어땠어?

M: 멋졌어. 가족이랑 하와이로 여행을 갔어.

W: 와우, 그거 멋지다. 얼마동안 거기에 있었어?

M: ① 2주!

② 20달러.

③ 우리는 비행기로 거기 갔어.

④ 우리는 호텔에 머물렀어.

20 W: 오늘 며칠이야?

M: 9월 18일.

W: 내 생일이 다가오고 있어.

M: 오, 언제야?

W: ① 10월 5일.

② 다음 주 화요일.

③ 난 새 자전거를 원해.

④ 내 생일은 너랑 같아.

Word Check
본책 p. 136

01 necklace 목걸이

02 maybe 아마

03 grocery 식료품

04 near 근처에

05 enough 충분한

06 hold 들다

07 vegetable 야채

08 ice hockey 아이스하키

09 theater 극장

10 understand 이해하다

11 harmonica 하모니카

12 trumpet 트럼펫

13 dinosaur 공룡

14 musical instrument 악기

15 flea market 벼룩시장

Sentence Check
본책 p. 137

01 Please look for it in the drawer.

02 I wish I could, but I have to ask my dad first.

03 I would like to check out these books.

04 You can only borrow the books for two weeks.

05 My favorite sport is hockey.

06 I'm free that day.

07 Smoking is bad for both smokers and nonsmokers.

08 I want to learn how to play it.

09 They play tennis twice a week.

10 I left my wallet at home.

11 A woman is putting groceries into a cart.

12 The flea market opens here every Saturday.

13 I am reading a science magazine about dinosaurs.

14 I took a trip to Hawaii with my family.

15 My birthday is coming up.

1 ④	**2** ②	**3** ①	**4** ①	**5** ①	**6** ④	**7** ①	**8** ④	**9** ②	**10** ③
11 ①	**12** ④	**13** ①	**14** ②	**15** ③	**16** ③	**17** ①	**18** ④	**19** ④	**20** ③

듣기 대본 본책 p. 142

1
W: May I help you?
B: Yes, I'm looking for running shoes.
W: How about these ones? These are very popular among teens.
B: They look nice. How much are they?
W: These are 100 dollars, but you can get a 20% discount.

2
W: Kevin, where are you going?
M: I'm going to the park to take a walk. Will you come with me?
W: Sure. But can we go to the drugstore first. I need some medicine for my headache.
M: Is it far from here?
W: No, it's just around the corner.
M: Okay. Let's go there first.

3
B: Did you hear tomorrow's weather?
G: They said it would be sunny. Do you have any special plans?
B: I'm going to the amusement park tomorrow.
G: That sounds exciting. Who are you going with?
B: My dad.
G: Have a great time!

4
B: Mom, what are you looking for?
W: I can't find my ring.
B: Where did you put it?
W: I thought I put it on the table, but it's not there.
B: Oh, there it is. It's in the top drawer of the side table.

5
G: Who is this girl in the picture?
B: That's my older sister, Amy.
G: How old is she?
B: She's three years older than me.
G: Then, she's fifteen years old, isn't she?
B: You're right.

6
B: It's very cold now.
G: Do you want me to close the window?
B: That will be nice.
G: Sure, not a problem.

해석

1
W: 도와드릴까요?
B: 예, 운동화를 찾고 있어요.
W: 이거 어때요? 이게 10대들 사이에서 매우 인기 있어요.
B: 좋아 보이네요. 그거 얼마예요?
W: 100달러인데 20% 할인받을 수 있어요.

2
W: 케빈, 어디 가고 있어?
M: 산책하려고 공원에 가고 있어. 나랑 같이 갈래?
W: 물론. 그런데 약국 먼저 갈 수 있니? 두통약이 좀 필요해.
M: 여기서 멀어?
W: 아니, 모퉁이 근처야.
M: 좋아. 거기 먼저 가자.

3
B: 너 내일 날씨 들었니?
G: 날이 맑을 거라고 했어. 특별한 계획이 좀 있니?
B: 내일 놀이공원에 갈 거야.
G: 신나겠다. 누구랑 같이 가?
B: 아빠랑.
G: 즐거운 시간 보내!

4
B: 엄마, 뭐 찾고 계세요?
W: 내 반지를 찾을 수가 없어.
B: 어디 두셨는데요?
W: 탁자 위에 두었다고 생각했는데, 거기 없어.
B: 오, 있어요. 협탁 맨 위 서랍에 있어요.

5
G: 사진에 이 소녀 누구야?
B: 내 누나 에이미야.
G: 몇 살이야?
B: 나보다 세 살 더 많아.
G: 그러면, 열다섯 살이네, 그렇지 않니?
B: 맞아.

6
B: 지금 너무 추워.
G: 내가 창문 닫아줄까?
B: 그러면 좋을 거 같아.
G: 알았어, 문제없어.

7 B: Christine, what did you do yesterday?
G: I went to my cousin's birthday party.
B: How was the party?
G: It was a lot of fun. How about you, Paul?
B: I stayed home all day.
G: Why? Were you sick?
B: No, I helped my mom clean the house.

8 B: Where is your brother?
G: He's playing baseball with his friends over there. He is wearing shorts.
B: Is he wearing glasses?
G: No, he isn't. He is catching the ball right now.
B: Oh, I found him.

9 G: What did you get for your birthday?
B: I got something I needed from my mom.
G: What did you get from your mom?
B: I got a new smartphone.
G: Wow! You got a big gift. Can I see it?
B: I put it on the desk. I'll go and bring it.

10 [Cellphone rings.]
G: Hello?
B: Hello, Susan. This is Mike. Are you free this Wednesday?
G: Well, I have a piano lesson, but it finishes at 3. I will be free after that. Why?
B: I got two K-pop concert tickets. Do you want to go with me?
G: Of course.
B: The concert starts at 7. Let's meet at the subway station at 6.
G: Okay. See you then.

11 ① W: Excuse me. Which bus goes to the beach?
M: Please take the bus number 17.
② W: Can I help you?
M: Could you please open the door?
③ W: Would you like to order?
M: Not yet. I'm looking at the menu.
④ M: I have a cold.
W: You should go see a doctor.

7 B: 크리스틴, 어제 뭐했어?
G: 내 사촌 생일 파티에 갔어.
B: 파티 어땠어?
G: 무척 재미있었어. 너는 어때, 폴?
B: 하루 종일 집에 있었어.
G: 왜? 아팠니?
B: 아니, 엄마가 집 청소하는 걸 도와드렸어.

8 B: 네 남동생 어디에 있어?
G: 저쪽에서 친구들이랑 야구하고 있어. 반바지 입고 있어.
B: 안경 쓰고 있니?
G: 아니, 그렇지 않아. 지금 공을 잡고 있어.
B: 오, 찾았어.

9 G: 네 생일에 무엇을 받았어?
B: 엄마한테 내가 필요했던 것을 받았어.
G: 엄마한테 뭐 받았는데?
B: 새 스마트폰을 받았어.
G: 와우! 큰 선물 받았네. 볼 수 있니?
B: 책상 위에 뒀어. 가서 가져올게.

10 [휴대폰이 울린다.]
G: 여보세요?
B: 안녕, 수잔. 나 마이크야. 이번 주 수요일에 한가하니?
G: 음, 피아노 수업이 있고 3시에 끝나. 그 이후에는 한가해. 왜?
B: K팝 콘서트 표가 두 장 있어. 나랑 같이 갈래?
G: 물론.
B: 콘서트는 7시에 시작해. 6시에 지하철역에서 보자.
G: 좋아. 그때 보자.

11 ① W: 실례합니다. 어떤 버스가 해변에 가죠?
M: 17번 버스를 타세요.
② W: 도와줄까요?
M: 문을 열어주시겠어요?
③ W: 주문하시겠어요?
M: 아직이요. 메뉴 보고 있어요.
④ M: 감기에 걸렸어.
W: 너 병원에 가는 게 좋겠어.

12 W: Let's eat out for dinner.

M: Okay. Do you have any place in mind?

W: No, I don't.

M: Then, how about going to the Vietnamese restaurant?

W: All right. I like Vietnamese food because it is cheap and healthy.

12 W: 저녁 외식하자.

M: 좋아. 마음에 둔 장소가 있어?

W: 아니, 없어.

M: 그러면, 베트남 식당 가는 거 어때?

W: 좋아. 난 싸고 건강해서 베트남 음식 좋아해.

13 B: I'd like to tell you some good news.

G: What is it?

B: We are going on a field trip next month on October 15.

G: Do you know where we are going?

B: We are going to the zoo.

G: Great.

13 B: 너한테 좋은 소식을 알려줄게.

G: 뭔데?

B: 다음 달 10월 15일에 현장학습을 가.

G: 우리가 어디로 가는지 알아?

B: 우리 동물원에 갈 거야.

G: 멋지다.

14 ① B: Jessica, how was Christmas?

G: It was great.

② B: I am sorry. I'm late.

G: Sounds good. Thanks.

③ B: Hi, Linda. How are you doing?

G: I'm doing very well.

④ B: Who's calling please?

G: This is Amy.

14 ① B: 제시카, 크리스마스 어땠어?

G: 멋졌어.

② B: 미안해. 늦었어.

G: 좋은 생각이야. 고마워.

③ B: 안녕, 린다. 어떻게 지내?

G: 난 무척 좋아.

④ B: 전화 거신 분 누구세요?

G: 나 에이미야.

15 B: I'd like to introduce my mom to you. She works at a bank. My mom goes to work early in the morning and comes home around 5 p.m. She has long, black hair and wears glasses. She likes playing the piano in her free time.

15 B: 저희 엄마를 소개해 드릴게요. 그녀는 은행에서 일하세요. 엄마는 아침 일찍 직장에 가서서 집에 5시경에 돌아오세요. 그녀는 긴 검은 머리에 안경을 쓰고 계세요. 그녀는 여가시간에 피아노 치는 것을 좋아하세요.

16 W: Dennis, what are you doing here?

M: I'm looking for my puppy. When I was talking on the phone, it ran away.

W: What does it look like?

M: It's small and black. Can you help me find it?

W: Sure.

16 W: 데니스, 여기서 뭐하고 있어?

M: 나 내 강아지 찾고 있어. 내가 전화 통화할 때 달아났어.

W: 어떤 모습이야?

M: 작고 검은색이야. 찾는 거 도와줄 수 있니?

W: 물론.

17 M: I have something to tell you.

W: What is that?

M: My older sister is going to get married this Saturday.

W: Wow, that's surprising! What time is the wedding?

M: ① It's at 3 p.m.

② Congratulations.

③ She's 27 years old.

④ It's far from here.

17 M: 너한테 할 얘기가 있어.

W: 뭔데?

M: 내 누나가 이번 주 토요일에 결혼해.

W: 와우, 놀랍다! 결혼식이 몇 시야?

M: ① 오후 3시야.

② 축하해.

③ 27살이야.

④ 여기서 멀어.

18 B: I didn't see you at school yesterday. What happened?

G: Oh, I went to see a doctor with my mom.

B: Why? Were you sick?

G: ① Yes, she is.

② I was busy yesterday.

③ Yes, my mom is a doctor.

④ I had a cold, but I'm better now.

19 G: Bob, were you at the bookstore yesterday?

B: Yes, I was there with my younger sister.

G: Oh, it was you! I saw you there.

B: Really? My sister wanted to buy a book, so I took her there.

G: What kind of book did she get?

B: ① She likes reading books.

② She wants to be a writer.

③ I like reading science magazines.

④ She bought some comic books.

20 G: What did you have for lunch?

B: I had pasta and bread.

G: Was it delicious?

B: Yes, it was good. What about you?

G: ① I had pizza.

② I ate fried rice.

③ I'd like to have some coffee.

④ I'm on a diet, so I don't eat lunch.

18 B: 어제 학교에서 너 못 봤어. 무슨 일 있었어?

G: 오, 엄마랑 병원에 갔었어.

B: 왜? 아팠어?

G: ① 응, 엄마가 아팠어.

② 나는 어제 바빴어.

③ 응, 엄마가 의사야.

④ 감기에 걸렸지만, 지금은 나아졌어.

19 G: 밥, 어제 서점에 있었니?

B: 응, 내 여동생이랑 거기 갔어.

G: 오, 너였구나! 거기서 너 봤어.

B: 정말? 내 여동생이 책을 사고 싶어 해서 거기 데리고 갔었어.

G: 무슨 종류의 책을 샀어?

B: ① 책 읽는 거를 좋아해.

② 그녀는 작가가 되고 싶어 해.

③ 나는 과학 잡지를 읽는 것을 좋아해.

④ 그녀는 만화책을 좀 샀어.

20 G: 점심으로 뭐 먹었어?

B: 나 파스타하고 빵을 먹었어.

G: 맛있었어?

B: 응, 맛있었어. 너는 어때?

G: ① 나는 피자 먹었어.

② 나는 볶음밥을 먹었어.

③ 나는 커피를 좀 먹고 싶어.

④ 나는 다이어트 중이라 점심을 안 먹었어.

Word Check
본책 p. 148

01 popular 인기 있는

02 teens 십대

03 discount 할인

04 drugstore 약국

05 around 근처에, 대략

06 corner 모퉁이

07 happen (일이) 발생하다, 일어나다

08 yet 아직

09 cheap 싼

10 healthy 건강한

11 Christmas 크리스마스

12 surprising 놀라운

13 wedding 결혼

14 side table 협탁

15 subway station 지하철역

Sentence Check
본책 p. 149

01 These are very popular among teens.

02 I need some medicine for my headache.

03 It's just around the corner.

04 It's in the top drawer of the side table.

05 I helped my mom clean the house.

06 He is catching the ball right now.

07 Let's meet at the subway station at 6.

08 You should go see a doctor.

09 We are going on a field trip next month.

10 I'd like to introduce my mom to you.

11 I have something to tell you.

12 What time is the wedding?

13 My older sister is going to get married this Saturday.

14 I went to see a doctor with my mom.

15 I was there with my younger sister.

| **1** ② | **2** ③ | **3** ④ | **4** ② | **5** ④ | **6** ④ | **7** ③ | **8** ① | **9** ④ | **10** ② |
| **11** ③ | **12** ① | **13** ③ | **14** ① | **15** ③ | **16** ③ | **17** ④ | **18** ③ | **19** ① | **20** ① |

듣기 대본　　　　　　본책 p. 154

해석

1 M: ① People are eating at the restaurant.
　② People are standing in line at the bus stop.
　③ The children are waiting for their teacher.
　④ People are getting on the bus at the bus stop.

1 M: ① 사람들이 식당에서 음식을 먹고 있다.
　② 사람들이 버스정류장에서 줄을 서고 있다.
　③ 아이들이 그들의 선생님을 기다리고 있다.
　④ 사람들이 버스정류장에서 버스를 타고 있다.

2 W: Mike, what do you have for breakfast?
M: I usually have bread and milk. How about you?
W: I have salad and fruit.
M: Fruit? What kind of fruit do you have for breakfast?
W: Apples or bananas. Do you like fruit?
M: Yes, I like strawberries.

2 W: 마이크, 아침으로 뭐 먹니?
M: 나는 보통 빵과 우유를 먹어. 너는 어때?
W: 나는 샐러드와 과일을 먹어.
M: 과일? 무슨 과일을 아침으로 먹어?
W: 사과나 바나나. 너 과일 좋아하니?
M: 응, 나는 딸기를 좋아해.

3 ① B: Why are you so upset?
　G: Someone broke my bike.
② B: What did you do last night?
　G: I watched a movie with my dad.
③ B: What's your favorite subject?
　G: I like math.
④ B: Why are you crying?
　G: The movie is so sad.

3 ① B: 왜 그렇게 화났니?
　G: 누가 내 자전거를 고장 냈어.
② B: 지난밤에 뭐했어?
　G: 아빠랑 영화를 봤어.
③ B: 네가 좋아하는 과목이 뭐야?
　G: 나는 수학을 좋아해.
④ B: 왜 울고 있어?
　G: 영화가 너무 슬퍼.

4 B: Jenny, are you interested in K-pop?
G: Yes, I am. Why?
B: Why don't you join the K-pop club?
G: What is the K-pop club?
B: The K-pop club is a space for students to learn more about Korean pop music, dance, and culture.
G: That's cool. How can I join the club?
B: You can do it online.
G: Okay. Let's do it now.

4 B: 제니, 너 K팝 음악에 관심 있니?
G: 응, 그래. 왜?
B: K팝 동아리에 가입하는 거 어때?
G: K팝 동아리가 뭐야?
B: K팝 동아리는 학생들이 한국 팝 음악, 춤, 문화에 대해 더 배우는 공간이야.
G: 그거 멋지다. 어떻게 동아리에 가입할 수 있니?
B: 온라인으로 가입할 수 있어.
G: 좋아. 지금 가입하자.

5 B: Did you see the new science teacher?
G: Not yet. What does she look like?
B: She is tall and slim.
G: Is she the woman wearing a blue blouse and a red skirt over there?
B: Yes, that's her.

5 B: 너 새로 오신 과학 선생님 봤니?
G: 아니, 아직. 어떻게 생기신 여자분이신데?
B: 키가 크고 날씬하셔.
G: 저쪽에 파란 블라우스에 빨간 치마 입고 계신 분이야?
B: 응, 맞아.

6 B: Cathy, there are sharks in the tank.

G: Yes, they are very big.

B: Where are the penguins? I want to see them.

G: There aren't any penguins in this aquarium.

B: Then, let's go look at the dolphins.

G: Okay. They are just around the corner.

6 B: 캐시, 탱크 안에 상어들이 있어.

G: 응, 무척 커.

B: 펭귄은 어디에 있어? 나 그들을 보고 싶어.

G: 이 아쿠아리움에는 펭귄이 없어.

B: 그럼, 돌고래 보러 가자.

G: 좋아. 모퉁이 근처에 있어.

---

7 B: The history museum is not open yet.

G: What time is it now?

B: It's 9:10.

G: It opens at 9:30, so we have to wait for 20 minutes.

B: I wonder what time it closes.

G: It closes at 6 in the afternoon.

7 B: 이 역사박물관은 아직 개관을 안 했어.

G: 지금 몇 시야?

B: 9시 10분이야.

G: 9시 30분에 여니까 20분 기다려야겠다.

B: 몇 시에 닫는지 궁금해.

G: 오후 6시에 닫아.

---

8 W: This is an animal. It lives in the sea. It doesn't have a spine. It has a soft, rounded body, and large eyes. It also has eight long arms. It can change the color of its skin quickly.

8 W: 이것은 동물이에요. 이것은 바다에서 살아요. 이것은 척추가 없어요. 이것은 부드러운 둥근 몸과 커다란 눈이 있어요. 이것은 또한 긴 팔이 여덟 개 있어요. 이것은 몸의 색을 빠르게 바꿀 수 있어요.

---

9 B: Where are you going?

G: I'm going to the gym to play volleyball.

B: Do you know that our national volleyball team won the silver medal at the Olympic Games?

G: Yeah! That game was so exciting.

B: They are great players, and I like them.

G: I like them, too. I want to be a volleyball player.

9 B: 너 어디 가고 있어?

G: 배구 하려고 체육관에 가고 있어.

B: 너 우리나라 대표 배구팀이 올림픽에서 은메달 딴 거 아니?

G: 그럼! 그 경기는 정말 흥미진진했어.

B: 그들은 훌륭한 선수들이고 나는 그들이 좋아.

G: 나도 그들이 좋아. 나는 배구 선수가 되고 싶어.

---

10 [Cellphone rings.]

G: Hello?

B: Hello, Susan. This is Kevin. I'm sorry, but I can't see you today.

G: What happened?

B: I fell down while riding my bicycle yesterday. I hurt my leg.

G: I'm sorry to hear that. I hope you get well soon

10 [휴대폰이 울린다.]

G: 여보세요?

B: 안녕, 수잔. 나 케빈이야. 미안한데 오늘 너를 못 만나.

G: 무슨 일이야?

B: 어제 자전거를 타다가 넘어졌어. 다리를 다쳤어.

G: 그 말 들으니 안됐다. 빨리 낫기를 바라.

---

11 G: Can you believe tomorrow will be the last day of June?

B: Yes, it's going to be already July!

G: July is my favorite month of the year.

B: Why?

G: Every July we go on a family trip.

B: Where are you going this year?

G: We are going to Jeju Island.

11 G: 내일이 6월 마지막 날이라는 걸 믿을 수 있니?

B: 응, 벌써 7월이야!

G: 7월은 일 년 중에 내가 제일 좋아하는 달이야.

B: 왜?

G: 7월마다 가족 여행을 가거든.

B: 올해는 어디로 가는데?

G: 우리 제주도에 갈 거야.

12 M: What are you going to do this afternoon?

W: I will go to the park.

M: What for?

W: I will walk my dog there.

M: Can I join you? I miss your dog Blackie.

W: Of course. Let's meet at 3 in front of the park.

12 M: 오늘 오후에 뭐할 거야?

W: 나는 공원에 갈 거야.

M: 뭐하러?

W: 거기서 개를 산책시킬 거야.

M: 같이 가도 되니? 네 개 블래키가 보고 싶어.

W: 물론이지. 공원 앞에서 3시에 만나자.

13 M: Hi, can I get two tickets for *Spiderman*.

W: Sure. What about the time?

M: When does the next movie start?

W: It starts at 5:15.

M: Okay. That sounds fine. How much is it?

W: Your total is 18 dollars. You can enter the theater 10 minutes before the movie starts.

13 M: 안녕하세요, 〈스파이더맨〉 2장 주실 수 있나요?

W: 예. 시간은요?

M: 다음 영화가 언제예요?

W: 5시 15분에 시작해요.

M: 알겠어요. 좋을 것 같네요. 얼마예요?

W: 모두 18달러예요. 영화 시작 10분 전에 극장에 들어갈 수 있어요.

14 B: Gina, what did you do last Saturday?

G: I went skiing with my family. How about you?

B: I went to the amusement park.

G: Really? Did you ride the roller coaster.

B: Yes, I rode it twice.

G: Wow, you must have had a lot of fun.

14 B: 지나, 지난 토요일에 뭐했어?

G: 가족과 스키 타러 갔어. 너는 어때?

B: 나는 놀이공원에 갔어.

G: 정말? 롤러코스터 탔어?

B: 응, 두 번이나 탔어.

G: 와우, 재미있게 보낸 게 틀림없네.

15 ① G: What are you doing?

B: I am preparing for the English test.

② G: Did you finish the science homework?

B: No, I'm doing it now.

③ G: You look sad. What's the matter?

B: I like Korean food.

④ G: Let's go get ice cream.

B: Sounds good to me.

15 ① G: 뭐하고 있어?

B: 영어 시험을 준비하고 있어.

② G: 과학 숙제 다했니?

B: 아니, 지금 하고 있어.

③ G: 너 슬퍼 보여. 무슨 일이야?

B: 나는 한국 음식을 좋아해.

④ G: 가서 아이스크림을 사자.

B: 난 좋아.

16 W: May I help you?

M: Yes, I'm looking for apples. Where can I find them?

W: They're here.

M: How much are these apples?

W: They are one dollar each.

M: Okay. I'll take five.

16 W: 도와드릴까요?

M: 예, 사과를 찾고 있어요. 어디서 찾을 수 있나요?

W: 여기에 있어요.

M: 이 사과들은 얼마예요?

W: 하나에 1달러예요.

M: 알겠어요. 다섯 개 주세요.

17 M: Can I see your passport, please?

W: Here you are.

M: How long will you stay in Hawaii?

W: About two weeks.

M: Where are you going to stay?

W: ① I'll be there by bus.

② I'm going to buy some food.

③ I don't have a car.

④ I'll stay at the Sunny Hotel.

17 M: 여권 볼 수 있나요?

W: 여기 있어요.

M: 얼마 동안 하와이에 머무나요?

W: 대략 2주일이요.

M: 여기서는 어디에 묵으시나요?

W: ① 거기에 버스로 갈 거예요.

② 음식을 좀 살 거예요.

③ 자동차가 없어요.

④ 써니 호텔에 머물 거예요.

18 M: Good morning, ma'am. May I help you?
　　W: I want to buy some strawberries.
　　M: The strawberries are over there.
　　W: I like these strawberries. How much are they?
　　M: ① It's okay.
　　　　② It's very fresh.
　　　　③ It's five dollars for one box.
　　　　④ I'd like to, but I can't.

19 G: Sam, can you come with us to the baseball game between Korea and Japan?
　　B: Sure. When is it?
　　G: It's on April 4 at 6 p.m.
　　B: What day is it?
　　G: ① It's Thursday.
　　　　② It will be sunny.
　　　　③ It's not far from here.
　　　　④ I'm busy every Monday.

20 W: Are you ready to order?
　　M: Yes. The mushroom pasta, please.
　　W: What would you like to drink?
　　M: ① No problem.
　　　　② What do you have?
　　　　③ I would like a Coke, please.
　　　　④ Can I have some water please?

18 M: 안녕하세요. 도와드릴까요?
　　W: 딸기를 좀 사고 싶어요.
　　M: 딸기는 저쪽에 있어요.
　　W: 이 딸기가 좋네요. 얼마예요?
　　M: ① 좋네요.
　　　　② 정말 신선하네요.
　　　　③ 한 상자에 5달러예요.
　　　　④ 그러고 싶은데 그럴 수 없어요.

19 G: 샘, 한국이랑 일본 야구경기 보러 갈래?
　　B: 물론. 언제야?
　　G: 4월 4일 오후 6시야.
　　B: 무슨 요일이야?
　　G: ① 목요일이야.
　　　　② 맑을 거야.
　　　　③ 여기서 멀지 않아.
　　　　④ 나는 월요일마다 바빠.

20 W: 주문하시겠어요?
　　M: 예. 버섯 파스타로 주세요.
　　W: 음료는 무엇을 드릴까요?
　　M: ① 문제없어요.
　　　　② 뭐가 있어요?
　　　　③ 콜라로 주세요.
　　　　④ 물을 좀 주시겠어요?

Word Check　　　　　　　　　　　　　　　　　　　　　　　本책 p. 160

01 prepare 준비하다　　**05** culture 문화　　**09** wonder 궁금하다　　**13** passport 여권

02 upset 화난　　**06** online 온라인으로　　**10** spine 척추　　**14** sliver medal 은메달

03 someone 누군가　　**07** shark 상어　　**11** believe 믿다　　**15** family trip 가족 여행

04 space 공간　　**08** dolphin 돌고래　　**12** enter 들어가다

Sentence Check　　　　　　　　　　　　　　　　　　　　　　本책 p. 161

01 People are standing in line at the bus stop.

02 I usually have bread and milk.

03 Someone broke my bike.

04 You can do it online.

05 She is tall and slim.

06 There aren't any penguins in this aquarium.

07 The history museum is not open yet.

08 I wonder what time it closes.

09 It can change the color of its skin quickly.

10 I fell down while riding my bicycle yesterday.

11 I hope you get well soon.

12 I am preparing for the English test.

13 They are one dollar each.

14 Can I see your passport, please?

15 What would you like to drink?

영어 듣기 모의고사

본책 p. 162

| 1 ④ | 2 ② | 3 ③ | 4 ④ | 5 ② | 6 ② | 7 ④ | 8 ② | 9 ④ | 10 ② |
| 11 ① | 12 ② | 13 ② | 14 ③ | 15 ① | 16 ① | 17 ④ | 18 ① | 19 ④ | 20 ④ |

듣기 대본 본책 p. 166

1
B: Catherine! What did you do yesterday?
G: Yesterday? I stayed home.
B: Why didn't you go to the library?
G: My parents went out, so I had to babysit my younger brother.
B: You're a very good older sister.

2
B: What do you do when you are free?
G: I enjoy going to the movies.
B: Sounds interesting! How often do you go to the movies?
G: I go three or four times a month.
B: Wow, that's a lot.

3
B: Jina, who is the man in this picture?
G: He's my favorite pianist Alfred Brendel.
B: Do you want to be a musician like him in the future?
G: Yes. I want to be a great pianist someday.
B: That's cool.

4
[Cellphone rings.]
G: Hello.
B: Hello, Jessie.
G: Hi, Daniel. What's up?
B: I'm calling to ask you a favor. My printer isn't working. Can you print out my science report for me?
G: Sure. Just email me your file.
B: Okay. I will send it to you in a minute.

5
B: Mike's birthday is next week.
G: Right. What birthday present will you get for him?
B: I'll buy him a baseball cap.
G: He already has a few caps.
B: How about a baseball bat?
G: That's a good idea. He'll love it.

6
G: Billy, how about going to the flower festival after school?
B: Okay. How do we get there?
G: We can take the subway.
B: But the subway station is too far from here.
G: Right. Then, what about riding our bikes?
B: Sounds good.

해석

1
B: 캐서린! 어제 뭐했어?
G: 어제? 나 집에 있었어.
B: 왜 도서관에 안 갔니?
G: 부모님이 외출하셔서 남동생을 돌봐야 했어.
B: 너 매우 좋은 누나구나.

2
B: 너 한가할 때 뭐해?
G: 나는 영화 보러 가는 거 즐겨.
B: 재미있겠다! 얼마나 자주 영화 보러 가?
G: 한 달에 서너 번 정도 가.
B: 와우, 많이 간다.

3
B: 지나, 사진 속 이 남자 누구야?
G: 그는 내가 좋아하는 피아니스트 알프레드 브렌델이야.
G: 너는 장래에 그처럼 음악가가 되고 싶어?
G: 응. 나는 언젠가 훌륭한 피아니스트가 되고 싶어.
B: 멋지다.

4
[휴대폰이 울린다.]
G: 여보세요.
B: 안녕, 제시.
G: 안녕, 데니얼. 무슨 일이야?
B: 너한테 부탁할 게 있어서 전화했어. 내 프린터가 작동을 안 해. 내 과학 보고서를 프린트해 줄 수 있니?
G: 물론. 나한테 네 파일을 이메일로 보내.
B: 알았어. 곧 보낼게.

5
B: 마이크의 생일이 다음 주야.
G: 맞아. 너는 무슨 생일 선물을 살 거야?
B: 나는 야구모자를 살 거야.
G: 이미 야구모자가 몇 개 있어.
B: 야구방망이는 어때?
G: 좋은 생각이야. 좋아할 거야.

6
G: 빌리, 방과 후에 꽃 박람회에 가는 거 어때?
B: 좋아. 어떻게 갈까?
G: 지하철 타고 갈 수 있어.
B: 하지만, 지하철역은 여기에서 너무 멀어.
G: 맞아. 그러면, 자전거 타는 거는 어때?
B: 좋아.

7 M: May I help you?

G: Yes. I'm looking for a purse for my mom.

M: What about this one with a ribbon on it? It's our most popular one.

G: I like the ribbon, but it's not my mom's favorite color. Do you have one in red?

M: Yes, here it is.

G: Great! I'll take it.

7 M: 도와줄까요?

G: 예. 엄마에게 드릴 지갑을 찾고 있어요.

M: 리본이 달린 이거 어때요? 가장 인기 있는 거예요.

G: 전 리본이 좋은데, 엄마가 좋아하시는 색이 아니에요. 빨간색 있나요?

M: 예, 여기 있어요.

G: 멋져요! 그걸로 살게요.

8 M: Good morning, everybody! This is the weather report. It's raining outside now. So don't forget to take your umbrella. The rain will stop tonight. Tomorrow will be windy and very cold. Be careful not to catch a cold.

8 M: 안녕하세요, 모두들! 일기예보입니다. 지금 밖에는 비가 오고 있습니다. 따라서 우산 가지고 가는 거 잊지 마세요. 비는 오늘 저녁 그칠 것입니다. 내일은 바람이 불고 매우 춥겠습니다. 감기 걸리지 않도록 조심하세요.

9 ① B: Is something wrong, Jenny?

G: I don't feel good. My stomach hurts.

② B: Did you make this pizza, Susan?

G: Yes, I did. Do you like it?

③ B: Alice! How are you doing these days?

G: Hi, Jio. I'm doing well.

④ B: Jina, what time is it now?

G: It opens at 9 o'clock.

9 ① B: 제니, 뭐 잘못됐어?

G: 몸이 좋지 않아. 배가 아파.

② B: 이 피자 네가 만들었니, 수잔?

G: 응, 그래. 맛있니?

③ B: 앨리스! 요즘 어떻게 지내?

G: 안녕, 지오. 잘 지내고 있어.

④ B: 지나야, 지금 몇 시야?

G: 그것은 9시에 열어.

10 G: Jack, what does your dad do?

B: My dad is a teacher.

G: I never knew that. What subject does he teach?

B: He teaches science at a middle school.

G: No way! My dad is also a science teacher!

B: Really? What a coincidence!

10 G: 잭, 네 아빠는 무슨 일 하셔?

B: 아빠는 선생님이야.

G: 나 결코 몰랐어. 무슨 과목 가르치셔?

B: 중학교에서 과학을 가르치셔.

G: 말도 안 돼! 우리 아빠도 과학 선생님이야!

B: 정말? 이런 우연이!

11 [Cellphone rings.]

B: Hello.

G: Hello, Sam. This is Susan.

B: Hi, Susan. What's up?

G: I'm sorry, but I can't go to your birthday party.

B: Why?

G: My dog is sick, so I have to take care of it.

B: Oh, I see. I hope your dog gets better soon.

11 [휴대폰이 울린다.]

B: 여보세요.

G: 안녕, 샘. 나 수잔이야.

B: 안녕, 수잔. 무슨 일이야?

G: 미안한데 나 네 생일 파티에 못 갈 거 같아.

B: 왜?

G: 내 개가 아파서 돌봐야 할 거 같아.

B: 오, 알았어. 개가 곧 회복되기를 바라.

12 W: Sam, did you buy a gift for Jim's birthday?

M: No. What about you?

W: I didn't, either. Why don't we go to the mall together?

M: Okay. Let's meet tomorrow morning at 11.

W: Umm... That's a little early for me. How about 12:30?

M: No problem. See you tomorrow.

12 W: 샘, 짐 생일 선물 샀니?

M: 아니, 너는 어때?

W: 나도 아직 못 샀어. 함께 쇼핑몰에 갈래?

M: 좋아. 내일 아침 11시에 만나자.

W: 음... 그건 나한테 좀 이른 거 같아. 12시 30분 어때?

M: 문제없어. 내일 보자.

13 B: Look at these roses here.

G: Wow! They're really beautiful.

B: There are so many kinds of flowers in this flower shop.

G: I like those yellow tulips.

B: Me, too. Let's buy those yellow tulips for Mom.

G: Okay. That's a good idea.

13 B: 여기 이 장미들을 좀 봐.

G: 와우! 정말 아름답다.

B: 이 꽃 가게에는 정말 많은 종류의 꽃들이 있어.

G: 나는 저 노란 튤립이 좋아.

B: 나도 그래. 엄마를 위해서 저 노란 튤립을 사자.

G: 그래. 좋은 생각이야.

---

14 B: Alice, is this your dog?

G: Yes, my dad gave it to me for my birthday.

B: Oh, he has long ears. How old is he?

G: He is two years old.

B: What's his name?

G: His name is Happy.

14 B: 앨리스, 얘가 네 개니?

G: 응, 아빠가 생일날 주셨어.

B: 오, 긴 귀를 가졌네. 몇 살이야?

G: 2살이야.

B: 이름이 뭐야?

G: 이름이 해피야.

---

15 W: Jake, what are you doing?

B: I'm drawing my future job, Mom.

W: Your future job?

B: Yes, I want to be a veterinarian.

W: Oh, that's nice. Are they zebras?

B: Yes! I want to work at a zoo as a veterinarian.

W: Cool!

15 W: 제이크, 뭐하고 있니?

B: 내 미래 직업을 그리고 있어요, 엄마.

W: 네 미래 직업?

B: 예, 저는 수의사가 되고 싶어요.

W: 오, 그거 좋다. 이것들은 얼룩말이니?

B: 예! 저는 동물원에서 수의사로 일하고 싶어요.

W: 멋지다!

---

16 G: Can you do me a favor?

B: What is it?

G: Could you help me with my science homework after school?

B: I'd love to, but I can't. I have a dentist appointment today.

G: Oh, I see.

B: Why don't you ask David for help?

G: Okay, I will. Thanks.

16 G: 부탁 들어줄 수 있니?

B: 뭔데?

G: 방과 후에 내 과학 숙제 도와줄 수 있니?

B: 그러고 싶은데 안 돼. 나 오늘 치과 예약이 되어 있어.

G: 오, 알았어.

B: 데이비드한테 물어보는 거 어때?

G: 알았어, 그렇게 할게. 고마워.

---

17 G: How was Jim's birthday party?

B: It was a lot of fun.
We ate a lot of delicious food.

G: What kind of food did you eat?

B: ① I like Korean food.

② Pizza is my favorite food.

③ I'd like to eat Chinese food.

④ We ate chicken, pizza, and ice cream.

17 G: 짐의 생일 파티 어땠어?

B: 무척 즐거웠어.
우리는 맛있는 음식을 많이 먹었어.

G: 무슨 종류의 음식을 먹었는데?

B: ① 나는 한국 음식을 좋아해.

② 피자가 내가 좋아하는 음식이야.

③ 나는 중국 음식이 먹고 싶어.

④ 우리는 치킨, 피자, 그리고 아이스크림을 먹었어.

18 B: Kelly, where are you going?

G: Oh, hi, John. I'm on my way to tennis practice right now.

B: I didn't know you play tennis.

G: I have been playing tennis for 3 years.

B: Can I go and watch you play?

G: ① Of course. Let's go.

② No, I can't play tennis.

③ No, I don't want to watch it.

④ No, I don't like tennis.

19 M: Let's go to the science museum tomorrow.

W: Great! What time does it open?

M: It opens at 9:30.

W: Then, let's meet at the entrance of the museum at 11 o'clock.

M: ① Let's take a taxi.

② It will be sunny tomorrow.

③ Okay. Here we are.

④ Okay. See you there at eleven.

20 B: Is that your sister by the window?

G: No, that is my cousin. She came from South Korea.

B: Wow! She's very tall.

G: Yes, she is taller than me.

B: Can she speak English?

G: ① A little bit.

② Yes, she can.

③ No, she can't.

④ Yes, she will study English.

18 B: 켈리, 어디 가고 있어?

G: 오, 안녕, 존. 나는 지금 테니스 연습 가는 길이야.

B: 네가 테니스 치는지 몰랐어.

G: 테니스 친 지 3년 됐어.

B: 내가 가서 너 하는 거 봐도 되니?

G: ① 물론. 가자.

② 아니, 나는 테니스를 치지 못해.

③ 아니, 나는 그걸 보고 싶지 않아.

④ 아니, 나는 테니스를 좋아하지 않아.

19 M: 내일 과학박물관에 가자.

W: 좋아! 몇 시에 열어?

M: 9시 30분에 열어.

W: 그러면, 박물관 입구에서 11시에 만나자.

M: ① 택시를 타자.

② 내일 맑을 거야.

③ 좋아. 여기 있어.

④ 좋아. 11시에 거기서 보자.

20 B: 창문 옆에 저 사람 네 언니야?

G: 아니, 내 사촌이야. 대한민국에서 왔어.

B: 와우! 매우 키가 크다.

G: 응, 나보다 키가 커.

B: 영어로 말할 수 있니?

G: ① 아주 조금.

② 응, 할 수 있어.

③ 아니, 못 해.

④ 응, 그녀는 영어를 공부할 거야.

Word Check

본책 p. 172

01 babysit 아이를 돌봐주다

02 someday 언젠가

03 purse 지갑

04 everybody 모두

05 forget 잊다

06 stomach 위

07 never 결코 ~ 아닌

08 coincidence 우연

09 either 역시

10 a little 조금(셀 수 없는)

11 delicious 맛있는

12 entrance 입구

13 veterinarian 수의사

14 flower festival 꽃 박람회

15 middle school 중학교

Sentence Check

본책 p. 173

01 I had to babysit my younger brother.

02 I enjoy going to the movies.

03 I want to be a great pianist someday.

04 I'm calling to ask you a favor.

05 The subway station is too far from here.

06 Be careful not to catch a cold.

07 He teaches science at a middle school.

08 Why don't we go to the mall together?

09 My dad gave it to me for my birthday.

10 I want to work at a zoo as a veterinarian.

11 I have a dentist appointment today.

12 We ate a lot of delicious food.

13 I have been playing tennis for 3 years.

14 Let's meet at the entrance of the museum.

15 She came from South Korea.

1 ②	2 ①	3 ②	4 ④	5 ②	6 ①	7 ③	8 ①	9 ④	10 ③
11 ③	12 ①	13 ④	14 ③	15 ②	16 ④	17 ④	18 ①	19 ③	20 ③

듣기 대본

본책 p. 178

1 B: Amy, are you going to the book festival tomorrow?
G: Yes, I am. What about you?
B: Me, too. Let's go together.
G: Sure. Why don't we meet at 2 at the bus stop?
B: I want to get there early. How about 12:30?
G: Okay. See you then.

2 B: Is your uncle in this room?
G: Of course. He's sitting on the sofa.
B: You mean the man wearing the blue T-shirt?
G: No, he's wearing a black T-shirt. He is drinking coffee now.
B: Oh, I see him.

3 G: Mike, could you do me a favor?
B: What is it?
G: Can I borrow your bike?
I'm late for my piano lesson.
B: Sure. Go ahead.
G: Thank you. I will return it by 6 o'clock.

4 W: I am an animal. I live in Africa. I am the tallest animal on the Earth. I have a long neck and four long legs. I eat leaves on a tree.

5 W: Damon, are you still playing computer games?
M: Yes, I am. Why?
W: I'm hungry. Let's order some food.
M: What kind of food do you want?
W: How about fried chicken?
M: Sounds good. Do you know the number of the chicken shop?
W: No, I don't. Let's search for it on the Internet.

6 B: Sue, did you have a good weekend?
G: Yes, I went camping with my family. How about you?
B: I went to the park with my friends.
G: What did you do there?
B: We planted trees in the park.
G: Really? Let me join you next time.

해석

1 B: 에이미, 내일 도서 박람회에 갈 거니?
G: 응, 그래. 너는 어때?
B: 나도. 함께 가자.
G: 좋아. 버스정류장에서 2시에 보는 거 어때?
B: 난 거기에 일찍 가고 싶어. 12시 30분은 어때?
G: 좋아. 그때 보자.

2 B: 네 삼촌이 이 방에 계시니?
G: 물론. 소파에 앉아 있어.
B: 파란 티셔츠 입고 있는 사람 말하는 거야?
G: 아니, 검은 티셔츠 입고 계셔. 지금 커피 마시고 계셔.
B: 오, 발견했어.

3 G: 마이크, 부탁 하나 들어줄래?
R: 뭔데?
G: 네 자전거 빌릴 수 있니?
내가 피아노 강습에 늦었어.
B: 물론. 가져가.
G: 고마워. 6시까지 돌려줄게.

4 W: 나는 동물이다. 나는 아프리카에 산다. 나는 지구에서 가장 키가 큰 동물이다. 나는 긴 목과 네 개의 다리를 가지고 있다. 나는 나무의 나뭇잎을 먹는다.

5 W: 데이먼, 너 아직 컴퓨터 게임하고 있니?
M: 응, 그래. 왜?
W: 나 배고파. 음식을 좀 주문하자.
M: 무슨 종류 음식을 원해?
W: 프라이드치킨 어때?
M: 좋은 거 같아. 너 치킨 가게 번호 아니?
W: 아니. 인터넷으로 찾아보자.

6 B: 수, 주말 잘 보냈니?
G: 응, 나 가족이랑 캠핑 갔어. 너는 어때?
B: 나는 친구들이랑 공원에 갔어.
G: 거기서 뭐했는데?
B: 우리는 공원에서 나무를 심었어.
G: 정말? 다음번에는 나도 함께하자.

7 B: Excuse me. Can I take my dog into the museum?

W: ① Sure. No problem.

② I'm sorry to hear that.

③ I'm sorry, but you can't.

④ It's not your fault.

7 B: 실례합니다. 박물관 안으로 개를 데리고 갈 수 있나요?

W: ① 물론이죠. 문제없어요.

② 그 말을 들으니 안됐다.

③ 죄송한데 안 돼요.

④ 그것은 제 잘못이 아니에요.

8 G: Jim, what are you eating?

B: I'm eating pizza. You want some?

G: No, I don't like pizza.

B: Then, what's your favorite food?

G: I like bibimbap.

B: Why do you like it?

G: It's healthy.

8 G: 짐, 뭐먹고 있어?

B: 나 피자 먹고 있어. 좀 먹을래?

G: 아니, 나 피자 좋아하지 않아.

B: 그러면, 네가 좋아하는 음식은 뭐야?

G: 난 비빔밥 좋아해.

B: 왜 그것을 좋아해?

G: 건강에 좋잖아.

9 G: I'll introduce my family to you. There are five people in my family. They are my grandmother, my father, my mother, my younger sister, and me. My father is a firefighter. He is very brave. My mother is a cook. She works at a restaurant. My younger sister is 6 years old. She goes to kindergarten.

9 G: 내 가족을 너에게 소개해줄게. 내 가족은 다섯 명이야. 할머니, 아버지, 어머니, 내 여동생과 나야. 아버지는 소방관이야. 그는 매우 용감해. 어머니는 요리사야. 그녀는 식당에서 일해. 내 여동생은 6살이야. 유치원에 다녀.

10 B: Christine. I have something to ask you.

G: What is that?

B: What are you going to buy for Jim's birthday?

G: I'm thinking of buying him a backpack. How about you?

B: I haven't decided yet.

G: Why don't you buy him running shoes? His shoes are very old.

B: Oh, that's a good idea.

10 B: 크리스틴. 너에게 말할 게 있어.

G: 그게 뭔데?

B: 짐의 생일에 무엇을 사줄 거야?

G: 배낭을 살까 생각 중이야. 너는 어때?

B: 나는 아직 결정 못했어.

G: 그한테 운동화 사주는 거 어때? 운동화가 많이 낡았어.

B: 오, 그거 좋은 생각이야.

11 ① M: What can I do for you?

G: I'm looking for a bag.

② M: Where is your cellphone?

G: It's on the table.

③ M: Excuse me, which bus goes to the airport?

G: It will take 20 minutes.

④ M: What a pretty scarf! It looks so nice on you.

G: Thank you, Dad.

11 ① M: 무엇을 도와드릴까요?

G: 가방을 찾고 있어요.

② M: 네 휴대전화 어디에 있니?

G: 탁자 위에 있어요.

③ M: 실례지만, 무슨 버스가 공항으로 가나요?

G: 20분 걸릴 거예요.

④ M: 무척 예쁜 스카프구나! 너한테 잘 어울린다.

G: 감사해요, 아빠.

12 B: Do you know where my science magazine is?

W: I think I saw it on the desk in the morning.

B: No, it's not there.

W: Then, check your backpack.

B: It's not there, either.

W: Hmm. Did you look on the shelf?

B: Oh, there it is! It's on the top shelf.

12 B: 제 과학 잡지 어디에 있는지 아세요?

W: 아침에 책상 위에서 본 거 같은데.

B: 아니요, 거기 없어요.

W: 그러면, 배낭을 확인해 보렴.

B: 거기도 역시 없어요.

W: 음, 선반 위는 봤니?

B: 오, 있어요. 맨 위 선반에 있어요.

13 G: Wow! John, you're good at playing the guitar.

B: Thank you for saying that.

G: Where did you learn to play?

B: I joined the school music club last year.

G: I want to learn how to play the guitar.

B: Then, how about joining our club?

G: That sounds good.

13 G: 와우! 존, 너 기타를 잘 치는구나.

B: 그렇게 말해줘서 고마워.

G: 어디서 치는 거 배웠어?

B: 나 작년에 학교 음악동아리에 가입했어.

G: 나도 기타 치는 법 배우고 싶어.

B: 그러면 우리 동아리 가입하는 거 어때?

G: 좋은 생각이야.

14 G: Jack, are you going to Tony's birthday party tomorrow?

B: Yes, I am.

G: I don't know where his house is. Can we go together?

B: Sure. Let's meet at 4 o'clock at the bus stop.

G: Well, that's too early. How about 5 o'clock?

B: No problem.

14 G: 잭, 너 내일 토니 생일 파티에 갈 거니?

B: 응, 그래.

G: 나 그의 집이 어디인지 몰라. 함께 갈래?

B: 좋아. 버스정류장에서 4시에 만나자.

G: 음, 너무 일러. 5시에 보는 거 어때?

B: 문제없어.

15 M: May I help you?

W: I'm looking for a cup.

M: How about the cup with a cat on it?

W: Hmm... It looks good, but I don't like cats.

M: Then, how about this cup with a flower?

W: Oh, that's good. How much is it?

M: It's 2 dollars.

15 M: 도와드릴까요?

W: 컵을 찾고 있어요.

M: 고양이가 있는 컵 어때요?

W: 음... 좋아 보이는데 제가 고양이를 좋아하지 않아요.

M: 그러면, 꽃이 있는 이 컵은 어때요?

W: 오, 그거 좋아요. 얼마예요?

M: 2달러예요.

16 M: ① A man is taking care of a girl.

② A nurse is looking out the window.

③ A doctor is sitting on the sofa.

④ A nurse is taking care of a patient.

16 M: ① 한 남자가 소녀를 돌보고 있다.

② 한 간호사가 창문 밖을 보고 있다.

③ 한 의사가 소파에 앉아 있다.

④ 한 간호사가 환자를 돌보고 있다.

17 W: May I help you?

M: Yes, I'm looking for apples.

W: How many apples do you want?

M: I want three.

W: ① Look over there,

② I don't have money.

③ Yes, that's all. Thank you.

④ Here you are. Anything else?

17 W: 도와드릴까요?

M: 예, 사과를 찾고 있어요

W: 얼마나 많은 사과를 원하세요?

M: 세 개요.

W: ① 저기 살펴보세요.

② 저는 돈이 없어요.

③ 예, 그게 다예요. 감사해요.

④ 여기 있어요. 다른 것은요?

18 G: Jack, what did you do yesterday?

B: I watched TV at home.

G: Oh, did you? What program did you watch?

B: I watched a soccer game. What about you?

G: ① I went shopping with my mom.

② It was very cold yesterday.

③ I don't feel good today.

④ That's too bad.

18 G: 잭, 어제 뭐했어?

B: 나 집에서 TV 봤어.

G: 오, 그랬어? 무슨 프로그램 봤는데?

B: 나 축구 경기 봤어. 너는 어때?

G: ① 나는 엄마랑 쇼핑 갔어.

② 어제 무척 추웠어.

③ 오늘 몸이 좋지 않아.

④ 그거 안됐다.

19 W: What are you going to do this weekend?

M: I'm going to go camping with my cousins.
Do you have any special plans?

W: No, I don't. I will just stay home.

M: Why don't you come with us?

W: ① I'm sorry to hear that.

② I'm going to eat pizza.

③ Really? It sounds good.

④ Oh, I went there last year.

20 M: Do you have breakfast every day?

W: Yes, I do.

M: What do you have for breakfast?

W: I usually have bread and eggs.
How about you?

M: ① I have a chicken salad.

② I don't eat breakfast.

③ I don't like eggs.

④ I usually have some cereal and fruit.

19 W: 이번 주말에 뭐할 거야?

M: 내 사촌들과 캠핑 갈 거야.
너는 특별한 계획 있니?

W: 아니, 없어. 그냥 집에 있을 거야.

M: 우리랑 함께 가는 거 어때?

W: ① 그 말 들으니 안됐다.

② 나는 피자를 먹을 거야.

③ 정말? 좋을 거 같아.

④ 오, 나는 작년에 거기에 갔어.

20 M: 너는 매일 아침을 먹니?

W: 응, 그래,

M: 아침으로 무엇을 먹어?

W: 나는 보통 빵이랑 달걀을 먹어. 너는 어때?

M: ① 나는 치킨 샐러드를 먹어.

② 나는 아침을 안 먹어.

③ 나는 달걀을 좋아하지 않아.

④ 나는 보통 시리얼이랑 과일을 먹어.

Word Check
본책 p. 184

01 together 함께

02 mean 의미하다

03 leaf 나뭇잎

04 search 찾다

05 Internet 인터넷

06 fault 잘못

07 healthy 건강에 좋은

08 kindergarten 유치원

09 decide 결정하다

10 introduce 소개하다

11 magazine 잡지

12 patient 환자

13 weekend 주말

14 book festival 도서 박람회

15 running shoes 운동화

Sentence Check
본책 p. 185

01 I want to get there early.

02 I will return it by 6 o'clock.

03 I am the tallest animal on Earth.

04 Let's search for it on the Internet.

05 We planted trees in the park.

06 Let me join you next time.

07 There are five people in my family.

08 Why don't you buy him running shoes?

09 It looks so nice on you.

10 I think I saw it on the desk in the morning.

11 I want to learn how to play the guitar.

12 I don't know where his house is.

13 A nurse is taking care of a patient.

14 I'm going to go camping with my cousins.

15 I usually have bread and eggs.

memo

memo

memo

Longman
Listening
mentor joy Series